ENERGY UNDER THE OCEANS

A Technology Assessment of Outer Continental Shelf Oil and Gas Operations

University of Oklahoma Press   :   Norman

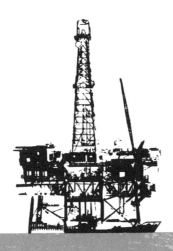

Energy Under the Oceans

A Technology Assessment of Outer Continental Shelf Oil and Gas Operations

The Technology Assessment Group
Science and Public Policy Program

DON E. KASH
IRVIN L. WHITE
KARL H. BERGEY
MICHAEL A. CHARTOCK
MICHAEL D. DEVINE
R. LEON LEONARD
STEPHEN N. SALOMON
AND HAROLD W. YOUNG

Foreword by Joseph Coates

Library of Congress Cataloging in Publication Data

Oklahoma. University. Science and Public Policy
  Program. Technology Assessment Group.
  Energy under the oceans.

  Includes bibliographical references.
    1. Petroleum in submerged lands—United States. 2. Gas, Natural—United States.
  3. Continental shelf—United States. 4. Technology assessment—United States.
  5. Environmental policy—United States. I. Kash, Don E. II. Title.
  TN872.A5062   1973   301.24'3   73-8374

Foreword

THE MANAGEMENT of technology for the commonweal is, if not the central problem of our society, certainly an issue of paramount and expanding urgency.

To a substantial degree, the publics interested in any particular technology as well as decision-makers in the private sector and in the government find themselves forced to act, or at least take a stand, with inadequate knowledge of the technological alternatives and their possible consequences. The growing interdependence of our society on major technological developments, the incredibly large commitments of money and manpower, and the long period to realization for major projects all demand more reliable methods of forecasting and anticipating consequences of technology. The demands for foresight are exacerbated by the growing number of negative consequences of technology which could have been mitigated, moderated, or limited if effective early warnings had been sounded.

Technology assessment, of which this study is one example, is the name for a class of policy studies intended to anticipate and explore the full range of consequences of the introduction of new technology or the expansion of an old technology in new and different ways. Men have always been interested in the consequences of technological development. One might reasonably ask, therefore, what's new about technology assessment? Several things are new.

First is the attempt to expand the study of the anticipated consequences well beyond the conventional considerations of economic costs and benefits or immediate implications for the perpetrator or user of technology. The extension into the full range of social, economic, political, international, legal, and other societal impacts demands a degree of skill and sophistication rarely brought to the management of technology. The second feature of technology assessment is its focus as a policy study on informing the interested publics and the decision-makers of the possible ranges of consequences for new actions. Sound assessments should put into the hands of all interested parties reliable information to help them formulate their decisions and to generate more socially desirable management strategies. Furthermore, there should be cumulative benefits from making the discussions and the implementations of the management of technology far more sophisticated than they have been in the past. A third aspect of technology assessment is the attempt to organize and draw policy guidance from both what is known with some certitude and what is not known.

Normally one anticipates that policy flows out of knowledge; but in the effective management of technology, viable policies must flow out of both what we know and what we do not know. Consequently, one may anticipate that among the consequences of a technology assessment will be one or more of the following:

Modifying the project or technology to reduce disbenefits or to increase benefits

Defining a monitoring or surveillance program with regard to the technology as it becomes operational

Stimulating research and development to:
   (a) Define risks more reliably
   (b) Forestall anticipated negative effects
   (c) Identify alternative methods of achieving the goal of the technology
   (d) Identify feasible corrective measures for negative effects

Identifying regulatory or other control needs

Encouraging the legislative development of a technology into new areas to exploit anticipated benefits

Identifying needed institutional changes or innovation

Providing sound inputs to all parties at interest

Preventing a socially destructive technology from developing (an unusual but not impossible outcome)

The material covered in this book relates to many of these possible actions.

This particular study is one of many at various stages sponsored by the Office of Exploratory Research and Problem Assessment in the Research Applications Directorate in the National Science Foundation. The general goals of the NSF technology assessment program are:

To provide a substantive, comprehensive, useful input into public policy formulation and decision-making with regard to the application of particular technologies

To explore and encourage technology assessment and the application of systematic methods, techniques, protocols, and approaches to complex, policy-related problems

To encourage the growth of organizational capability to conduct impartial, comprehensive technology assessments

To encourage the extension of the concept of impact analysis to include the impacts of social technology, social invention, and institutional change

To serve the growing needs in the federal agencies for advice, guidance, and assistance in technology assessment

To meet the mandated cooperative activities associated with the formulation of the Office of Technology Assessment by the Congress

With regard to any particular assessment of a technology, the sponsoring organization is faced by several difficulties: identifying organizations which can adequately perform the assessment; assuring that their methods, techniques, and strategies for conducting the study are adequate; assuring that the investigators not only have the widest latitude of independence, but also driving them to use their independence. An effective technology assessment is likely to be bad news to someone. Consequently, that bad news as well as the good and indifferent news, with regard to management of a particular technology must be brought forward in a way to inform the interested parties and illuminate the issues. In brief, quality control in the technology assessment must strike a balance between comprehensiveness, incisiveness, timeliness, completeness, independence, and focus.

The history of this particular project may interest both general readers and other organizations interested in sponsoring such assessments, and assist them in understanding how these goals were approached. First, the National Science Foundation as the sponsor of this project has no stake in the technology per se, having no federal mission in the area of offshore resource development. The University of Oklahoma team coming to us had no prior stake in the technology and no position which might in fact or in appearance influence its judgment. The proposal as generated by the principal investigators and their associates was put forward as a subject of timely and growing interest by a team who felt that they could make a useful contribution. Upon receipt of the proposal it was sent for review and comment to a wide range of professional and institutional parties, including representatives from federal agencies, the industry, environmental groups, public interest groups, and academics representing a variety of germane competences. Their collective criticism as well as that of the Foundation staff was cycled back to the principal investigators. They then put forward a stronger proposal, which again was resubmitted to the reviewers. On the basis of their advice, the project was funded.

To assure both completeness and balance, the investigators were urged to form an oversight committee (mentioned in the Preface) whose function was not to participate in the study, but to provide a divergent complementary sounding board, wise council, and in some cases access to knowledge and information not otherwise readily available. When the work had progressed to the point at which a substantial but tentative report was available, that is, the summer of 1972, the investigators held a one-week summer seminar on offshore oil resource development under the auspices of the Engineering Foundation. That meeting was supported by a separate grant from the National Science Foundation. The seminar, involving some sixty to seventy representatives of various parties, not only sharpened the judgment of the investigators but also began to inform the interested communities of what developments were taking place in this project.

As the study itself drew to completion, the principal investigators not only conducted their own quality control reviews with their oversight committee and other independent reviewers, but the National Science Foundation sent the proposal out to some fifteen people who had no previous contact with the project and solicited their independent evaluations. These evaluations ranged from critical to laudatory, but did not comprise a sufficiently large detailed volume of criticism to make it worthwhile to append them to the study. The gist of that criticism was anonymously fed back to the principal investigators to allow them to make any last corrections, adjustments, modifications, or compensations in their study.

On the basis of all that, this document is put forward with our institutional hope, if not expectation, that it will sharpen the discussion and illuminate the issues on the development of our offshore oil resources. While it is not expected that this is, by any means, the last word on the discussion, we do hope it will move the discussion perceptibly forward for all parties at interest and lead to a wiser and more thoughtful public policy for the management of these resources.

> Joseph F. Coates
> Program Manager for Technology Assessment
> Office of Exploratory Research and Problem Assessment
> National Science Foundation
> Washington, D. C.
> *June 28, 1973*

Preface

THIS BOOK is the report of a technology assessment of oil and gas operations on the U.S. outer continental shelf made by an interdisciplinary research team under the aegis of the Science and Public Policy Program at the University of Oklahoma. The analysis, funded by the National Science Foundation, was conducted over a twenty-month period beginning in September, 1971.

Co-principal investigators for the study were Don E. Kash and Irvin L. (Jack) White, both of the University of Oklahoma. Don E. Kash is the director of the Science and Public Policy Program and professor of political science. Irvin L. White is the assistant director of the Science and Public Policy Program and associate professor of political science. Other members of the research team, also of the University of Oklahoma, included: Karl H. Bergey, professor of aeronautical, mechanical and nuclear engineering; Michael A. Chartock, assistant professor of zoology; Michael D. Devine, assistant professor of industrial engineering; R. Leon Leonard, assistant professor of aeronautical, mechanical and nuclear engineering; Stephen N. Salomon, visiting assistant professor of physics; and Harold W. Young, professor of law. Each of these members of the research team is also a research fellow in the Science and Public Policy Program.

Charles C. Patton, director, petroleum and geological engineering and Halliburton Professor of Petroleum Engineering at the University, served as a technical advisor during the first twelve months of the study.

Continuing advice was provided by an Oversight Committee consisting of the following people: Edward D. Goldberg, Scripps Institution of Oceanography, Geological Research Division, University of California at San Diego; Robert Kay, chief, Policy Development Division, National Oceanic and Atmospheric Administration; Philip E. Jenson, production manager of Southern Region, Shell Oil Company; Vincent E. McKelvey, director, U.S. Geological Survey, Department of the Interior; Leo A. McReynolds, Research and Development Department, Phillips Petroleum Company; John P. Milton, at the outset of the project, director, International Programs, The Conservation Foundation, now at the Woodrow Wilson Center; and Edward Wenk, Jr., professor of engineering and public affairs, University of Washington. We wish to acknowledge their major contribution to this report.

In addition, a number of individuals, corporations, government agencies, and public interest groups contributed significantly to the study. H. O. "Bud" Harder, chairman of the Board of Trustees of the University of Oklahoma Foundation, provided invaluable assistance and support, particularly during the early stages of the project. Bud not only gave us the benefit of a lifetime of experience in the petroleum industry, but also provided useful contacts, sound advice, and continuing personal support. Other individuals who should be singled out include: Malcolm F. Baldwin, Woodrow Wilson Center; Rear Admiral William M. Benkert, U.S. Coast Guard; Charles L. Blackburn, Shell Oil Co.; S. J. Brady, Phillips Petroleum Co.; Vincent M. Brown, National Petroleum Council; E. E. Clark, Phillips Petroleum Co.; Donald D. Dunlop, consultant; Morris K. Dyer, Marshall Spacecraft Center; Robert F. Evans, U.S. Geological Survey; Stephen J. Gage, Council on Environmental Quality; Paul L. Gassett, Gulf Oil Co.; Robert L. Geyer, Seismograph Services Corp.; Captain Clarence R. Hallberg, U.S. Coast Guard; Charles O. Jones, Falk Professor of Politics, University of Pittsburgh; Arthur Lubinski, Amoco Production Co.; Phillip S. Massey, Phillips Petroleum Co.; Charles S. Matthews, Shell Oil Co.; Roger W. Mowell, Esso Production Research Co.; F. T. Pease, The Offshore Company; Harry Perry, energy consultant; Robin J. Robinson, Esso Production Research Co.; Calvin Saunders, Halliburton Services; O. J. Shirley, Shell Oil Co.; Schofner Smith, Phillips Petroleum Co.; Henry D. Van Cleave, Environmental Protection Agency; Thomas B. Stoel, Natural Resources Defense Council; Darrell G. Warner, Exxon; E. N. Washburn, Phillips Petroleum Co.; Russell G. Wayland, U.S. Geological Survey; Alvin C. Weingand, Get Oil Out!; and Joseph E. Wirsching, Exxon.

We also wish to express our appreciation to the following organizations: Exxon, Gulf, Halliburton, Phillips, Shell, and the U.S. Geological Survey. While we received wholehearted support from industry, government agencies, and interest groups generally, the study could not have been successfully completed without the assistance these particular organizations provided.

Conduct of the study was facilitated by Joseph F. Coates, program manager in the Exploratory Research and Problem Assessment Office of the National Science Foundation and Raymond D. Daniels and Taylor C. Anthony, director and assistant director of the Oklahoma Research Administration. Joe Coates, who monitored the project for NSF, contributed to the study in ways too numerous to detail here; Ray Daniels and Taylor Anthony administered the NSF grant supporting the project in a manner which considerably eased the task of management.

Robert J. Bauer, associate professor of English at the University of Oklahoma, served as an editorial consultant. While he bears no responsibility for the final editorial decisions, he contributed to the clarity and readability of the report.

Ginna H. Davidson did the graphics and several of the illustrations for the report. Her skills contributed significantly to the clarity of presentation.

We also wish to express appreciation to the staff of the Science and Public Policy Program. Ann M. Niemeyer and Peggy L. Neff organized and typed a seemingly endless number of research papers and drafts of the report. Janice K. Whinery assisted in preparation of this final account. Martha T. Jordan and Phillip C. Morgan provided continuing research assistance. Their efforts materially contributed to the completion of the study. Martha Jordan prepared the index and Phil Morgan prepared Appendix A on public opinion and designed several illustrations and graphics.

Although this project was funded by the National Science Foundation's program of Research Applied to National Needs (RANN) under NSF Grant Number GI–29942, the analyses, conclusions, and recommendations presented here do not necessarily reflect the views of the National Science Foundation. Neither the University of Oklahoma, the Oklahoma Research Administration, nor any of the numerous organizations and individuals identified as contributing to this project are responsible for this technology assessment of outer continental shelf oil and gas operations. The report is the sole responsibility of the Technology Assessment Group, Science and Public Program, the University of Oklahoma.

A Note on Data Sources

We have attempted to provide complete citations for data sources used in this study. However, we have respected requests for confidentiality and do not identify certain individuals and their professional affiliations. In some instances, respecting confidentiality has required that specific companies or agencies not be named. When analyses are based on data bases generated by the University of Oklahoma Technology Assessment Group, we have attempted to provide sufficiently detailed description to permit replication.

Table of Contents

Part Three: Policy Issues Raised by OCS Development

List of Illustrations

List of Tables

Acronyms and Abbreviations

API	American Petroleum Institute
BLM	Bureau of Land Management
BOP	blowout preventer
BTU	British thermal unit
CEQ	Council on Environmental Quality
CFR	Code of Federal Regulations
EPA	Environmental Protection Agency
FAA	Federal Aviation Administration
FAO	Food and Agriculture Organization (UN)
FPC	Federal Power Commission
FRA	Federal Railroad Administration
FWPCA	Federal Water Pollution Control Act
GOO!	Get Oil Out! Inc.
HEW	Department of Health, Education, and Welfare
ICC	Interstate Commerce Commission
IDOE	International Decade for Ocean Exploration
ISA	International Seabed Authority
LNG	liquid natural gas
LOS	Law of the Sea
LOT	load-on-top
NAE	National Academy of Engineering
NAS	National Academy of Sciences
NASA	National Aeronautics and Space Administration
NEPA	National Environmental Policy Act of 1969
NIH	National Institutes of Health
NOAA	National Oceanic and Atmospheric Administration
NPC	National Petroleum Council
NRC	National Research Council
NRDC	Natural Resources Defense Council, Inc.
NSF	National Science Foundation
NTSB	National Transportation Safety Board
OCS	outer continental shelf
OPEC	Organization of Oil Producing and Exporting Countries
OPPR	Office of Policy Planning and Research
OPS	Office of Pipeline Safety
OSHA	Occupational Safety and Health Act of 1970

OST   Office of Science and Technology
OTA   Office of Technology Assessment
PCB   polychlorinated biphenyl
RANN   Research Applied to National Needs
SCEP   Study of Critical Environmental Problems
SPS   subsea production system
TAPS   trans-Alaska pipeline system
USGS   U.S. Geological Survey

Table of Statutes

Coastal Zone Management Act (amendments to the Marine Resources and Engineering Development Act), 86 Stat. 1280, 16 U.S.C. § 1451.

Federal Water Pollution Control Act Amendments of 1972, 86 Stat. 816, 33 U.S.C. § 1251.

Marine Protection, Research and Sanctuaries Act of 1972, 86 Stat. 1052, 16 U.S.C. § 1431.

Merchant Marine Act of 1920, 41 Stat. 988, 46 U.S.C. § 861.

Morse Public Information Act, 81 Stat. 54, U.S.C. § 552.

National Environmental Policy Act of 1969, 83 Stat. 852, 42 U.S.C. § 4321.

Occupational Safety and Health Act of 1970, 84 Stat. 1590, 29 U.S.C. § 651.

Outer Continental Shelf Lands Act, 67 Stat. 462, 43 U.S.C. § 1313.

Submerged Lands Act, 67 Stat. 29, U.S.C. § 1301.

Part One

An Introduction to a Technology Assessment
of OCS Oil and Gas Operations

This book is divided into five major parts. The two chapters in Part I introduce the study: Chapter I covers the background of the study and the social context within which it has been conducted, and Chapter II describes how the study was conducted.

I. Technology Assessment and OCS Development

IN THE PAST, most decisions to develop and apply a technology seem to have been made primarily on the basis of two criteria: whether it was technologically feasible and/or whether it would be economically profitable. When the question of social desirability has been asked, it usually has been in terms of whether applying the technology promised to produce some immediate, tangible social benefit. But it is now widely recognized that applied technologies frequently produce not only sought for benefits, but other—often unanticipated—desirable and/or undesirable consequences as well.

Recently it has been the negative or socially undesirable, unanticipated consequences that have attracted the most attention. And many social critics have blamed inadequately informed past technological decisions for environmental degradation, persistent unemployment, and a variety of other undesirable impacts on the "quality of life." One consequence has been the development of a belief that we, as a society, have somehow gone wrong in our scientific and technological decision-making. This belief has been reinforced by several major trends in our development as a society, including:

1. a recognition of the growing complexity of our technological society;
2. an appreciation of just how interdependent and interrelated physical and social systems are; and
3. shifts in societal values which call for re-examining and, in some cases, reordering national priorities.

Largely because of these trends, efforts are now underway to improve scientific and technological decision-making. The goal is to improve not only the decision-making process but the quality of scientific and technological decisions as well. One kind of effort is being called technology assessment.

WHAT IS TECHNOLOGY ASSESSMENT?

Technology assessment is an attempt systematically to identify, analyze, and evaluate the potential environmental, legal/political, and other social impacts of a technology.[1] Technology assessment is being developed as a policy-making tool, a tool for alerting public and private policy makers to the likely consequences of making a decision either to employ a particular technology or to choose from among alternative technologies. Technology assessors examine the relationships between a technology and its physical, ecological, and social environment. They ask what will be the effect of introducing a new technology and what impacts can be anticipated if changes are made in either the technology or in legal/political systems. In short, technology assessors assume that unanticipated impacts can be as powerful, pervasive, and durable as the anticipated impacts of technological developments and their goal is to insure that technological policy-making is as well-informed as possible with regard to these impacts.

The technology assessment concept was formally proposed in a 1966 report of the Subcommittee on Science, Research and Development of the House Committee on Science and Astronautics. This report called for the development of a mechanism in the Congress for "keeping tabs on the potential dangers, as well as the benefits in new technology." The concept was legitimized by means of hearings, reports, seminars, and a series of studies, including those conducted by the National Academies of Science, Engineering and Public Administration, and by what is now the Congressional Research Service. These efforts led to the passage in 1972 of a bill establishing an Office of Technology Assessment (OTA) in the Congress. (Acronyms and abbreviations are listed on pages xxi–xxii.)

In the executive branch, the recently dismantled Office of Science and Technology (OST) promoted development of the technology assessment concept. In 1970, OST, together with the MITRE Corporation, funded an effort to develop a technology assessment methodology. More recently, the National Science Foundation (NSF), particularly the program on Research Applied to National Needs (RANN), has become the principal sponsor of efforts to develop a technology assessment capability. RANN is supporting studies designed to assess the impacts of technologies on man and his environment, and either to develop or to refine methods and techniques for predicting and assessing these impacts. One of the studies is the assessment of outer continental shelf (OCS) oil and gas operations being reported here, one of several NSF-supported efforts focusing on some aspect of policy-making for energy and/or the environment.

ENERGY AND THE ENVIRONMENT

Policy makers in the United States are being pressured by the often conflicting demands of individuals and groups concerned with energy and the environment. They are having to attempt to find some means for satisfying growing demands for energy while at the same time responding to the widespread pressures for more stringent controls aimed at either assuring or improving environmental quality.

ENERGY DEMAND

Any discussion of energy demand must recognize that economic growth continues to be a high-priority goal in the United States. Historically economic growth and energy consumption have been linked with the demand for energy increasing at approximately the same rate as the gross national product. This relationship might be modified, but such a modification would require major changes in governmental policy. Specifically it would require much more comprehensive planning and the implementation of controls over the uses of energy. There is little evidence of either a societal or governmental capacity, let alone willingness, to institute these kinds of changes.

The meaningful question is not whether, but at what rate, energy demand will increase. There have been numerous projections of what energy demand will be over the next fifteen years, and most of them have been subjected to similar criticism. A summary of their purported inadequacies was stated by Senator Henry Jackson. Based on a survey of thirty energy-demand studies conducted as a part of the Senate Interior and Insular Affairs Committee's National Fuels and Energy Policy Study, he concluded that "... [their] definitions and assumptions are rarely spelled out ... and [they] contain no information as to how consumption of energy and of particular fuels would be influenced by changes in prices, technology, or public policy."[2] In fact, most studies of energy demand have not taken change into account at all, relying instead almost exclusively on trend analysis, projecting past use patterns into the future.

The most recent study, and one which attempts to respond to these criticisms, was conducted by the National Petroleum Council (NPC).[3] In making its projections, NPC indicates that "... decreases in demand resulting from efficiency improvements were considered as were possible reductions from variations in the other principal factors influencing energy consumption: economic activity, population, cost of energy, and environmental controls."[4] NPC projects that the annual range of growth in energy consumption will be between 3.4 and 4.4 percent over the 1971–1985 period. This is consistent with projections made by most other studies. In fact, the demand range projected by NPC encompasses the various demand levels presented in all the major studies done since 1968,[5] and we have elected to use NPC's demand projections as the basis for this assessment.

Major changes either in societal values or energy availability could significantly reduce growth in energy consumption. Some people believe that such a reduction would be beneficial, whatever the cause. It is not our purpose in this study to address the question of desirable rates of growth. Our use of NPC's demand projections is not an endorsement; NPC's projections are used because they are recent and generally consistent with the projections made in most other studies.

According to NPC, the U.S. energy demand in 1985 will be in the range of 23 million barrels of oil per day[6] and 36 trillion cubic feet of gas per year.[7] Together these two sources are expected to satisfy approximately 70 percent of the total U.S. energy demand in 1985.[8]

ENERGY SUPPLY

Potential alternatives to conventional oil and gas as energy sources include geothermal power, solar energy, fast breeder reactors, thermonuclear fusion, energy from refuse, hydroelectric, wind power, conventional nuclear reactors, coal (including synthetic gas and liquids), tar sands, and oil shale. Most of these potential sources utilize newly developed or developing technologies. These include geothermal, solar, fast breeders, fusion, refuse, synthetic products from coal, as well as tar sands and oil shale. None of these is in widespread service, and some are still in the research stage. Hence, with any of these sources, additional problems will have to be solved before they can provide reliable and economical energy, given current societal constraints. A major federal effort could accelerate the availability of some of these sources, but no such effort presently exists. Without such acceleration there are not likely to be major new alternatives to oil and gas between now and 1985.

Of those alternatives now in use, hydroelectric resources are limited because of the limited number of available dam sites; and conventional nuclear reactors and coal are likely to be constrained by environmental considerations. In short, as indicated in Figure 1, the choice of supply sources for the nation up to 1985 is between imported oil and gas and domestic oil and gas. This is the situation even if one uses the most conservative estimates of demand.

Some observers have suggested that energy for many new activities could be provided by the introduction of more efficient equipment and procedures. A recent interagency study, led by the Office of Emergency Preparedness, suggested that such efficiencies could reduce demand by an equivalent of 7.3 million barrels of oil per day by 1980.[9] Most observers believe this to be unduly optimistic short of a large-scale government crash program aimed at improved efficiency. In fact, even the interagency group doubts that this reduction can be obtained. The difficulty in establishing the necessary governmental controls together with the long lead time

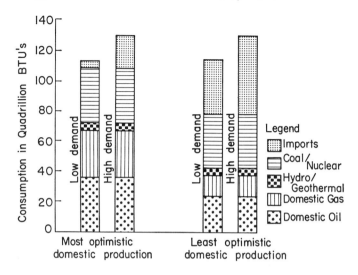

Fig. 1. U.S. Energy Supply and Consumption in 1985

Source: National Petroleum Council, Committee on U.S. Energy Outlook, *U.S. Energy Outlook: A Summary Report* (Washington: National Petroleum Council, 1972), p. 6.

needed to alter existing equipment are the major reasons for skepticism.[10] Another constraint is that while oil and gas can be used as a substitute for almost any other primary fuel, the reverse is not so. For instance, Figure 2 shows that 24.6 percent of the total energy used domestically in 1971 was in transportation; in this sector there is no available substitute for petroleum. Figure 2 also indicates that 20.7 percent is used in the household/commercial sector, where significant substitution would be difficult over the next fifteen years.

Another consideration which plays a role in determining the substitutability of one energy source for another is the location of supply vis-á-vis demand. For example, domestic geothermal sources are mainly located in the West (that is, the U.S. West) while heavy demand for electricity is in the East. Oil and gas supplies are presently in the West, Southwest, and Alaska, again with major demand in the East and Midwest. This means that transportation of the energy source becomes a major constraint in interchangeability. (See the major supply and production areas identified in Figure 3.)

In summary, given increased energy consumption, there is no alternative to an increase in the demand for the use of oil and gas. The question of supply over the next fifteen years centers on the level of dependence on oil and gas imports.

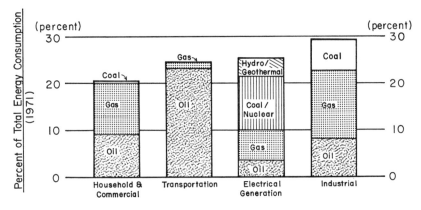

Fig. 2. Energy Consumption by Source and Consuming Sector (1971)

Source: U.S., Executive Office of the President, Office of Emergency Preparedness, *The Potential for Energy Conservation*, Staff Study (Washington, D.C.: Government Printing Office, 1972), Appendix A, p. A–2.

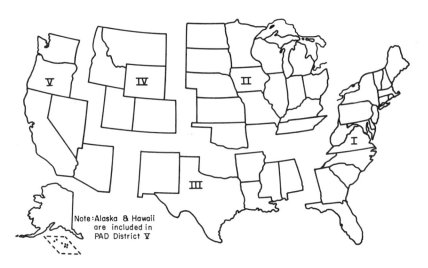

Fig. 3. 1970 Petroleum Demand and Production by District

(stated in million barrels per day)

Source: National Petroleum Council, Committee on U. S. Energy Outlook, *U.S. Energy Outlook: An Initial Appraisal, 1971–1985; an Interim Report* (Washington: National Petroleum Council, 1971), Vol. 2, pp. xv and 59.

District	Demand	Production
I	5.966	0.057
II	4.037	1.433
III	2.537	7.812
IV	0.376	0.708
V	2.070	1.318

OIL AND GAS SOURCES

In 1970, imports provided 12 percent of our energy supply. The possible range of imports in 1985 is extreme. In the lowest demand–highest domestic production situation, imports would represent only 3 to 4 percent of supply. In the highest demand–lowest domestic production situation, imports would supply approximately 40 percent of domestic energy. The most likely situation is that imports will supply between 20 and 28 percent of our total energy. This is between 9 and 14 million barrels of oil per day and between 3.2 and 3.9 trillion cubic feet of gas per year.[11]

Any increase in dependence on imports generates grave concerns on the part of many people both within and outside the government. These concerns fall into four categories: (1) economics, (2) environmental protection, (3) national security, and (4) multiple use—all of which generate great pressure for increasing domestic oil and gas production.

Increased domestic oil and gas production is possible in four areas: (1) onshore lower 48 states, (2) Alaska, (3) state offshore, and (4) the OCS. If we assume maximum feasible domestic production, 60 percent of the domestic oil would come from onshore in 1985. A substantial portion of this will result from the use of secondary and tertiary recovery processes on already developed fields.[12] Somewhere between one-half and two-thirds of the domestic gas will be produced onshore in the lower 48 states.[13]

Again if we assume maximum domestic production in 1985, approximately 20 percent (or 2 to 2.6 million barrels) of oil per day and approximately 15 percent (or 4.4 trillion cubic feet) of gas per year will come from Alaska.

Although state-controlled offshore lands hold promise for increased production, their percentage of 1985 domestic production is much less significant than the OCS. Development in these areas may be difficult also because of local opposition.

The OCS is likely to contribute the major portion of the oil and gas produced offshore in 1985. If we assume maximum development of domestic oil and gas, approximately 20 percent (or 2 to 2.6 million barrels) of oil per day and 30 percent (or 9.1 trillion cubic feet) of gas per year will come from offshore in 1985.

The OCS is also attractive because of its location. A number of the favorable geological structures are located close to high-demand areas, particularly those off the East Coast and California. Additionally, those in the Gulf of Mexico can be readily linked into already established transportation networks.

Industry has made heavy investments in the technologies necessary to develop OCS oil and gas. The projected demand together with expected

OCS resources, their favorable location, and the already heavy industry commitment of capital pressure for continued OCS development seem promising.

In practice the only feasible alternative to the OCS seems to be increased oil and gas imports. (The OCS, the trans-Alaska pipeline (TAPS), and imports are compared in Chapter XII.)

ENVIRONMENTAL CONSTRAINTS

Continued development of OCS oil and gas, however, will take place within the context of continuing demands for environmental quality. OCS oil and gas operations appear to be identified in the minds of many citizens with the environmental concerns generated in the late sixties and early seventies. Union's blowout at Santa Barbara is repeatedly mentioned as a major catalyst for the environmental movement and therefore as a major turning point for public policy. (Although referred to as "Union's blowout," Union Oil Company had three partners: Gulf, Mobil, and Texaco.) In California, for example, the moratorium on leasing state offshore lands imposed after Santa Barbara is still in effect; and on November 7, 1972, California voters passed Proposition 20, the Coastal Zone Conservation Act. This Act established a statewide Coastal Zone Conservation Commission and six regional Commissions to oversee a state plan for the preservation, protection, restoration, and enhancement of the environment and ecology of the coastal zone.[14]

Another indication of public reaction to oil spills has been reported by Hazel Erskine in a study of public opinion polls relating pollution to industry. She found that after Santa Barbara, the oil industry was viewed as the major source of water pollution by people living in the western region of the United States. This had not been so before the Santa Barbara spill, and Erskine attributes the change to widely publicized oil spills on the Pacific Coast.[15] (An analysis of public opinion on pollution is presented in Appendix A.)

Tanker accidents, such as the *Torrey Canyon*, had probably made the public more aware of oil spills, and the reaction was doubtless sustained by three accidents on platforms in the Gulf of Mexico which followed within the next two years.

Concern with OCS oil and gas operations as a major area of environmental problems has been heightened by two other factors. First, a general concern with the environment developed in the late sixties as represented by such issues as the pesticides controversy. As several congressmen noted, the environment became important enough to influence the way people voted. Second, Santa Barbarans had a history of opposing oil and gas development in the channel, and their efforts in opposition to further development after the blowout focused national attention on oil and gas operations for a sustained period of time.

Environmental quality is now an issue of national concern. The change in the social climate is illustrated in the comparison of the reactions to the OCS accidents during the 1969–1971 period with those to a platform fire in the Gulf of Mexico on October 15, 1958.[16] In this case two oil wells ignited and it took over a month to re-establish control. So little public concern was generated that no public estimates of oil spilled or environmental damage existed. Recently, observers have noted that the 1969–71 period was a high point in terms of the level of public concern with the environment. This point is made because there have been a number of spill incidents since 1971, some of which have not been widely reported in the media. The ones that have been reported have not generated the kind of public reaction associated with Santa Barbara.

But even if Santa Barbara was unique, it contributed to developments which will be of continuing importance for OCS oil and gas operations. The most important of these was to open up decision-making for the OCS. Two elements are involved in this change. One is the continuing interest of individuals, groups, and government agencies not previously concerned with OCS operations. The other is the expansion of the criteria that must be taken into account when decisions are made for the OCS in the future. These expanded criteria apply to the procedures to be used in making decisions as well as to the substance to be considered.

An early response to the expanded concern with the OCS was imposition of stricter operating standards by the United States Geological Survey (USGS). And the trend is toward even stricter regulation.

One result of the general concern with the environment was the passage of the National Environmental Policy Act (NEPA, the statute and code citations for which are listed on page xxii) which required use of procedural criteria that assured new individuals and groups access to the decision-making process—public hearings, for example—as well as consideration of new substantive criteria—the assessment of environmental impacts. Passage of the Federal Water Pollution Control Act (FWPCA) is another example of the establishment of stricter procedural and substantive criteria which impact on OCS operations. And the creation of the Environmental Protection Agency (EPA) introduced a new and different kind of federal agency into the arena.

Concern with the impact of OCS oil and gas development has led to the creation of public interest groups and/or attracted the interest of already existing groups. These groups now exist at national, state, and local levels and appear likely to be continuing participants in the OCS policy-making arena.

Sufficient concern with the OCS has been developed among congressmen and state legislators to insure continuing scrutiny by legislative bodies. Although the level of citizen concern and attention by the mass media appears to vary from one part of the country to another, there is now an environmental constituency among the public at large. Leaders in both government and industry have begun to recognize that this is a continuing constituency and to respond to its concerns.[17] To date most of the attention has been focused on pollution, but the expansion of the OCS policy arena will doubtless require assessment of the trade-offs with broader social concerns such as alternative uses and land-use planning.

In summary, then, future OCS oil and gas operations will take place in a context that has changed substantially in the past four years and one that will continue to change. The change will involve participants in this policy arena who represent new values and who will demand that the criteria laid down in recent legislation are applied scrupulously. It will be a setting in which any future dramatic accidents on the OCS hold the possibility of increasingly strict regulation. Future OCS operations then will take place within a complex set of constraints.

The net effect of enlarging the OCS policy-making arena over the past four years has been to slow development. Optimal future development of these resources will require planning and administration which is responsive to these new participants and criteria.

Given the social context just outlined, every effort must be made to carry out OCS operations in an optimal manner. This requires that the technologies involved be responsive to a changed social climate. It is the objective of this technology assessment to contribute to that responsiveness. What follows, then, is an investigation of how the technologies can most effectively contribute to a broad and sometimes conflicting set of social goals.

This assessment has been carried out within certain boundary conditions. Those conditions are of four kinds: limiting definitions, assumptions, purposes, and value standards. We have defined the limits of the study as follows:

1. Geographically it is limited to the outer continental shelf of the lower 48 states and Alaska.

2. In time it is limited to the next fifteen years.

3. Alternative sources of oil and gas, alternative energy forms, and alternative energy mixes have not been assessed in detail. We begin by

asking "if the development of OCS oil and gas resources continues during the next fifteen years, how can social benefits be maximized and social costs be minimized?" Therefore, consideration of alternative sources, forms, and mixes has been limited to their feasibility as replacements for OCS oil and gas during that fifteen-year time period.

4. Since tankers and barges are used on the OCS only infrequently, or in special circumstances, our consideration of these technologies has been limited. We restrict our examination of tankers and barges to their use for temporary storage and for an initial, temporary transportation alternative.

Our operating assumptions have been as follows:

1. Continuing development of the OCS will occur due to the demand for oil and gas and the limitations of alternative energy sources.

2. A major war will not occur, nor will international conditions result in either exaggerated OCS development or its delay.

3. Concern for the non-economic, non-energy impacts of OCS development will be sustained.

Our purposes are to:

1. Assess the broad range of social impacts flowing from OCS oil and gas operations;

2. Contribute to an information base for rational OCS policy-making;

3. Contribute to the formulation of a social-technological system for the development of OCS oil and gas resources which is responsive to a broad set of social concerns; and

4. Make specific recommendations for changes in government policy and administration, and industry management and technologies which will contribute to optimal resources development on the OCS.

In selecting our recommendations we have applied the following standards:

1. In the absence of knowing what the effects of changes will be, OCS oil and gas operations should be conducted to produce minimum change.

2. Achieving minimum change requires the widest possible public access to information and the decision-making process for the OCS.

This study has been conducted by an interdisciplinary research team including a marine biologist, a lawyer, a physicist, two political scientists, and three engineers. It was funded by NSF's RANN program and was conducted over a twenty-month period extending from September, 1971, through March, 1973.

1. Vary Coates, *Technology and Public Policy: The Process of Technology Assessment in the Federal Government, Summary Report* (Washington: Program of Policy Studies in Science and Technology, George Washington University, July, 1972), p. 1.

2. U.S., Congress, Senate, Committee on Interior and Insular Affairs, Henry M. Jackson, Chairman, *Press Release*, August 1, 1972.

3. National Petroleum Council, Committee on U.S. Energy Outlook, *U.S. Energy Outlook: A Summary Report* (Washington: National Petroleum Council, December, 1972).

4. *Ibid.*, p. 3.

5. U.S., Congress, House, Committee on Interior and Insular Affairs, *Energy "Demand" Studies: An Analysis and Appraisal*, Committee Print (Washington: Government Printing Office, 1972).

6. National Petroleum Council, Committee on U.S. Energy Outlook, *U.S. Energy Outlook* (Washington: NPC, 1972), p. 272.

7. *Ibid.*, p. 133.

8. *Ibid.*, Table 21, p. 36.

9. U.S., Executive Office of the President, Office of Emergency Preparedness, *The Potential for Energy Conservation*, Staff Study (Washington: Government Printing Office, 1972).

10. One assessment of limiting demand is in "Energy Options: Limiting Demand," by Joel Darmstadter of Resources for the Future, Inc., a talk before the Upper Midwest Council Conference on the "Outlook for Energy," Minneapolis, Minn., December 9, 1972.

11. NPC, *U.S. Energy Outlook*, 1972, pp. 23, 58.

12. *Ibid.*, p. 36.

13. *Ibid.*, p. 37.

14. George H. Murphy, *Proposed Amendments to Constitution: Propositions and Proposed Laws* for the General Election, Tuesday, November 7, 1972 (Distributed by Edmund G. Brown, Jr., Secretary of State, State of California), p. 51.

15. Helen Erskine, "The Polls: Pollution and Industry," *Public Opinion Quarterly*, 36 (Summer, 1972), p. 264.

16. This was on CAGC's Platform "E" in West Delta Block 45, OCS0138. CAGC is the acronym for Continental, Atlantic, Getty, and Cities Service.

17. V.E. McKelvey, "Petroleum Exploration and the Public Consent," *The Landman*, 17 (February, 1972), pp. 8–13.

II. The Research Strategy

THE DEFINITION OF technology which we use has been an important factor in determining our research strategy in this technology assessment. We assume that technology includes interacting social and physical components. Specifically, OCS oil and gas technologies are a combination of physical technologies (hardware, for example) and social technologies (organizational and management arrangements and procedures, for example): that is, we understand technology to refer to a complex man-machine system whose parts cannot be separated in the real world.

An adequate methodology for assessing technology would allow us to investigate and understand these integrated man-machine systems. No demonstrably successful methodologies are available. There was, however, at the time this study was initiated, some agreement concerning the elements to be included in an assessment. These, summarized in a widely read study of technology assessment methodology prepared by the MITRE Corporation, were built into our research design.[1] These elements include:

1. defining the assessment task;
2. describing relevant technologies;
3. developing state-of-society assumptions;
4. identifying impact areas;
5. making preliminary impact analysis;
6. identifying possible action options;
7. completing impact analysis.

The technology assessment process as outlined in these seven steps assumes physical technologies to be causal factors and therefore the starting point for assessments. This view was central to our research strategy for assessing offshore oil and gas operations. Starting with the physical technologies, we expected to trace through the consequences of these technologies for both the social technologies and for society at large. An objective was to identify those points where changes in either the physical technologies or the social technologies would result in significantly different consequences for society. It should be emphasized, however, that our initial strategy assumed that physical technologies were the primary factors, the engine driving the system.

Our assessment had two objectives: to test the view that an appropriately organized interdisciplinary team could overcome the lack of a technology

15

assessment methodology; and to conduct a substantive assessment of value to policy-makers. Our organizational goal was to develop a capability to identify and assess the second and higher-order consequences of scientific–technological innovations. Our approach reflected the widely held belief that no method or theory exists which will adequately explain society's ability to develop complex technologies. Rather that capacity is largely a product of organizational and managerial skills and as much an art form as a science.[2] Complex technologies are a product of organizational synthesis. Organizational synthesis involves taking men who are informed in-depth and, by means of appropriate organization and management methods, combining their knowledge and insights to produce a complex product. Our objective was to use the same kind of organizational synthesis to assess the second-order consequences of offshore oil and gas technologies.

As for our second objective, we sought to provide a better information base for making policy for developing offshore oil and gas resources. We chose offshore technologies as a focus because they appeared to be evolutionary in character and it was therefore highly probable that we would be able to describe the physical technologies that would be available fifteen years in the future. In addition, offshore oil and gas was an important aspect of a broader energy policy problem area.

INITIAL DATA COLLECTION FOR SYSTEMS ANALYSIS

In our initial research plan, we defined offshore operations as a system. For analytical purposes, we divided that system into three subsystems: (1) exploration; (2) drilling and production; and (3) pipelining, storing, and transporting. The task at this point was to prepare a detailed description of contemporary offshore operations. Each of the subsystems was divided into physical technologies and social technologies. At this point we identified the specific pieces of hardware—downhole safety devices, for example—that make up the physical technologies subsystems. We also identified specific social technologies—rules, regulations, and procedures, for example—and responsible regulatory organizations, for example, the U.S. Geological Survey (USGS). Our goal was to develop a matrix which would indicate how physical and social technologies interact.

Parallel to this, we identified an extensive list of the categories of societal impacts which offshore operations might generate, impacts on marine biosphere and impacts on multiple use, for example. We collected data which would allow identification of how physical technologies linked to social technologies and produced impacts on society. Data collection was aimed at providing a base for subjecting the offshore system to three levels of analysis: (1) specific technologies, (2) technological subsystems, and (3) the total offshore system.

The second stage of our research involved four tasks, to:

1. fill in gaps and refine already collected data;
2. describe the technologies that would be available in fifteen years;
3. describe an "accident response" subsystem;* and
4. develop societal impact categories to be used in constructing an impact matrix.

During the initial stage of our research we had developed descriptions of physical technologies relying primarily on published literature and interviews with operations people in the petroleum industry. Our efforts to identify the technologies of the future relied on interviews with research and development people in the industry. This effort marked a major turning point in the study. We concluded that the physical technology systems in use in the late 1980's would be substantially the same as those in use today. This conclusion does not mean that the technologies are unchanging; rather incremental improvement will continue on a component by component basis. There is no evidence, however, that new physical technology systems will be available over the next fifteen years. We include as an existing technology the prototype subsea production systems presently undergoing tests. The point of emphasis is availability, for there are numerous proposals in the literature for radically different systems, but we could find no evidence of the likelihood of their use within the time period of our study. Finally, it is necessary to note that our conclusions were based on two sources: publicly available information and what we were told by the domestic industry. As a consequence, we may be unaware of proprietary developments within the industry, developments which companies have kept secret in order to gain a competitive advantage.

Our findings concerning the incremental development of the technologies raised serious questions concerning the basic assumption of the assessment, that the engine driving the system was the physical technologies.

* In our first stage of data collection we found that these technologies comprised a distinctive subsystem.

PRELIMINARY IMPACT ANALYSIS

Our preliminary impact analysis involved tracing the impact physical technologies would have on society. This involved the three levels of analysis previously identified: specific technologies, technological subsystems, and the total system. Our goal at this point was to quantify the system to the maximum possible extent.

Several conclusions were drawn from this impact analysis. We were able to identify few impacts that could be expected in the future not already known to observers of offshore operations and already recorded in the literature. The reasons for this were two-fold: (1) the technology of the future was likely to be much like that of the present, and (2) so little knowledge and information exists concerning impacts that it was frequently impossible to determine which impacts were costs and which were benefits, let alone give them specific weights—for example, the impact of platforms on fishing.

In attempting to identify quantitative impacts, we experimented with three methods: (1) an adaptation of a Forrester-style model applied specifically to oil discharges in the waters of the Gulf of Mexico, (2) a gaming model using matrix algebra, and (3) Delphi. In each case, our lack of a data base or the nature of the data gave the efforts an unreal character. We found that the mechanics of Delphi would require more time than seemed warranted given the expected results. In summary, we found that these methods were for the most part inapplicable and we elected not to use them in making our assessment.

In addition to recognizing our limited ability to identify new impacts, the work to this point isolated two other problem areas. One was that we should limit the study to the outer continental shelf (OCS). We came to this conclusion because of the complexity and difficulty of collecting data on state legal/administrative systems and the relatively minor role these areas will play in the future. And, second, as previously noted, our research strategy had to be modified since it was clear that the physical technologies did not drive the system.

REDESIGN OF THE ASSESSMENT

Our initial research strategy provided for conducting what the National Academy of Engineering (NAE) has labeled "technology-initiated analysis."[3] NAE used the analogy of an inverted funnel to illustrate this assessment approach. "The assessment process begins with the new technology at the small end and emerges as a complex pattern of consequences at the large end." Given our findings concerning the relative stability of the technology, we reversed our research strategy, adopting instead what the NAE has labeled "problem-initiated analysis."[4] Again using the funnel analogy, this "process begins at the large end of the funnel, and the optimum solution to a given problem emerges at the small end."

Specifically, we prepared a catalogue of all the negative impacts of OCS operations which had been identified by observers. At this juncture we made no effort to judge the criteria upon which they were labeled as negative impacts. From these impacts, we traced causes back through the social technologies to the physical technologies.

Using a "problem-initiated analysis" strategy, we identified weaknesses in specific technologies and the overall system of physical technologies. Based on this analysis, we concluded that correction of virtually all physical technology problems was within state-of-the-art capabilities. In practice, many of the weaknesses in physical technologies could be corrected if equipment and designs already in existence were used.

It became evident that the major modifications required were in the social technologies (rules, regulations, procedures, etc.). Changes were needed which would induce the use of the best available physical technologies. Or, where needed, social technologies should be capable of generating pressures for developing improved physical technologies. For instance, through the use of regulation and new research and development (R and D), government could stimulate the creation and use of new physical technologies over the next fifteen years.

This redefinition of our assessment cast it much more in the light of a traditional policy analysis. Indeed a major objective now was the understanding of an incremental policy-making system, one in which policy is the accumulated result of many specific decisions and actions.[5] This understanding was necessary because we now defined our objective as making recommendations aimed at improving the OCS system for the future. The lack of alternative systems of physical technologies had effectively eliminated the initial objective of cost-benefiting alternative physical technologies.

EXECUTION OF THE PROBLEM-INITIATED ANALYSIS

Based upon our redefinition of the study as a problem-initiated analysis, the task now was to identify the policy issues (causes of negative impacts), define alternative ways of dealing with those issues, and recommend the most desirable alternatives.

It should be noted that the assessment was still focused on the future. Our goal still was to find ways to correct deficiencies and improve OCS oil and gas operations.

Since we were recommending specific policy alternatives, we had to establish a value standard. Our findings concerning data and measures for determining the nature and quality of impacts had already demonstrated the practical inability of establishing substantive standards in most impact areas. Therefore, we adopted procedural standards. Our objective was to assure that OCS operations resulted in minimum change unless the effects of the change are known: that is, specific substantive standards should be set only when it is generally agreed that the resulting changes will produce an improved balance between overall social benefits and costs. This objective clearly required recommending dynamic social technologies. In addition, we posited as an instrumental value that to achieve our stated objective would require the widest possible public access to OCS policy-making. Our recommended policy alternatives are based on these two standards.

Our policy analysis involved several steps. First, using the large number of impacts that had been identified, we selected out those impacts which appeared to be most significant. To be significant, the impacts had to have broad social importance and be likely to continue over the next fifteen years unless corrective action was taken. These decisions were based on the collective judgment of the research team. When questions arose which the team was unable to resolve, we sought the judgments of outside consultants.

Significant issues were then divided into physical and social technologies issues. Social technologies issues were subdivided into the four issue categories: (1) information and data, (2) environmental quality, (3) government management, and (4) jurisdiction. Only one category of physical technologies issues was analyzed, those which raised questions concerning the adequacy of specific physical technologies.

Each issue within each category was defined as a policy issue, and causes and parties of interest were identified.

A range of alternative means for dealing with each of the issues was then developed based on three major sources: proposals that had already been made, proposals made by consultants to our group, and proposals generated within our group itself.

On the basis of our policy analyses of the alternative means proposed for dealing with each of the issue categories, we summarized a set of desirable changes. These proposals were then reviewed by nine consultants representing public interest groups, a variety of academic disciplines and government agencies, and the petroleum industry.

Based on the desirable changes developed for each of the issue categories, we then developed an integrated set of recommendations for improving the operation of the OCS system. The criteria employed in selecting these recommendations provided for a standard of minimum possible change technologically and economically achievable in impact areas and the widest possible public participation in OCS policy-making. It is our intention in the recommendations to provide an overall design for the operation of the OCS system, a design which will allow optimal development of these resources.

1. Martin V. Jones, *Project Summary*, summary volume of *A Technology Assessment Methodology*, The MITRE Corporation (7 vols.; Washington: The MITRE Corporation, 1971), p. 7.

2. Don E. Kash and Irvin L. White, "Technology Assessment: Harnessing Genius," *Chemical & Engineering News*, 49 (November 29, 1971), p. 38.

3. National Academy of Engineering, Committee on Public Engineering Policy, *A Study of Technology Assessment*, Report to the Committee on Science and Astronautics, U.S. House of Representatives (Washington: Government Printing Office, July, 1969), pp. 15–16.

4. *Ibid.*, p. 15.

5. Charles Lindblom, *Intelligence of Democracy* (New York: Free Press, 1965).

Part Two

The Development of OCS Oil and Gas Resources

In this part of the report, we provide an overall description of how OCS oil and gas resources are developed. We begin, in Chapter III, with a chronological description of the various functional activities to be performed and the physical technologies used to perform them. In Chapter IV, we provide summary descriptions of the petroleum industry which develops OCS resources and the governmental system established to oversee their development. And, in Chapter V, we discuss how public policy for the OCS has been made and administered and how new policy objectives, particularly a general concern for protecting and restoring the environment, have affected public policy-making and administration in this policy area.

III. How OCS Oil and Gas Resources Are Developed

THE UNITED STATES first claimed exclusive ownership of the natural resources of the continental shelf adjacent to its coasts in a Presidential Proclamation issued by President Harry S. Truman in September, 1945.[1] This unilateral claim was subsequently affirmed by the multinational 1958 Geneva Convention on the Continental Shelf. The portion of the shelf to be under federal jurisdiction was defined in the Outer Continental Shelf Lands Act and the Submerged Lands Act, both enacted in 1953. (Throughout the report statutes are referred to by title; see the List of Statutes for statute and U.S. Code references.) These statutes provide for a division which assigns to the states a band extending from the coastline three miles seaward. The area beyond that, the outer continental shelf (OCS), is assigned to the federal government. This division has been and is being challenged by a number of coastal states, successfully so far by only Texas and Florida.[2]

OCS resources are public resources. The federal government is responsible for managing and controlling them and this responsibility is assigned to specific federal agencies by statute. The basic legislation establishing public policy for the development of resources in this area is the OCS Lands Act. Qualified U.S. nationals acquire the right to develop a specific tract through a competitive lease bid system authorized by this Act. Although the actual development is by private persons, government agencies, principally the Department of the Interior, are responsible for establishing and enforcing regulations which will achieve established public policy objectives.

The first sale for leasing oil and gas rights on the OCS to private persons took place in October, 1954. Actually, however, the petroleum industry had been developing oil and gas resources offshore for many years before that. In California, oil has been produced from piers extending offshore since the late 1800's, the first such well being drilled near Santa Barbara in 1897. In the Gulf of Mexico, most of the early activity was in marshlands and near-shore areas under state jurisdiction. The first offshore well on a platform out of sight of land was completed in 1947 in the Ship Shoal area of the Creole field off the coast of Louisiana.

More than 16,000 wells have now been drilled in state and federal offshore lands.[3] Of these, approximately 10,000 wells are still producing oil or gas.[4] In 1971, these wells produced 616 million barrels of oil and 3.8 trillion cubic feet of gas. This was about 17 percent of all oil and gas produced in the United States in 1971. Cumulative offshore production at the end of 1971 was reported by the Department of the Interior to be 4.8 billion barrels of oil and 20.7 trillion cubic feet of gas.[5]

In this chapter, we describe the technologies currently being used and developed by the petroleum industry in its OCS oil and gas operations. We also describe the activities involved in developing these resources and indicate the permits and permissions that must be obtained, which government agencies are responsible for overseeing the various aspects of development, where other parties interested in OCS development can attempt to influence the administration of public policy for the OCS, and the general economics of producing OCS petroleum. Our objective is to provide the reader, particularly those who make and/or administer policies affecting OCS development, with an overall description of the activities and technologies for finding, developing, producing, and transporting oil and gas on the U.S. OCS. To accomplish this objective, we have organized our discussion into six major categories: exploration, field development, production, transportation, accident response, and economics. The first four of these are major phases in the normal development process and include a description of steps taken to prevent accidents from occurring, the fifth focuses on the activities and technologies available for responding when accidents do occur, and the sixth provides a general overview of OCS economics.

EXPLORATION

Exploratory activities are undertaken to locate geological formations which are potential oil and gas reservoirs. These activities, the first step in the process of developing OCS resources, progress through three principal phases:

1. regional surveys to identify promising geological formations;
2. detailed surveys upon which to base the evaluation of specific tracts; and
3. exploratory drilling to determine whether oil and gas are actually present.

Both industry and government require good exploratory data for making decisions concerning OCS development. Industry needs the data for determining the value of tracts being offered for sale. Since this is one of the principal determinants of a company's bonus bid, the better the data and its presentation and interpretation, presumably the more competitive a company can be.

Government also requires the data for determining the value of the tracts which it plans to sell. In addition, government agencies need the data to be able to determine the environmental risk associated with developing a particular tract, and as a basis for prescribing and enforcing rules to prevent waste and to conserve the natural resources of the OCS as required by the OCS Lands Act.

EXPLORATORY PERMIT

A permit must be obtained before any exploratory activity may be undertaken on the OCS (see Figure 4). Section 11 of the OCS Lands Act provides that:

> any agency of the U.S. and any person authorized by the Secretary [of the Interior] may conduct geological and geophysical explorations in the outer Continental Shelf which do not interfere with or endanger actual operations under any lease maintained or granted pursuant to this Act, and which are not unduly harmful to aquatic life in such area.

In practice these permits are issued by the Area Oil and Gas Supervisor of the U.S. Geological Survey (USGS).

The Area Supervisor issues the permit after he ascertains that the requirements of cooperative agreements between the Department of the Interior and the states of Alabama, California, Florida, Georgia, Louisiana, or Texas have been met. These agreements require that permission be obtained from the Corps of Engineers (Corps) and that a stipulation be filed with the Area Supervisor and with the appropriate agencies of states adjoining the areas to be explored (see Figure 4). In the stipulation, the applicant agrees to comply with all regulations of the adjoining states which govern and, in some cases, restrict the exploratory techniques which may be used. The Corps' permission is intended to prevent obstructions to navigation; the stipulation is intended to insure that aquatic life is protected and conserved.

In the case of exploration off all other coastal states, permission does not have to be obtained from the Corps and the stipulation has to be filed with only the Area Supervisor.

As a further means of insuring against adverse environmental impacts during exploration, there are cooperative agreements among the National Marine Fisheries Service, the Bureau of Sports Fisheries and Wildlife, the Bureau of Land Management (BLM), and USGS concerning pollution, the use of explosives, and obstructions to fishing.[6]

Phase I Exploration

Industry is engaged almost continuously in broad area reconnaissance. The

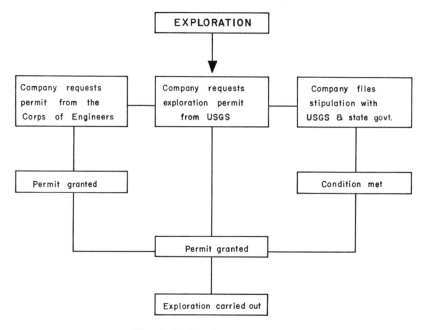

Fig. 4. Exploration Procedures

methods used in this activity are generally passive in nature and include either air- or ship-borne measurements of changes in the earth's magnetic field, local variations in the earth's gravity, and the existence of natural oil seeps. Gravimetric methods have been used extensively in locating salt dome structures in the Gulf of Mexico, and natural seeps gave early indications of oil deposits off southern California.

A number of more advanced techniques have been suggested including satellite photography and infrared measurements. The National Aeronautics and Space Administration's (NASA) Earth Resources Technologies Satellites and Skylab projects include tests of one or more of these sensors. It is not clear at this time how useful these techniques will be in locating offshore petroleum resources.

Since these reconnaissance techniques are almost entirely passive, their physical impacts on the environment are minor. Furthermore, interference between users of these technologies and other users of air space and ocean space above the OCS appears to be negligible.

Phase II Exploration

When the decision is made to undertake a more detailed investigation of a particular area on the OCS, a number of exploratory tools are available in addition to the passive methods used in reconnaissance. These include seismic surveying, bottom sampling, and coring. All are active techniques and have a physical impact on the environment in which they are employed.

Seismic Surveying: Seismic surveying is by far the most frequently employed technique in the pre-lease sale phase of exploration. In a seismic survey (as shown in Figure 5), an energy source is used to generate sound waves which are reflected and refracted by the underlying geologic strata. The echos are picked up on hydrophones and recorded on magnetic tape. These data are used to prepare cross sections of the subsurface structure in the area being surveyed. Combinations of cross sections can be used to obtain a three-dimensional picture showing the location of geologic structures of the types known to be favorable for the accumulation of oil and gas.[7]

Until a few years ago, the energy source used in seismic surveying at sea

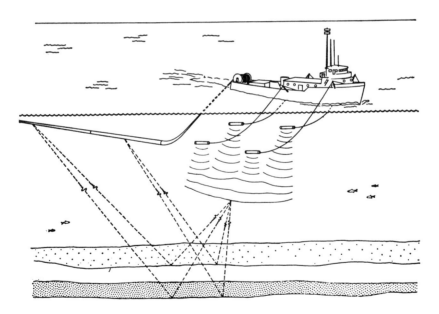

Fig. 5. Seismic Surveying

Source: OTC 1120, *1969 Offshore Technology Conference, May 18–21, Houston, Texas, Preprints,* Vol. 2, p. 421. Used by permission of Esso Production Research Co. and the Society of Exploration Geophysicists.

Fig. 6. Propane-Oxygen Gun

Source: Esso Production Research Company. Used by permission.

was usually a charge of dynamite or other explosive material. Since the use of explosives at sea caused damage and killed marine life, other energy sources have been developed. Currently almost all marine seismic work is done with these substitute energy sources; almost none is now done with explosives.

There are two principal types of substitutes, those which involve the contained explosion of a gas mixture, and those which use a continuous electronic vibrator with a variable frequency. Esso Production Research Company's propane-oxygen gun, illustrated in Figure 6, is typical of the first type. Propane and oxygen are detonated inside a rubber sleeve which transmits the energy directly to the water. Continental Oil Company's "VIBROSEIS," an example of the second type, is shown in Figure 7. The "VIBROSEIS" uses a high-powered oscillator whose frequency changes continuously over a period of a few seconds. Neither of these new energy sources appears to have any significantly adverse environmental impacts;

nor does their use appear to conflict with other kinds of activities in the areas being surveyed.

The most significant limitation in exploration has been the inability to locate hydrocarbons without drilling. Although sophisticated instrumentation and advanced computer methods are used in both gravimetric and seismic exploration, the interpretation of the data depends heavily on the skill of geological specialists. The most promising means for improving the reliability and quality of exploratory data appears to be in the continuing refinement of computer methods for reducing, enhancing, and then displaying data taken during multi-sensor surveys. The quality of this data has recently improved to such a point that geologists are asserting that they can detect "direct indications of hydrocarbons in seismograph data."[8] Hydrocarbon concentrations in overlaying rocks have also been detected through physico-chemical tests.[9]

Bottom Sampling and Coring: The general USGS authorization to conduct geological and geophysical exploration does not include the right to take bottom samples or cores. If, in the opinion of USGS, either bottom sampling or coring is necessary to evaluate the potential of a particular area, limited permits may be issued so long as the likelihood of environmental damage is small. When permitted, samples obtained must be made available to USGS.

Recently, USGS has required applicants to furnish shallow-focus seismic data prior to granting a permit for either technique to be used. Where coring has been permitted, penetration of the sediment has been limited to 1,000 feet. Most permits allow penetration of 500 feet of sediment without restriction, but drilling must cease after sampling the first 20 feet of consolidated formation below a depth of 200 feet. The purpose of these restrictions is to reduce the possibility of blowouts or other adverse environmental effects and to preclude the testing of potentially productive formations in advance of a lease sale.

Bottom sampling and coring do have physical impact on the environment. Environmental damage is confined, however, to the immediate area within which the bottom is being sampled or the core taken. Permits are not issued often and, when they are, environmental impacts are supposed to be weighed against the advantages to be gained by acquiring the samples or cores. The use of these techniques is closely supervised, with USGS now requiring that one of its personnel be on board during bottom sampling or coring operations.

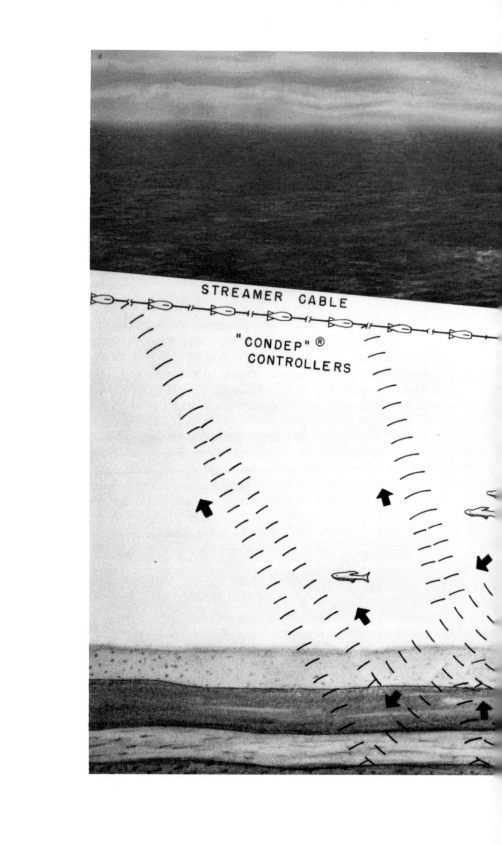

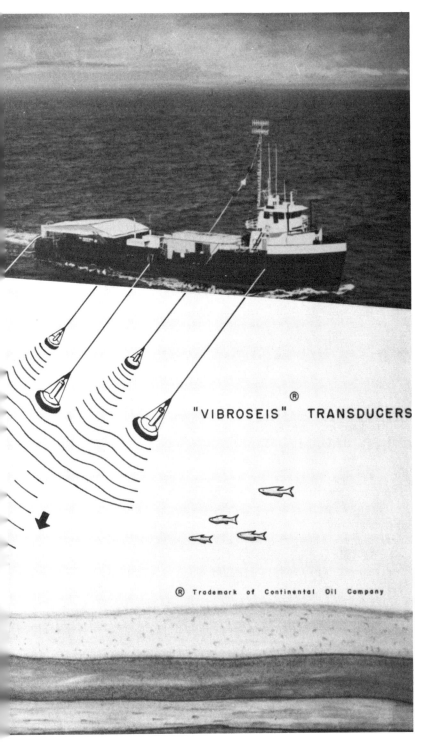

Fig. 7. "VIBROSEIS" System
Source: Continental Oil Company. Used by permission.

Phase III Exploration

Exploratory drilling is not permitted until after a tract has been purchased in a lease sale. Under Section 8 of the OCS Lands Act, the Secretary of the Interior is authorized "to grant to the highest responsible bidder by competitive bidding . . . oil and gas leases on the outer Continental Shelf." In administering this system, the Secretary is responsible for: (1) meeting "the urgent need for further exploration and development of the oil and gas deposits of the submerged lands of the outer Continental Shelf . . . ;"[10] (2) providing "for the prevention of waste and conservation of the natural resources of the outer Continental Shelf . . .;"[11] and (3) protecting and restoring the environment.[12]

Within the Department of the Interior, the Bureau of Land Management (BLM) is directly responsible for administering the leasing system (see Figure 8). BLM issues a call for nominations specifying the general location within which nominations will be received. The Director of BLM selects the tracts to be sold from those nominated by private individuals, by companies, by the Secretary (upon the advice of the Director of USGS), or by BLM.

Since OCS lease sales are considered to be major federal actions significantly affecting the quality of the human environment, environmental impact statements are required and are now prepared by BLM for each proposed sale. A draft statement is circulated to all interested parties at least 90 days before the proposed sale date. If a public hearing is to be held, as has been the case before each recent sale, the draft statement must be available at least 15 days beforehand.

BLM receives the requested comments and modifies the statement as appropriate. The final environmental statement, together with comments, is made public no later than 30 days before the scheduled sale. (It is at this point that environmental interest groups have participated in policy-making for the OCS, primarily by challenging the adequacy of the statement.) If the statement is not challenged or if the challenge is not successful, the sale may then be held on the proposed date.

Sealed bids are submitted in advance and must be accompanied by information qualifying the bidder as one legally entitled to participate—a responsible U.S. national—together with a certified check for 20 percent of the amount bid. Bids are opened at a public meeting (see Figure 9). The Director of BLM has 30 days in which to decide whether to accept or reject the highest bid for each tract. When bids are rejected, it is usually because they are considered to be too low.

The award of a lease assigns to the lessee "the exclusive right and privilege to drill for, mine, extract, remove and dispose of oil and gas deposits,

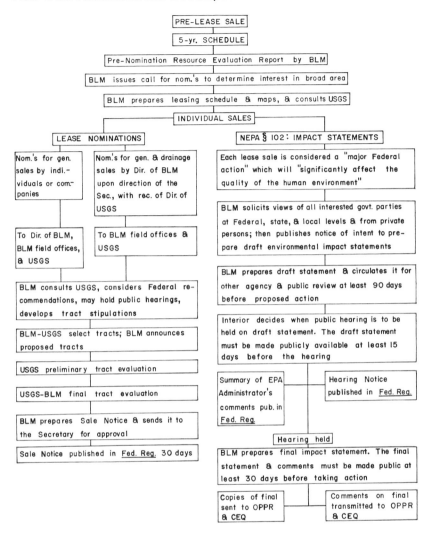

Fig. 8. Pre-Lease Sale Procedures

except helium gas, in or under" the area described in the lease agreement.[13] These rights extend "for a period of five years and so long thereafter as oil or gas may be produced from the area in paying quantities, or drilling or well reworking operations as approved by the Secretary are conducted thereon."[14]

The lessee is obligated to proceed diligently to develop the tract he has

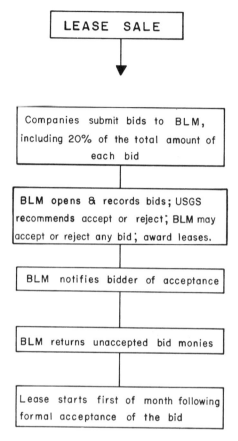

Fig. 9. Lease Sale Procedures

won.[15] Although additional seismic work may be carried out before proceeding, it is necessary to drill wells in order to determine whether commercial accumulations of oil or gas underlie the tract.

Exploratory Drilling Platforms: The drilling equipment used for drilling offshore exploratory wells is similar to that used on land. The most significant difference is that offshore operations require a platform to support the drill rig and associated equipment. Four basic types of platforms are now being used to support exploratory drilling offshore: barges, drill ships, jack-ups, and semi-submersibles.

Barges were used extensively in drilling the first shallow water wells in the Gulf of Mexico. Compartments in these early barges were controlled-flooded until the barge sat on the seabed. This technique was limited to water depths permitting the upper structure of the barge to be high enough

DISCOVERER III

Fig. 10. Drill Ship

Source: The Offshore Company. Used by permission.

above water for drilling operations to be conducted. In contrast, most new barges are floaters. Although they are neither ship-shaped nor self-propelled, they are used much like drill ships. Barges of this type are suitable for drilling in water depths of 600 feet or more.[16] This is primarily a limitation imposed by the anchor and chain systems used for maintaining position. However, barges also have a weather limitation since, given their hull shapes, they have poor motion characteristics.

Drill ships (see Figure 10) generally have the same lines as traditional merchant ships. They are self-propelled and therefore are capable of moving from one drilling location to another without assistance. Positioning

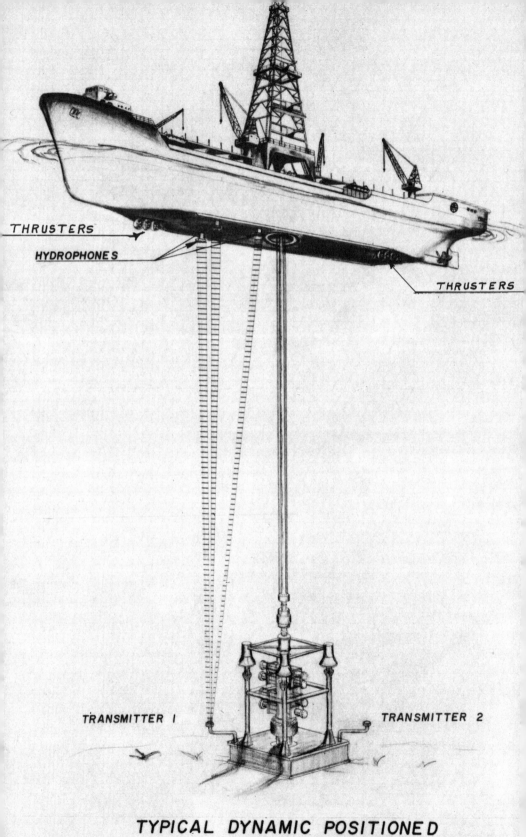

THRUSTERS

HYDROPHONES

THRUSTERS

TRANSMITTER 1

TRANSMITTER 2

TYPICAL DYNAMIC POSITIONED
DEEP WATER DRILL SHIP

is accomplished by either a mooring system of anchors and chains or a dynamic positioning system. This latter system consists of a series of propellers or thrusters coupled to sensors which detect and compensate for movement (see Figure 11). Drill ships are now being constructed that can drill and re-enter wells in water depths of up to 3,000 feet of water[17] and are expected eventually to have an almost unlimited depth capability.

Jack-up rigs are platforms with legs that can be moved up and down (see Figure 12). When the legs are extended, the platform can elevate itself above water and temporarily become a bottom standing platform. By retracting its legs, the jack-up becomes a floater and, with assistance, can be moved from one location to another. At the present time, jack-ups can drill in water depths of up to 350 feet.[18]

The semi-submersible is the newest type of drilling rig available and is the best suited for severe weather environments (see Figure 13). These rigs have a platform deck supported by columns which are connected to large underwater displacement hulls or large vertical caissons or some combination of the two.[19] The columns, displacement hulls, or caissons are flooded on site "to reduce wave forces by locating the major buoyancy members beneath the surface or beneath the wave action."[20]

Semi-submersibles may or may not be self-propelled. And they share the positioning limitations of all floating drilling rigs. Most are presently positioned with mooring systems although some are also equipped with dynamic positioning systems. At the present time, semi-submersibles are limited to a water depth of about 2,000 feet, but the expectation is that these rigs eventually will be able to drill in any water depth.

All floating rigs share another problem in addition to those identified above: platform motion induced by wave action which affects drilling. Marine risers (see Figure 14) have been developed to conduct the drill string from the platform to the hole being drilled and are designed to permit some lateral and vertical movement during drilling operations without breaking off the drill string. Risers are currently available for water depths of up to 1,500 feet and are being developed for deeper water.

Exploratory Drilling Permits: Detailed requirements for most phases of finding, developing, producing, and transporting oil and gas on the OCS are set forth in OCS Orders for each of the USGS Areas. USGS is the agency with the broadest responsibility for overseeing these activities. However, the Corps of Engineers, Coast Guard, Environmental Protection

---

Fig. 11. Dynamic Positioning System
Source: The Offshore Company. Used by permission.

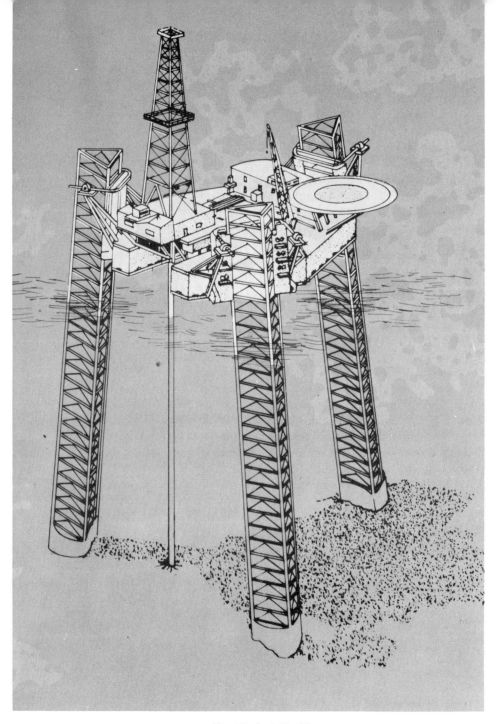

Fig. 12. Jack-Up Rig

Source: Esso Production Research Company. Used by permission.

Fig. 13. Semi-Submersible Rig

Source: The Offshore Company. Used by permission.

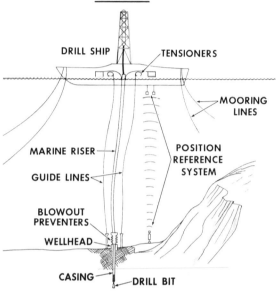

FLOATING DRILLING SYSTEM

DRILL SHIP — TENSIONERS

MOORING LINES

MARINE RISER

POSITION REFERENCE SYSTEM

GUIDE LINES

BLOWOUT PREVENTERS

WELLHEAD

CASING — DRILL BIT

Fig. 14. Marine Riser

Source: Esso Production Research Company. Used by permission.

Agency (EPA), and Occupational Safety and Health Administration have certain responsibilities as well: the Corps must approve all offshore structures, including movable drilling rigs;[21] the Coast Guard sets requirements for marking structures and artificial islands, for specifying personnel safety equipment and procedures,[22] and for monitoring pollution on the OCS;[23] EPA sets pollution standards, issues discharge permits, and consults with the other agencies on questions of the environmental impact of OCS operations;[24] and the Occupational Safety and Health Administration promulgates standards for and conducts inspections of the working environment.[25] Most of these requirements have to be met before commencing exploratory drilling operations.

USGS permission is required before exploratory drilling can begin (see Figure 15). The lessee submits an exploratory drilling plan to the Area Supervisor which includes:

(1) a description of drilling vessels, platforms, or other structures showing the location, the design, and the major features thereof, including features pertaining to pollution prevention and control; (2) the general location of

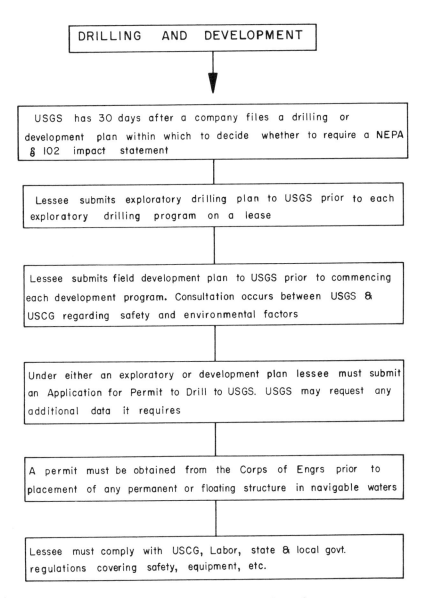

DRILLING AND DEVELOPMENT

USGS has 30 days after a company files a drilling or development plan within which to decide whether to require a NEPA § 102 impact statement

Lessee submits exploratory drilling plan to USGS prior to each exploratory drilling program on a lease

Lessee submits field development plan to USGS prior to commencing each development program. Consultation occurs between USGS & USCG regarding safety and environmental factors

Under either an exploratory or development plan lessee must submit an Application for Permit to Drill to USGS. USGS may request any additional data it requires

A permit must be obtained from the Corps of Engrs prior to placement of any permanent or floating structure in navigable waters

Lessee must comply with USCG, Labor, state & local govt. regulations covering safety, equipment, etc.

Fig. 15. Drilling and Development Procedures

each well including surface and projected bottom hole location for direction-ally drilled wells; (3) structural interpretations based on available geological and geophysical data; and (4) such other pertinent data as the supervisor may prescribe.[26]

Under current Department of Interior rules, the Area Supervisor has 30 days within which to determine whether granting the permit would con-stitute a major federal action of significant impact on the human environ-ment. Ordinarily approval of an exploratory drilling plan does not require an impact statement; however, if the request involves drilling in an en-vironmentally sensitive area, a statement may be required. If a statement were to be required, this would provide another access point for environ-mental interest groups to participate in OCS policy-making.

Even though an exploratory drilling plan has been approved, a separate "Application for Permit to Drill" has to be submitted prior to drilling operations. It must meet USGS requirements for controlling wells and be consistent with the exploratory drilling plan.[27] The application describes the integrated program for blowout prevention which includes the mud, casing, and cementing programs.

Exploratory Drilling: Drilling methods and much of the equipment used offshore are identical to those used on land. The hole is drilled using a rotary drill: that is, the hole is drilled by rotating a drill bit on the bottom of a string of drill pipe (see Figure 16). Cuttings from the drill face are removed by a fluid called drilling mud which is pumped down through the drill string, out through the bit, and circulated back to the surface via the annular space between the drill string and the bore hole. In addition to removing cuttings, drilling mud acts to prevent blowouts by counter-bal-ancing formation pressures and preventing the flow of liquids or gases from the formation zones penetrated as the hole is drilled. The necessary balance is accomplished by: (1) regulating the specific weight of the mud being used and thereby the weight of the mud column, and (2) controlling the mud flow rate. At the present time, the tool pusher (driller) usually has limited information available to him on bore hole pressure, mud volume, and mud circulation rate. Variations or rates of change in all three are po-tentially important in detecting unwanted downhole pressure changes which could result in a blowout.

Since blowouts are dangerous, expensive, environmentally damaging, and attract public attention, a number of safeguards in addition to drilling mud are used to minimize the likelihood of their occurrence. These include setting casing and installing blowout preventers (BOP's).

Casing, which consists of relatively large-diameter steel pipe, is set and

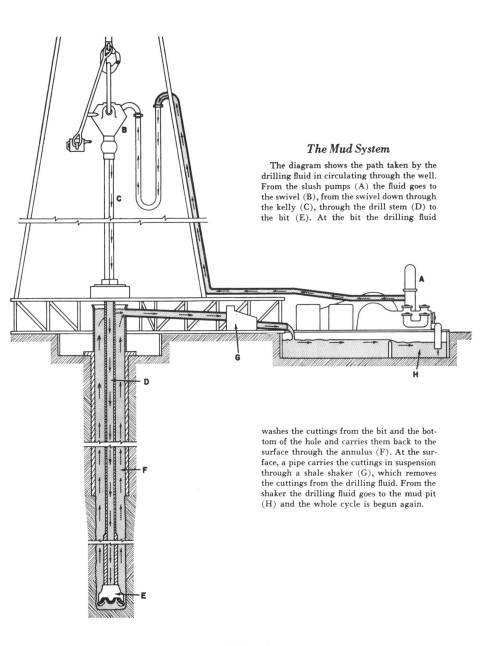

The Mud System

The diagram shows the path taken by the drilling fluid in circulating through the well. From the slush pumps (A) the fluid goes to the swivel (B), from the swivel down through the kelly (C), through the drill stem (D) to the bit (E). At the bit the drilling fluid washes the cuttings from the bit and the bottom of the hole and carries them back to the surface through the annulus (F). At the surface, a pipe carries the cuttings in suspension through a shale shaker (G), which removes the cuttings from the drilling fluid. From the shaker the drilling fluid goes to the mud pit (H) and the whole cycle is begun again.

Fig. 16. Drilling System

Source: University of Texas at Austin, Division of Extension, Petroleum Extension Service, *A Primer of Oil Well Drilling* (2nd ed.; Austin: Petroleum Extension Service, University of Texas, 1957), p. 35. Used by Permission.

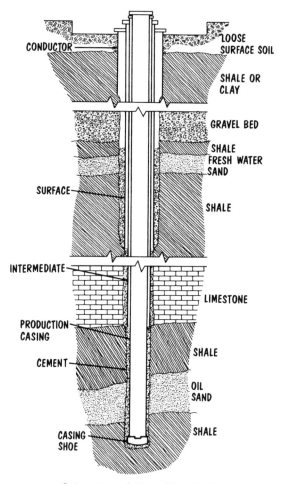

CONDUCTOR

LOOSE SURFACE SOIL

SHALE OR CLAY

GRAVEL BED

SHALE
FRESH WATER
SAND

SURFACE

SHALE

INTERMEDIATE

LIMESTONE

PRODUCTION CASING

CEMENT

SHALE

OIL SAND

CASING SHOE

SHALE

Casing strings and pipe used in an oil well.

Fig. 17. Casing
Source: University of Texas at Austin, Division of Extension, Petroleum Extension Service, *A Primer of Oil Well Drilling* (3rd ed.; Austin: Petroleum Extension Service, University of Texas, 1970), p. 48. Used by permission.

cemented to a depth specified by OCS Order No. 2 issued by the appropriate USGS Area Supervisor. The casing is, in effect, a liner for the bore hole and may be as large as 36 inches in diameter. Specific requirements are established on the basis of the sub-surface structural features and pressures which are expected to be encountered (see Figure 17).[28]

Surface casing also provides an attachment for the BOP stack. The stack, shown in Figure 18, consists of a series of control valves which are capable

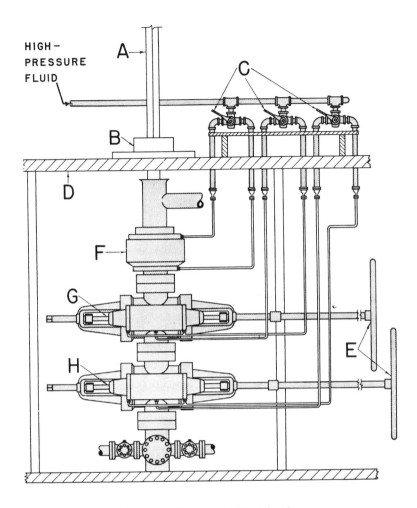

HIGH–PRESSURE FLUID

Fig. 18. Blowout Preventer Stack

Source: University of Texas at Austin, Division of Extension, Petroleum Extension Service, *A Primer of Oil Well Drilling* (2nd ed.; Austin: Petroleum Extension Service, University of Texas, 1957), p. 45. Used by permission.

A = Kelly; B = Rotary table; C = Hydraulic controls on derrick floor; D = Derrick floor; E = Manually operated controls on side of substructure; F = Top preventer, which contains large rubber element capable of sealing around any tool protruding through casing head; G = Pipe rams, which close off hole, provided drill string is removed.

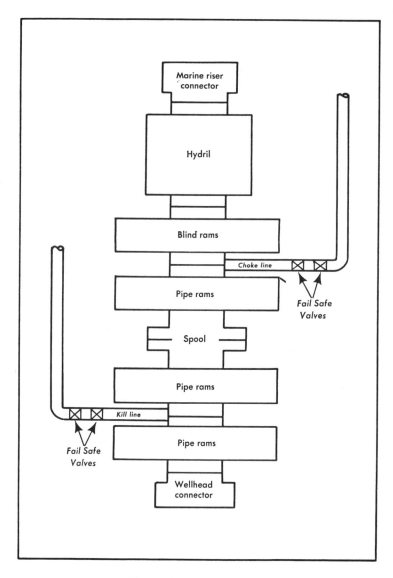

Fig. 19. Subsea BOP Stack

Source: L. M. Harris, *An Introduction to Deepwater Floating Drilling Operations* (Tulsa: Petroleum Publishing Co., 1972), p. 99. Used by permission.

of either closing around the drill string to seal off the annular space or closing off the hole completely. On land and on bottom-standing platforms offshore, the BOP stack is attached to the top of the surface casing just beneath the rotary table. In the case of floating rigs, the stack is attached to the top of the surface casing on the ocean floor (see Figure 19).

In the case of floating rigs, the BOP's located on the seafloor are hydraulically activated and are controlled from the ship. In deep water, the time required to activate the preventers from the surface may pose a problem and some new floating rigs are being equipped with electronically activated systems in order to achieve a shorter response time. Whether hydraulically or electronically controlled, BOP's are activated manually, not automatically.

FIELD DEVELOPMENT

After commercial accumulations of oil or gas have been found and defined during the exploratory phase, plans must be formulated for developing the field so that it can be produced. Actually several exploration and field development activities overlap. For example, while the exploration department of a company is drilling wells to determine the extent of the field and the recoverable reserves, the production department may be preparing

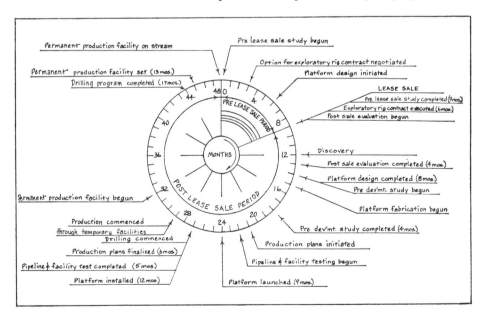

Fig. 20. A Hypothetical Four-Year Offshore Planning and Field Development Program

the production plan and placing orders for major equipment. The hypothetical planning and development program outlined in Figure 20 illustrates how activities are integrated from before the lease sale until permanent production facilities are put into operation.

DEVELOPMENT PLAN

The field development phase formally begins with the submission of a development plan to the Area Supervisor (see Figure 15).[29] As with the exploratory drilling plan, this plan is to include: (1) a detailed description of drilling vessels, platforms, and structures indicating where they are to be located as well as their major features; (2) the location of each well to be drilled including bottom hole location in the case of directionally drilled wells; (3) structural interpretations for these areas; and (4) any other data the supervisor may require. A separate drilling permit must also be requested; this is identical to the Application for Permit to Drill required for drilling exploratory wells. Both the development plan and drilling permit are subject to the Department of Interior rule providing for a 30-day period after submission of the application for the purpose of determining whether approval of the request would constitute a major federal action which might significantly affect the quality of the human environment.

Because of the comprehensive nature of the development plan, extensive planning must precede its submission. A major decision is the selection of a production facility. At the present time the two principal alternatives are fixed platforms and subsea completions. Subsea production systems are being tested and developed, and several intermediate alternatives, including buoyant towers and tension-leg platforms, have been proposed.

FIXED PLATFORMS

Fixed platforms such as the one pictured in Figure 21 have evolved from the simple wooden structures used by the industry in the bayous of Louisiana. These steel truss structures are now fairly well standardized within the industry. The platform, which is permanently attached to the ocean floor by steel pilings, supports one or more decks on which drilling and production equipment is mounted.

New platforms scheduled for the North Sea will operate in water depths of up to 550 feet. And Exxon is planning to use a fixed platform in 850 feet of water in the Santa Barbara Channel.

Although the limiting height of conventional fixed platforms has been estimated to be in excess of 1,000 feet, there is a good chance that the North Sea and Santa Barbara installations may represent the ultimate size. The

Fig. 21. Fixed Platform
Source: Shell Oil Company. Used by permission.

two major technological problems are foundations and dynamic response. But, in the end, the ultimate upper limit is really economic.

For both drilling and production, a large amount of equipment has to be mounted on a very compact platform; and this compactness contributes to many of the problems which occur on platforms. Although safety has not been neglected, overall safety systems, such as gas and flame detectors, fire containment design, fire control equipment, and rapid escape systems for personnel, have been identified as areas requiring additional attention. The situation is changing as both USGS and the operators apply lessons learned in the Chevron, Shell, and Amoco accidents in the Gulf, all of which involved fires that destroyed or extensively damaged the platform, required personnel evacuation, and in one case resulted in several personnel casualties.

SUBSEA COMPLETIONS AND PRODUCTION SYSTEMS

Subsea completions involve placing the wellheads on the ocean floor rather than on platforms. The produced liquids or gases are transferred from the wellhead either to a nearby fixed platform or to a shore facility for processing. At the present time, more than 70 subsea completions are in use in offshore U.S. waters.

Two prototype subsea production systems (SPS) are presently being tested under actual field conditions and another is in an earlier design stage, but the subsea production system can be considered a part of existing offshore technology. These systems come in a variety of configurations. They include both wet systems, in which the wellhead equipment is exposed to water, and dry systems which contain essentially conventional wellhead equipment within watertight chambers maintained at atmospheric pressure. These chambers are designed to permit workmen to perform maintenance activities in a shirtsleeve environment.

Figure 22 shows Standard of California's diverless subsea completion system (DSCS) which is being built by Regan Forge and Engineering Company. In this system, a template is lowered onto a flat spot on the ocean floor which was previously surveyed by sonar or television. After the template is set, the pilot bit and hole opener are guided into the central hole by guide arms from four guidelines. The permanent guideposts serve to land the BOP stack and other equipment. Although the installation itself does not require diver assistance, divers may be required for subsequent workover or repairs.

Fig. 22. SOCAL's Diverless Subsea Completion System
Source: Chevron Oil Field Research Company. Used by permission.

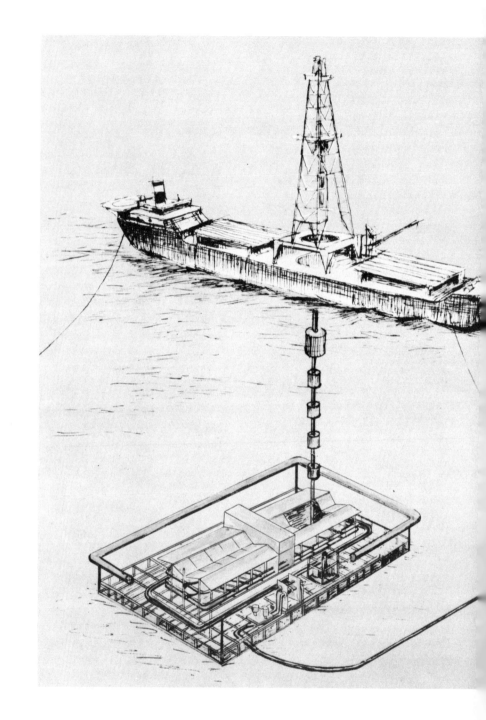

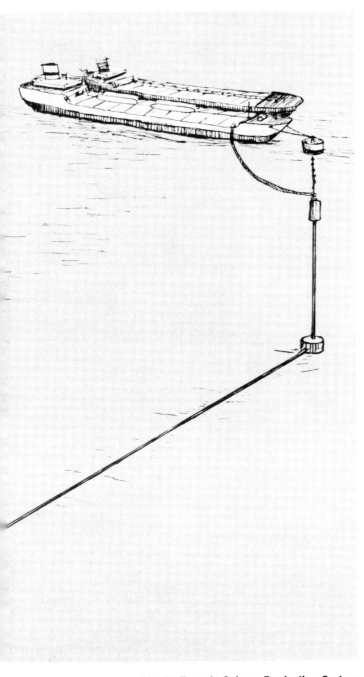

Fig. 23 Exxon's Subsea Production System
Source: Esso Production Research Company. Used by permission.

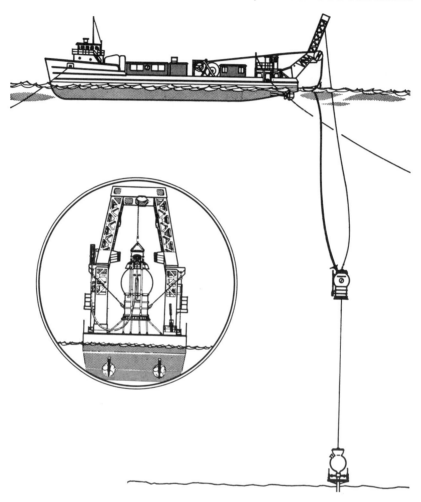

Fig. 24. Lockheed's Subsea Production System
Source: Lockheed Petroleum Services Ltd. Used by permission.

Another wet system approach is represented by the Exxon Subsea Production System shown in Figure 23. Exxon's SPS consists of an integrated
group of subsea wellheads and incorporates provisions for pumpdown
tools, gas lift, water flood, and production manifolding. A manipulator
robot runs on tracks around the manifold and is capable of servicing the
valves and other plumbing included in the system. The robot includes a
one-atmosphere diving bell which can be operated either manned or unmanned from the surface.

The one-atmosphere Lockheed dry system, shown in Figure 24, relies on a diving bell for personnel access. The bell, positioned by wire guidelines, mates and seals with the wellhead cellar into which the flowline bundle is inserted. The Lockheed system is designed for water depths of up to 1,200 feet. Studies for operations in deeper water have shown that the "one atmosphere encapsulated system can be economically extended to 3000 feet depths."[30] If this proves to be the case, the cost of subsea completions will be relatively insensitive to water depth and will therefore become relatively more attractive for deep water.

A somewhat more ambitious scheme, at least from the multi-wellhead enclosure standpoint, is the Subsea Equipment Associates Limited (SEAL) system. SEAL is a London-based consortium in which Mobil, Westinghouse, BP (British Petroleum), CFP (Compagnie Française des Pétroles), and Groupe DEEP (a group of 14 French Companies) have interests. Like the Lockheed system, the SEAL unit is designed to contain what are essentially standard dry-land wellheads by encapsulating them in a dry one-atmosphere compartment within which men may work.

Subsea manifold centers are now being developed for use with subsea systems. Studies are also being made of complete subsea production centers which would be fully equipped for separation and other treatment tasks. Except for gas production, the routine use of SPS's will require subsea separators or multi-phase pumping systems which can handle crude oil, gas, water, and sand simultaneously and deliver the mix to shore for separation.

The relative inaccessability of subsea production systems requires that reliability and redundancy be given a high priority in their design to avoid the consequences of catastrophic failure. Both API and USGS are working on specifications and regulatory procedures aimed at insuring the integrity of SPS installations. Although SPS's appear to have many advantages over conventional platforms in specific circumstances, they are not a panacea for all OCS production problems and can be expected to go through a process of development and refinement.

INTERMEDIATE PRODUCTION SYSTEMS

Although most industry spokesmen seem to believe the production will move directly from fixed platforms to subsea systems, several companies are examining intermediate alternatives. These include buoyant towers and tension-leg platforms. The buoyant tower consists of a heavy base secured on the ocean floor with a buoyant column attached to this base by a flexible coupling (see Figure 25). The buoyant column extends above the water surface, where, in response to wave forces, the platform pivots

Fig. 25. Buoyant Tower

Source: Dravo Ocean Structures Services Ltd. Used by permission.

around the base. Dravo Ocean Structures has demonstrated this system, but there are some disadvantages and few advantages compared to either fixed platform or subsea production systems: there is less single deck space than on fixed platforms; the articulated joint at the base of the column is expensive; and since the tower extends above water, it still can be considered an eyesore.

Several companies are examining the tension-leg platform alternative. This platform is similar to a semi-submersible with excess buoyancy being held down by tension cables or risers between the platform and anchors on the ocean floor. Although the platform maintains a horizontal deck, it, like the buoyant tower, is subject to wave action and is exposed to the weather. Apparently these platforms would not be cheaper than fixed platforms and they, too, could still be considered unsightly.

DEVELOPMENT DRILLING

The drilling procedures for field development are essentially identical to those for drilling exploratory wells. Alternatives to the rotary drilling process are being examined and include the use of a flexible drill string, a jetted particle system, high fluid pressure drilling, and the use of explosives. The flexible drill string is used to reduce the time necessary to make a trip—pulling the drill string out of the well to replace a bit or run a log. The use of jetted steel particles or high pressure fluid to augment the conventional drill bit is intended to speed up the drilling rate and decrease the number of bit changes needed to drill the well. Explosive drilling would replace the drill bit with a shaped explosive charge. None of these systems is likely to be put into widespread use in the next 15 years. In fact, the time required to drill a well is much more likely to be decreased by incremental improvements in existing rotary bits during that time period.

COMPLETION

If the well which has been drilled is dry, it is plugged with cement and abandoned.[31] If commercial accumulations of hydrocarbons are found, the well is completed. Completion is the term used to encompass the various activities required to transform a well into a producer of oil or gas. These activities are undertaken to permit safe and effective oil or gas production and to minimize the need to re-enter the well at some later time. Avoiding or minimizing re-entry is desirable for both safety and economic reasons.

Procedures for completing oil and gas wells are specified for both the Pacific and Gulf Coast Areas in OCS Order Nos. 5 and 6. Completion can include setting and cementing casing, perforating (cutting holes in the casing which will permit oil or gas to flow from the formation into the well hole), fracturing (applying pressure or using explosives to increase permeability), acidizing (using acid to enlarge openings in the formation), consolidating sand (to keep sand from filling the well bore), setting tubing (conduit for routing the oil or gas to the surface), and installing down-hole safety devices (valves installed to prevent blowouts during produc-tion). Several of these completion activities are aimed at increasing pro-duction rate. If performed after initial completion, they are considered servicing or workover operations.

It is estimated that the average ultimate recovery for OCS production will be about 45 percent of the oil known to be in place. The figure for Lou-isiana is 46.5 percent while that for California is only 23.6 percent. Overall, the average for U.S. domestic production, onshore and offshore, is about 31 percent.[32] Industry is attempting to improve these percentages, since a small percentage change in recovery would produce a significant increase in total cumulative domestic production.

The remaining completion activities are undertaken to insure that oil and gas can be produced safely. Unfortunately, the velocity-actuated down-hole safety valves installed during completion operations are among the most inadequate pieces of equipment used on the OCS, as demonstrated by their performance record. Until recently, USGS required that velocity-actuated valves be set in production tubing. They are operated by fluid velocities higher than the preset upper limit. When the pressure differential across the valve exceeds the preset value, the valve is supposed to close automatically, shutting off fluid flow in the well. Although no overall failure rate statistics are available, 25 to 40 percent of these valves failed to function properly in major accidents in the Gulf in 1970 and 1971.

Industry has recognized this inadequacy by undertaking programs to improve the performance of automatic downhole safety valves, but with only limited success. An inherently more reliable surface-actuated sub-surface safety valve is now required for most new wells by OCS Order Number 5. Existing wells are to be fitted with these surface-actuated valves when the tubing is pulled.

This safety valve problem illustrates what has been a major gap in the industry's offshore operations. A National Aeronautics and Space Admin-istration (NASA) study team commissioned by USGS for the purpose of improving safety and preventing pollution in OCS oil and gas operations, found that "the lack of identifiable quality control organizational elements, primary reliance on inspection and widespread objection to written pro-cedures or record-keeping indicates a significant lag in quality control and reliability technology in OCS operations."[33] The team's report goes on to say that "the need for improved equipment and methods for offshore operations is recognized; however, the need for and use of quality and

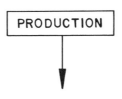

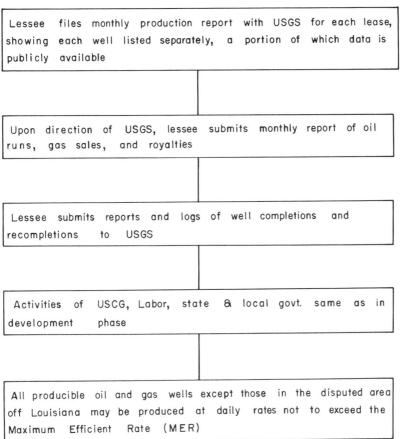

PRODUCTION

Lessee files monthly production report with USGS for each lease, showing each well listed separately, a portion of which data is publicly available

Upon direction of USGS, lessee submits monthly report of oil runs, gas sales, and royalties

Lessee submits reports and logs of well completions and recompletions to USGS

Activities of USCG, Labor, state & local govt. same as in development phase

All producible oil and gas wells except those in the disputed area off Louisiana may be produced at daily rates not to exceed the Maximum Efficient Rate (MER)

Fig. 26. Production Procedures

reliability techniques as aids to effecting this needed improvement are not yet generally appreciated by the industry."[34] In the year since this study was published, both USGS and the industry have responded positively to these findings. Organizational systems for documenting mechanical failures have been established by some of the major petroleum companies, and API has established a permanent standardization committee which expects to issue preliminary standards in 1973 for consensus approval by the offshore industry.

During the production phase, the lessee must file regular reports with the USGS on production, sales, and other field activities (as shown in Figure 26). The Maximum Efficient Rate (MER), noted in the last box, is an upper limit on the production rate for any given well in order to obtain maximum field recovery. It is set by agreement between the lessee and the regulatory agency.

PRODUCTION

From the wellhead, the produced fluids are run through various treatment facilities to prepare them for sale or discharge. They pass from the top of the well to the treatment equipment through a group of valves and fittings referred to in the industry as the Christmas tree. The purpose of this hardware is to direct the fluids to treating equipment, to close off the well in the event of malfunction or emergency, to limit the well-flow rate by the use of chokes, and to permit testing and workover or servicing operations to be performed on the well.

The nature of the treatment facilities into which the produced fluids pass from the Christmas tree is determined by the composition of the fluids and the requirements which must be satisfied for the fluids to be sold or discarded. To be discarded, sand must be free of oil, and discharged water must have an average of not greater than 50 parts per million of oil.[35]

If both oil and gas are produced, a separator is needed so that the oil and gas can be metered and pumped through separate lines. If water is produced with the oil, a tank to remove water which is not contained in an oil-water emulsion is often used. This tank is known as a free-water knockout. More sophisticated equipment is needed if water is produced as an emulsion with the oil, if sand is produced, or if the gas contains water vapor. After all the major contaminants have been removed, the gas or oil passes through Lease Automatic Custody Transfer (LACT) hardware where it is measured and its quality verified before entering the pipeline to shore.

When treatment facilities can be mounted on production platforms, the equipment is similar, if not identical, to onshore components. For subsea production, the processes may remain essentially unchanged, but the hardware becomes much more complex. It may turn out that the problems of extensive underwater operations are so severe or expensive that it may be preferable to transport the produced materials (gas, oil, water, and sand) either to close-in platforms or to onshore facilities for treatment. In either case, the availability of multi-phase pumping systems will be important to the successful expansion of subsea production systems.

Production activities are continuous and require hardware installed for the life of the field. Production problems occur, however, and sometimes the well bore has to be re-entered for various workover or servicing functions. The less serious of these may be handled by using wire-line or pumpdown servicing equipment which may be operated from the platform itself. A variety of tools can be introduced into the well bore to carry out functions such as scraping paraffin deposits from the tubing walls, logging data on formations and well behavior, retrieving and installing downhole safety valves, and fishing for junk left in the hole. More serious problems require workover procedures for which a drilling rig is used, and all of the equipment and precautions involved with drilling are employed.

TRANSPORTATION

Oil and gas may be transported from the OCS either by pipeline or by bulk carriers, such as tankers and barges. At the present time, all production from offshore California and 98 percent of all OCS production in the Gulf of Mexico is transported to shore by pipeline. Since nearly all current plans for developing petroleum resources within 200 miles of the coast incorporate pipelining in one form or another, it seems likely that pipelines will continue to dominate the transportation of OCS oil and gas to shore. Nevertheless, barges and tankers are used as a temporary means of transportation during field development or to transport oil from fields with low production rates.

BULK CARRIERS

Tanker and barge certification requirements are established and administered by the Coast Guard. Rate schedules and licensing for common carrier tankers and barges are supervised by the Federal Maritime Commission, which is also responsible for issuing the certificates of financial responsibility for oil pollution clean-up required for all vessels over 300 gross tons.

In bulk transport operations, the principal risk of spilling oil occurs either during transfer operations or as a result of collision. Since bulk carriers have a poor oil spill record in coastal waters, the alternative of

substituting tanker or barge transportation for pipelines is not attractive
at the present time. Furthermore, tanker and barge transportation can be
interrupted by severe weather which may necessitate shutting down production. Aside from the economic loss, shutdowns interrupt the supply to
onshore users.

OFFSHORE STORAGE

Offshore storage facilities can provide a buffer between the continuous
production of the wells and the discontinuities of tanker operations. Since
most oil and gas produced on the OCS is pipelined to shore, storage has
not been used to any great extent in U.S. waters. Consequently, the major
technological advances in offshore storage technology have been developed
in response to needs in other parts of the world.

Two new subsea or bottom-standing storage systems have been developed
recently for U.S. companies in their overseas operations. Continental's
Dubai installation in the Persian Gulf consists of three tanks, each with a
capacity of 500,000 barrels. The tanks, as shown in Figure 27, resemble
inverted wine glasses, the major portion being underwater and therefore
less susceptible to either weather or collision damage than surface tanks.

The tank being built for Phillips' North Sea Ekofisk field has a capacity
of one million barrels and is constructed of concrete. It has an outer baffle
to minimize potential damage to the tank, primarily from wave action
(see Figure 28).

Floating storage has also developed considerably in recent years. The
barge *Pazargad*, for example, has a nominal one million barrel capacity
and is serving in the Persian Gulf as a storage, desalting, and loading facility. It uses a single point mooring system which allows the barge to head
into the weather at all times.

It seems unlikely that storage facilities will be used on the U.S. OCS in
the foreseeable future. On the other hand, if refinery or distribution facilities cannot be located immediately onshore from the production field,
tanker transport may be required to carry the petroleum liquids to distant
ports for processing or transshipment. In such cases, the use of OCS
storage facilities may be necessary.

PIPELINES

Pipelines serve two major purposes on the OCS, gathering gas and produced fluids and transmitting them to land. Gathering lines move production to a central point for treatment, storage, or measuring. These lines
terminate at the final metering point under USGS jurisdiction. Pipelines

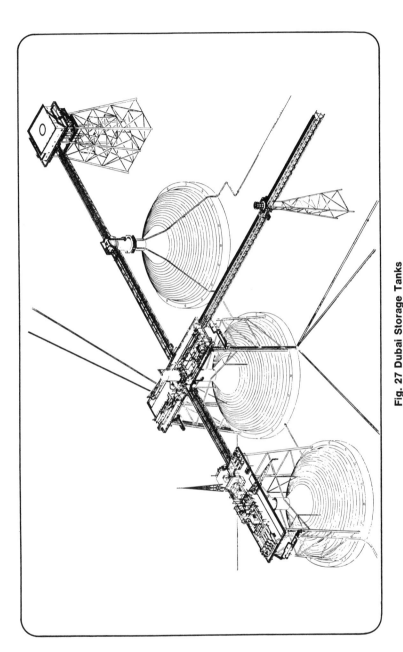

Fig. 27 Dubai Storage Tanks

Source: J. I. Horning and Gerald L. McCurry, "Dubai Expands Production System," *Oil and Gas Journal*, 70 (August 28, 1972), p. 54. Used by permission.

Fig. 28. Phillips-Ekofisk Storage Tank

Source: *Ocean Industry*, 6 (July, 1971), p. 21. Used by permission.

which move produced fluids and gas beyond this point are known as transmission lines.

The proposed location of gathering lines is included in the lease development plan. The USGS Area Supervisor approves the design of these lines. If they are located entirely on the lease, no right-of-use or easement is required, since these rights are explicit in the lease agreement itself. If gathering lines cross other leases, these lessees must be notified and an application for right-of-use or easement made to the Area Supervisor (see Figure 29). However, since these easements are considered an extension of lease production facilities, no rental fee is charged for their use.

Transmission lines may carry either oil or gas or both and are classified

TRANSPORTATION

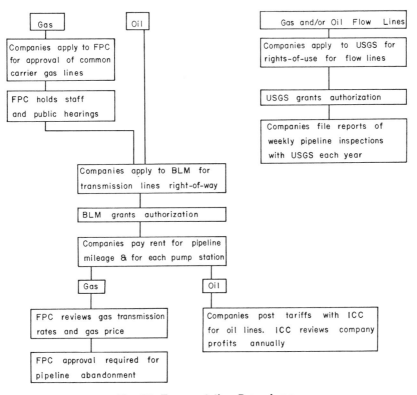

Fig. 29. Transportation Procedures

as either single custody or common carrier. Rights-of-way for common carrier lines are granted by BLM. The Interstate Commerce Commission (ICC) regulates rates and access for these lines. If the line transports gas, the Federal Power Commission (FPC) must grant a certificate of public convenience and necessity and both the FPC and the Office of Pipeline Safety (OPS) must approve the design. FPC also established the rate structure for common carrier gas pipelines (see Figure 29).

Regulatory responsibilities in the case of single custody lines is less clear. Oil transported in these lines is generally metered onshore and, therefore, the lines are likely to be considered as gathering lines falling under USGS jurisdiction. Even when final metering is conducted offshore, however, it appears that, in practice, USGS continues to exercise authority over single custody oil transmission lines. From the regulatory standpoint, it appears that most lines transporting gas to shore are treated as common carriers.

PIPELAYING

There are three primary techniques used to lay pipeline offshore. The most common is the lay barge or "stovepipe" technique in which sections of the pipe, usually coated with concrete, are welded together on a so-called lay barge and released into the water as the barge moves forward. Lay barges have been used for pipe as small as 4 inches in diameter and as large as 52 inches in diameter (see Figure 30).

A second technique is the reel barge, in which long sections of pipe are welded on land, wound onto a large reel on the barge and then laid directly from the reel. Currently, this technique is limited to pipe diameters of 12 inches or less. For pipe diameters in the 4- to 10-inch range, reel barges are often more economical than conventional lay barges.

A third method is to pull pipe from make-up facilities onshore into the water. Because of the stress on the pipe owing to frictional drag, the pull method is limited to lengths of 2 to 4 miles. A related technique is called float-and-sink. In this approach, a length of pipe is assembled onshore, given auxiliary buoyancy with strapped-on tanks, floated to location, then sunk and connected to other sections with underwater welds. Its use is sharply limited by the requirement for calm seas and by the high cost of associated diving operations.

Although it was common in the past to lay pipe directly on the undersea surface, it is now more common to bury the pipeline to avoid damage from currents, storm waves, and anchors and other marine equipment. A burial barge is used to sink the pipe beneath the surface, usually by displacing soil with a high-pressure water jet.

Weather presents the greatest risk to a pipelaying program. In the Gulf of Mexico, a good year's work for a pipelaying barge is about 220 days. Although wave heights of 6 feet are usually sufficient to shut down a normal pipelaying operation, one recently built semi-submersible barge is said to be able to function in 16-foot seas.

The ecological effects of pipelines are related to spills and shoreline modification. The largest oil spill in the Gulf Coast OCS occurred in 1967 when a pipeline failed as a result of anchor damage sustained two years earlier. The leak was not discovered for ten days, by which time 167,000 barrels had been discharged. The other significant ecological problem has occurred primarily in the shore regions of Louisiana. Pipeline dredging has resulted in canals connecting bodies of water which would otherwise be separate. The resulting environmental changes have generally been adverse. Present practice is to dam these canals in order to attempt to prevent this intrusion.

The future of pipelines on the OCS is centered on the problem of water-

30. Lay Barge

Source: J. Ray McDermott & Co., Inc. Used by permission.

depth limitation. The current techniques for laying pipe of 12 inches in diameter or larger are limited to approximately 400 to 500 feet water depth. There are two basic problems, diver and structural limitations. In moving to deeper water, lay barges will use an articulated structure with adjustable buoyancy (known as the stinger) to support the pipe between the barge and the ocean floor. Another approach for increasing water depth capability is to use an inclined or a vertical assembly area for the pipe. This tends to reduce the overbend when the pipe is no longer supported by the stinger.

A number of techniques are being used to extend diver depths and at least one major diving contractor is now committed to offering its operational services down to 1,000 feet. This is accomplished by using a full saturation system and a diving bell, all of which add to the already high cost for diving services.[36] Because of these costs, efforts are also being made to develop diverless systems.

Finally, pipeline failures due to corrosion or other effects of age have been infrequent in the Gulf. Since some of these lines have been in place nearly 25 years, however, there is a growing concern with the condition of old pipe and a continuing need to monitor these lines and to attempt to detect potential rather than actual leaks.

ACCIDENT RESPONSE

Finding, developing, producing, and transporting oil and gas on the OCS is a potentially hazardous undertaking. In the past, accidents have occurred from time to time during the conduct of these activities and, for all practical purposes, it will be impossible to prevent them from occurring in the future. The best that industry and responsible government agencies can do is to take every possible precaution to prevent accidents and be prepared to respond rapidly and effectively when they do occur.

ACCIDENT PREVENTION

Both industry and government have focused a great deal of attention on improving equipment and procedures as a means for preventing accidents, and both agree that this is the most effective means of accident response available to them. Since the Santa Barbara blowout, there has been a general tightening of operational procedures and OCS orders are beginning to include more detailed requirements. Some of those changes, such as the revision of OCS Order No. 5 to require remotely actuated subsurface safety valves rather than velocity actuated valves, were mentioned earlier. But perhaps the best example of the USGS's more active regulatory role is the 1970 revision of OCS Order No. 8. This order now specifies that particular safety devices and controls must be used. The Gulf Coast Area Supervisor established requirements after reviewing existing components and systems. He then required the use of more reliable components and, in some cases, required back-up systems as well. At the same time pollution control requirements were added, both for oil spills and effluents. The purpose of this new USGS policy is to require all operators to use improved equipment and employ safer practices.

ORGANIZATIONAL RESPONSE

As recently as the *Torrey Canyon* spill off the coast of England in 1967, there was no provision for an organized response to oil spills off the coast of the U.S. Shortly after the *Torrey Canyon* accident, however, President Johnson required that a pollution contingency plan be developed. Santa Barbara was the plan's first test. Requirement for the plan, now known as the National Oil and Hazardous Substances Pollution Contingency Plan, has subsequently been written into the FWPCA.[37] The Plan established a structure for coordinated, integrated response by federal agencies, principally four primary agencies designated by the Plan: EPA, Interior (USGS), Transportation (Coast Guard), and Defense.

Industry's parallel response has been to organize a number of clean-up cooperatives. Although there are some 76 of these now, the two major ones are Clean Seas, Inc. in California and Clean Gulf Associates in Louisiana. Both purchase and maintain equipment and train personnel. When a member of the cooperative has an oil spill, he may draw equipment from the cooperative and have his own personnel operate it.

RESPONSE TECHNIQUES AND EQUIPMENT

Blowouts continue to be the most challenging accidents in OCS petroleum operations. Response to a blowout depends on whether the well is being drilled or is producing, and whether the escaping oil or gas is burning. If possible, the well is capped. When damage to the wellhead prevents capping or when serious environmental pollution will result if blowing oil is not consumed, the escaping gas and oil are allowed to burn at the surface and relief wells are drilled to the producing zone or zones. Mud, water, and/or cement are pumped down the relief well to close the formation and stop the blowout.

The drawbacks to this technique are that it is costly in both dollars and time. For an offshore well, relief drilling can often require up to four months or more to complete. (An Alaskan offshore well blew for 14 months in 1962–63 when weather conditions impeded efforts to regain control.) In addition, production lost during drilling can result in costs comparable to those of the relief wells themselves.

Containment

As for the oil spilled, the use of floating booms is the primary containment technique being used and developed both by industry and government agencies. The thickness of an unconstrained oil slick depends on the characteristics of the oil and the temperature of the water. It may vary from a thickness of only a few thousandths of an inch in temperate waters to as much as one-quarter of an inch in arctic waters. A successful containment boom prevents the spreading and thinning of the slick thereby increasing the likelihood of successful recovery.

Three environmental characteristics limit boom effectiveness: wave

Fig. 31. Exxon's Bottom Tension Boom and Skimmer in Operation
(lighter areas are oil, darker are water)

Source: Esso Production Research Company. Used by permission.

height, wind velocity, and current. The Coast Guard has tested a light-weight boom system which is supposed to be effective in 5-foot seas in combination with 20-mile-per-hour winds and 2-knot currents. However, the test was conducted in near calm conditions. It has also awarded a contract for development of a heavy-duty containment system which would perform effectively in seas of up to 10 feet in combination with winds of up to 40 miles per hour. Exxon has developed a heavy-duty bottom tension boom which has been shown to be effective in 6- to 8-foot seas with 20-knot winds and an imposed current of 1.25 knots (see Figure 31). Two West Coast clean-up cooperatives—Clean Seas, Inc. and Clean Bay, Inc. in San Francisco—are now receiving this boom in installments for their inventories. By summer, 1973, each will have 1,000 feet on hand.

In turbulent seas with wave heights in excess of 10 feet, a true oil slick does not exist. Oil droplets are distributed in the water column and, given the present state of the art, neither containment nor clean-up is possible.

A major factor in the success with which an oil spill can be contained is how rapidly the boom is deployed. Since the size of the oil spill on relatively calm water increases with time, rapid deployment reduces the length of boom necessary to contain the spill and increases the likelihood of effective containment. Both of the Coast Guard booms are to be air deployable. The goal is to be able to have the boom in place within four hours of mobilization. Such rapid deployment presents difficult design problems, and it appears that a compromise will have to be made between boom survival and boom effectiveness in heavy seas on the one hand and rapid deployment on the other.

Clean-up

Once a spill has been contained, clean-up measures can be instituted. The two major techniques used today are mechanical gathering and sorbent recovery. Mechanical recovery may be used without restriction in carrying out the contingency plan, while sorbents may be used "providing that these materials do not in themselves or in combination with the oil increase the pollution hazard."[38] Other methods include dispersing agents, sinking agents, biological agents, and burning agents, which may be used under limited circumstances and with specific approval of the appropriate federal and local agencies. This requirement has tended to inhibit their use.

Mechanical Devices: Most mechanical clean-up devices currently available are suitable for use only in calm water and operate at recovery rates between 1 and 5 barrels of oil per minute, depending largely on the thickness of the oil slick (see Figure 32). The most notable characteristics of mechanical clean-up devices are the variance between predicted and ex-

Fig. 32. Mechanical Clean-Up Device

Source: JBF Scientific Corporation. Used by permission.

perimentally verified clean-up capability. A 1970 study on oil spill clean-up prepared for API by the Dillingham Corporation reported that mechanical devices that are available are of limited capacity and suitable for use only in calm water.[39] Subsequently a number of new devices have been reported which proponents claim will operate in heavier seas. None of these has been proved effective yet.

The major difficulties encountered in heavier seas are the lack of stability of small vessels and the absence of a well-defined "slick" of oil. Recovery rate and effectiveness for clean-up devices drop off fairly rapidly when these relatively small devices have to compete with wind and wave action.

Sorbents: The National Petroleum Council contends that, after containment and mechanical recovery, sorbent materials are the most desirable method for controlling oil spills. However, there are logistical problems both in spreading and collecting these materials. And these problems are not yet adequately resolved by presently available equipment.

Sorbent materials are spread onto the oil surface, mixed with the oil, and the resulting oil-soaked mixture is collected. Wind is a major problem in distributing sorbents because of their low density. Baled fibrous materials such as straw can be distributed successfully with commercial mulchers which consist of hammer mills and blowers.

Recovery on a large scale in open waters appears to be possible by commercial purse seiners outfitted with special nets. The collected mixture may be disposed of by burning or, in the case of natural absorbents such as straw, by burial.

Straw is considered to be the most cost-effective of the sorbents currently available. It absorbs 5 times its weight in oil and costs $25 to $50 per ton. Since it is a natural, fibrous material, there are relatively few limitations in its use and it is generally effective with a greater variety of petroleum products over a greater range of temperatures than are many of the alternatives.

A number of other sorbent materials which are treated or manufactured are available on the market. Most of these absorb much larger quantities of oil than does straw, but they are not nearly so cost-effective.

Perhaps the greatest deterrent to the use of sorbent materials is their high handling cost. As indicated, they must be handled twice and then disposed of, giving them roughly twice the cost of dispersants or other singly handled materials.

Dispersants, Sinking and Burning Agents: Other techniques for disposal of an oil slick include use of dispersants and sinking, burning, and biological agents. The use of dispersants is sharply restricted in the Contingency Plan.[40] Sinking agents are restricted by the Contingency Plan to "marine waters exceeding 100 meters in depth where currents are not predominantly onshore, and only if other control methods are judged by EPA to be inadequate or not feasible."[41]

Burning agents have been used in a limited number of circumstances and

> ... may be used and are acceptable so long as they do not in themselves, or in combination with the material to which they are applied, increase the pollution hazard and their use is approved by appropriate Federal, State and local fire prevention officials.[42]

Microbial degradation has been studied in laboratories but has not been utilized in large-scale tests or on an actual spill. And the Contingency Plan states that "biological agents shall be used to treat spills only when such use is approved by the appropriate state and local public health *and* water pollution control officials."[43]

Fig. 33. Whittaker's Survival Capsule
Source: Whittaker Corporation. Used by permission.

Gravity escape boom

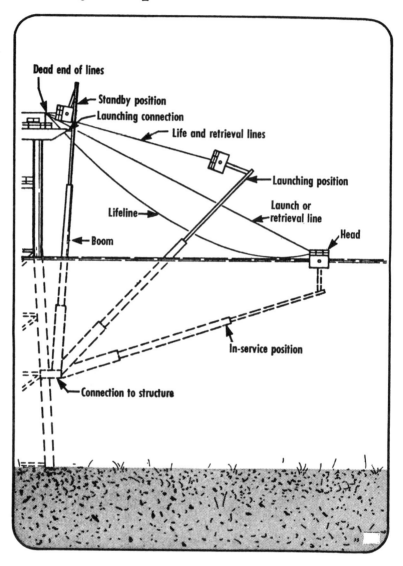

Fig. 34. Gravity (above) and Buoyant (opposite) Booms

Source: John L. Kennedy, "Offshore Escape Booms Are Designed for Speed, Simplicity," *Oil and Gas Journal*, 70 (October 16, 1972), p. 111. Used by permission.

Buoyant-boom concept

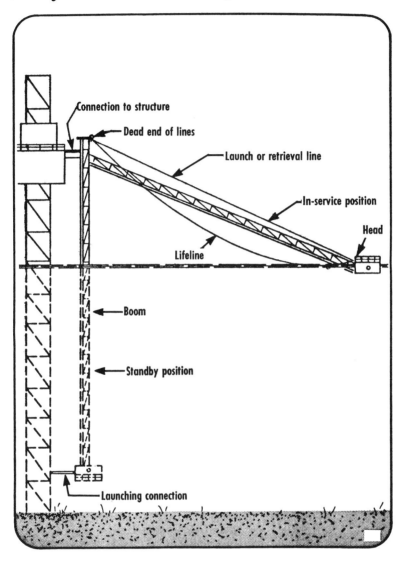

ACCIDENTS OTHER THAN OIL SPILLS

Although oil spills have received most of the public attention, accidents involving property damage, fire, and loss of life are a continuing problem offshore. In addition to Coast Guard requirements, OCS Order No. 8 requires that there be fire control and extinguishing systems on platforms. Since steel or other metal construction is used almost exclusively on offshore platforms, an important function of fire control techniques is to reduce the temperature on essential structural elements, generally by use of water sprays. Automatic water spray systems are a part of the OCS Order No. 8 requirements under certain circumstances. For instance, automatic water spray systems are required in unventilated wellhead areas.

Some problems of life saving are unique to offshore platforms. Their height above the water surface makes satisfactory launching arrangements difficult and renders traditional shipboard life saving equipment inadequate. One solution is a survival capsule which may be lowered rapidly from the platform surface and which provides escape and survival facilities for a crew of up to 28 men (see Figure 33). More recent developments include adaptation of the Boeing 747 inflatable slide escape system for platform use and the development of other escape booms such as those illustrated in Figure 34.

Storms have been a principal source of accidents not involving oil spills. A primary problem following storms is the availability of repair equipment, particularly derrick and pipe-laying barges. Inspections of structures are made by the USGS after storms to confirm their serviceability.

In addition to accidents involving rigs or platform damage, a number of death or injury accidents are associated with routine industrial operations of platforms. USGS accident statistics show 56 deaths and 83 serious injuries from OCS operations in the period from 1953 to 1971.[44] A Coast Guard tally of injuries and deaths reported 71 deaths and 82 injuries for the period 1966 through 1971, some of which occurred outside the U.S.[45] More comprehensive and detailed listings apparently are not available. (OCS accidents are discussed in detail in Appendix B.)

The Occupational Safety and Health Act will have an impact in this area, since it empowers the Occupational Safety and Health Administration to inspect and investigate working environments and to impose various penalties for hazardous working conditions, including shutting down the facility if this appears to be warranted.

Finally, from the standpoint of public concern, few aspects of environmental damage are of more importance than the actual or potential harm to birds. Because of this, and because the areas of heaviest OCS oil and gas operations are near large concentrations of water fowl and other birds, considerable effort has been expended by industry to prevent bird contamination and to clean up any birds that may be affected. Noisemakers have been used to frighten birds away from a contaminated area, but their efficiency has not been established.

ECONOMICS

In this section, the economics of offshore petroleum production is briefly described to indicate: (1) the relative magnitude of investments required, and (2) the factors that affect the cost of producing a barrel of oil. It is generally believed that the OCS and Alaska are the only domestic sources remaining that can offer increases in production (by simply selling more leases) without requiring increases in price. To the extent that some reserves are not recoverable due to the economics, then the higher the price of crude oil, the greater the quantity of recoverable reserves that may become available.

HISTORICAL COSTS

As a measure of the relative economic importance of each of the technological phases, the following list gives the average per barrel costs which have been incurred in the Gulf of Mexico:[46]

	Dollars/Barrel
Exploration (per equivalent barrel of reserves added): geophysical, geological, exploratory drilling; excludes bonus and royalties:	.15
Development: well drilling, etc.:	.77
Production: production equipment, operating expenses, overhead:	.59
Transportation: pipelines	.12
Lease Purchase (bonus):	.27
Total	$1.90

While geophysical exploration and exploratory drilling are crucial to the success of any company, the above figures show that the direct economic cost of these activities has been relatively small, although they are certainly the "higher risk" monies. The major cost of finding oil thus far has been the bonus bid costs.

The average per acre bonus bids for wildcat sales on the OCS of Louisiana are reported in Table 1. Bonus bids have risen sharply over the past five years, so that the $.27 bonus per barrel of reserves reported in the previous list has probably increased sharply over the past few years.

Table 1. Federal Wildcat Sales off Louisiana

Date	Acreage	Bonus (millions)	Average price/acre
October, 1954	394,721	$ 116.4	$ 294
July, 1955	252,806	100.1	395
February, 1960	464,047	246.9	532
March, 1962	1,879,557	445.0	237
June, 1967	744,456	510.1	685
December, 1970	543,898	845.8	1,043[a]
September, 1972	290,521	585.8	2,016
December, 1972	524,939	1,673.0	3,187

Source: *Offshore* (January, 1973), p. 34.

[a] There is an obvious error in the data as reported for December, 1970. If the acreage and bonus figures are correct, the average price would be $1,555.

For comparative purposes, it should be noted that the often quoted average price for crude oil is around $3.40–$3.50 per barrel, although the exact selling price of crude depends upon its grade. While this may seem to be a substantial profit margin ($3.50 — $1.90 = $1.60 per barrel), there are two factors which significantly affect an interpretation of what the margin actually is. First of all, one-sixth of the wellhead price of the crude oil is paid to the government as royalties; therefore, industry revenue is $2.92 per barrel produced (5/6 × $3.50); and second, the time value of money affects the economics since most of the expenditures (costs) are incurred early in the life of the project whereas the revenues are collected over a long period, say 15–20 years.[47] (When comparing the price of oil with its production cost, it should be recalled that the selling price of a particular grade of crude is set generally across the board, in no way reflecting the cost of producing that particular barrel of oil. For example, crude produced from a large, efficient reservoir at $.20 per barrel and crude produced from a low production well at $3.00 per barrel will both generally sell for the same price.)

The following are the total domestic offshore expenditures (includes state waters) through 1968:[48]

	Billions of Dollars
Exploration	1.5
Development	7.3
Production	1.7
Bonus and Rental	4.1
Royalty and Production Taxes	1.7
Total	16.3

COMPONENT COSTS

The primary difference between field development using fixed platforms and mobile rigs is that fixed platform development requires a large initial cost for the platform but a relatively small per day cost for the rig. On the other hand, mobile rig development using rental equipment does not require initial platform investment but does involve a high per day rig cost. Fixed platform development has generally proved to be more economical thus far. However, as the industry moves to deeper water, mobile rig development with the use of subsea wellheads and subsea production equipment is likely to become more attractive. Virtually all exploratory drilling is now done from mobile rigs.

Drilling Structures

The following list gives some cost estimates for various types of mobile rigs. These cost estimates were obtained from a major oil company (1972).

Type of Rig	Water Depth Capability	Day Rate
Jack-up	200 feet	$ 6,800
	225 feet	$ 8,400
	275 feet	$13,000
Semi-submersible	(essentially not a factor)	$22,000–$30,000
Drill ship	(essentially not a factor)	$16,000

Note that these are all bare rig costs; there would be approximately another $10,000 per day for boats, well-service companies, and other services. These day rates depend on demand and, during sharp rises in exploratory activity, can rise significantly. The two most important factors affecting the daily cost of a mobile rig are its water depth capability and its equipment.

In comparison to the mobile rig rates cited above, the rig rate for a fixed platform would be around $4,000–$6,000 per day. The two types of drilling rigs that can be used with the multiple well platform are the combination drilling rig and tender and the self-contained unit. The self-contained unit is used predominantly today. In either case the platform is constructed in the same manner. The tender is a floating barge that supports a crane and the remainder of the required rig equipment such as power plant, storage facilities, and living quarters. The self-contained unit thus requires a larger deck section because it will contain all of the rig equipment.

Some past and projected fixed platform costs in the Gulf of Mexico are presented in Figure 35. It can be seen that, for a given number of wells, the increase in cost with water depth is approximately linear. However, for a fixed water depth, the platform cost per well decreases rapidly as the

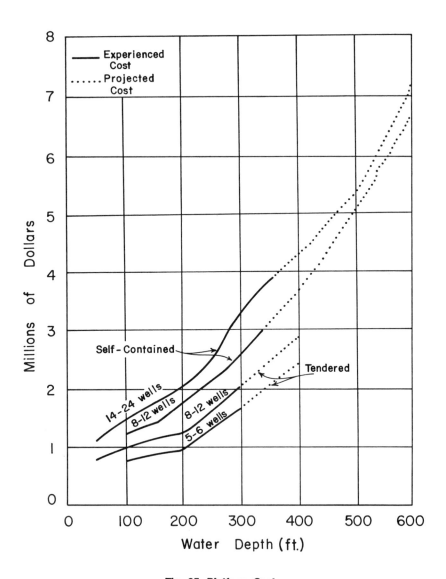

Fig. 35. Platform Costs

Source: U.S., Department of the Interior, Bureau of Land Management, *The Role of Petroleum and Natural Gas from the Outer Continental Shelf in the National Supply of Petroleum and Natural Gas*, Technical Bulletin 5 (Washington: Government Printing Office, 1970), p. 182.

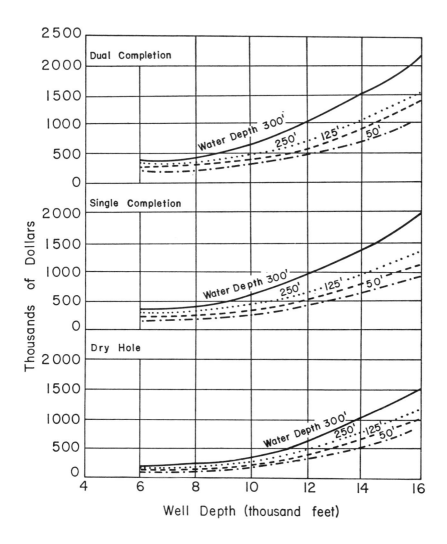

Fig. 36. Drilling Costs (Mobile Rig)

Source: BLM, *Role of Petroleum from the OCS*, p. 181.

number of wells is increased. For example, at 200 feet, a 12-well self-contained platform costs approximately $150,000 per well, while a 24-well platform costs approximately $85,000 per well. The economic pressures favoring the use of large multi-well platforms are apparent.

Well Drilling Costs

The cost of drilling from a mobile rig depends on the water depth and the well depth and consists primarily of the daily rig costs. Figure 36 shows cost estimates for drilling from a mobile rig at various water depths and to various well depths. Since most exploratory wells are plugged and abandoned, the bottom set of curves for "dry holes" best approximates exploratory drilling costs.

The approximate total cost for drilling and equipping a well from a self-contained platform in the Gulf Coast is presented in Figure 37. Since most development wells are drilled from fixed platforms, water depth ceases to be a significant factor in the drilling cost. The well depth referred to in Figure 37 actually means "length" and not vertical depth. The costs of deviated wells depend upon the vertical depth, "length" of the hole, and the angle of deviation, but generally costs are not categorized this way.

Production Costs

Production costs consist of initial equipment costs and everyday operating expenses. Production equipment cost estimates for a 9-well platform are presented in Figure 38. The cost of the oil production equipment includes production and test separators, oil skimmer, treaters, manifold, and related piping. The gas production equipment cost includes cost of heat exchanger, steam generator, production and test separator, skimmer, meter-proving vessel, manifold, and related piping. The estimated costs for both types of equipment are based on an installation in which all equipment is skid-mounted and coated.

Annual operating expense for a production system includes such things as expense for warehousing, office rental, house leases, transportation, salaries and allowances, communications, and compressor-operating expense.

Operating expenses are usually estimated by figuring a cost per well per month. These costs generally depend on whether the well is oil or gas, the depth of the well, the number of platforms, and the distance from shore. Some *typical* OCS average operating costs obtained from a major oil company are as follows:

Oil Wells: $4,950 per well per month (including well workover costs).
Gas Wells: $3,800 per well per month (including well workover costs).

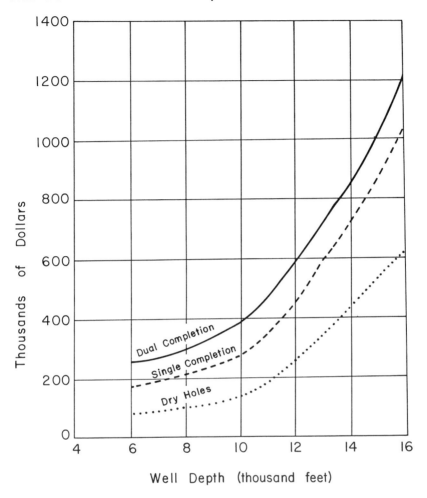

Fig. 37. Drilling and Equipment Costs (Fixed Platform)
Source: BLM, *Role of Petroleum from the OCS*, p. 183.

These costs include all direct operating costs plus allocated costs of the district office supervising the properties. They do not include general office or indirect overhead charges.

Pipelines

The cost of installing a pipeline system offshore depends mainly on the method of laying the pipe, the water depth, and the length and size of the

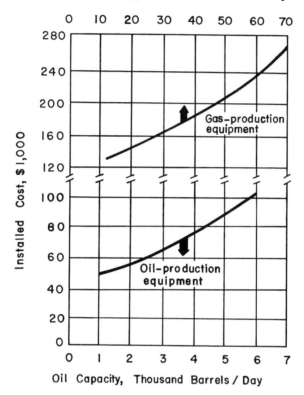

Fig. 38. Production Equipment Costs

Source: Darrell Williams, "Here's a Guide to Offshore Economics," *Oil and Gas Journal*, 67 (April 14, 1969), p. 119.

Table 2. Typical Gas Pipeline Cost per Mile, Gulf of Mexico

Pipeline Diameter	Water Depth		
	0–100 feet	100–200 feet	300–350 feet
36 inches	$435,000		
30 inches	330,000	$475,000	
26 inches	250,000	310,000	
24 inches	225,000	275,000	$400,000
20 inches	180,000	220,000	325,000
12 inches	100,000	125,000	165,000

Source: BLM, *Role of Petroleum from the OCS*, p. 195.

pipe. The two primary techniques used employ lay and reel barges, and a large portion of the installation cost is attributable to the day rate for the barge. For example, a lay barge 360 feet long by 72 feet wide with seven work stations and capable of laying two miles per day of 12-inch pipe has a day rate of about $31,000 per day.[49] The cost of material, coating, administration, communication, platform, etc., is added to the day rate cost to make up the total installation cost.

In Table 2, estimates of the cost per mile of various sizes of *gas* pipelines in relation to water depth in the Gulf of Mexico are reported.

Subsea Production Systems

It is difficult to compare the economics of subsea production to platform production systems for two reasons. First of all, some types of subsea production systems are still in the developmental stage, and much of the cost information is conjectural. While the basic equipment costs can be estimated with some accuracy, equally important installation and maintenance cost estimates are subject to a high degree of uncertainty.

Second, subsea production systems use an entirely different approach to field development. It is, therefore, difficult to make an economic comparison between platform production systems and SPS's. For a given field, an "optimal" subsea production plan should be compared to an "optimal" platform production plan. For example, if a given field might require 18 wells with a subsea production system, a platform production system might

Table 3. Cost Estimates for Oil Spill Clean-up Offshore

Combatant Method	2,380 barrels (100,000 gal)		245,000 barrels (35,000 tons)	
	Direct Costs[a]	Capital Costs[b]	Direct Costs[a]	Capital Costs[b]
Chemical Dispersion	$ 80,000	$ 51,600	$6,200,000	$862,500
Absorption (Straw)	113,000	79,300 (579,300)[c]	8,625,000	1,405,000 (6,405,000)[c]
Sinking	64,900	56,600	4,505,000	1,385,000
Combustion	82,200	49,500	6,171,000	675,000

Source: Arthur D. Little, Inc., "Combating Pollution Created by Oil Spills—Volume One: Methods," Report to the Department of Transportation, U.S. Coast Guard (June, 1969).

[a] Direct costs are those incurred directly for a specific spill, including material and operating costs.

[b] Capital costs are initial equipment and warehouse costs. Boom costs were not included. Persons conducting the study assumed spills in the open ocean which spread over areas so large as to make booms ineffective.

[c] Includes equipment for the collection of spent materials.

require 24 wells. In a recent study, the two systems were compared on this basis.[50] The authors came to the following tentative conclusions:

1. Platform systems have an advantage for:
   a. reservoirs with small areas
   b. shallow water depths
2. Subsea systems will in general be less sensitive to water depth and show their greatest advantage for:
   a. smaller reservoir volumes
   b. greater water depths
   c. larger areal extents for reservoirs

ECONOMIC COST OF OIL SPILLS

In this section, we briefly treat the economic costs of stopping or cleaning up polluting accidents. (The "social" costs of such incidents are discussed in Chapter XI.)

In a study by Arthur D. Little, Inc., the costs of cleaning up offshore oil spills of various sizes are projected. Selected results of that study are summarized in Table 3. The costs of some previous OCS accidents involving oil spills are reported in Table 4. These costs include all those costs incurred directly in stopping or cleaning up the spilled oil. They do not include the costs of fines (if any), costs of lawsuits for damages, or costs borne by other parties, for example, by commercial fishermen. (A more detailed description of offshore accidents can be found in Appendix B.)

Table 4. Cost of Some Previous OCS Accidents

Description/Location	Total Cost (in millions)
Union (Santa Barbara)	$10.6
Shell (Gulf of Mexico)	$30.0
Amoco (Gulf of Mexico)	$15.4
Chevron (Gulf of Mexico)	$15.0

1. U.S., *Statutes at Large*, Vol. 59, pt. 2 (1945), Presidential Proclamation 2667, September 28, 1945, pp. 884–85.

2. In *United States v. Louisiana (Florida)*, 363 U.S. 1, 121 (1960), the Court held that Texas and Florida each had a seaward boundary three marine leagues (approximately nine miles) from their Gulf coastlines. Some facets of claims made by Louisiana are still undecided [*Louisiana Boundary Case: United States v. Louisiana*, 394 U.S. 11 (1969)]; and the claims of Maine, New Hampshire, Massachusetts, Rhode Island, New York, New Jersey, Delaware, Maryland, Virginia, North Carolina, South Carolina, Georgia, and Florida (east coast of Florida) are still pending before the Court [*United States v. Maine, et al.*, 395 U.S. 955 (1969)].

3. U.S., Department of the Interior, *Statement, Questions and Policy Issues Related to Oversight Hearings on the Administration of the Outer Continental Shelf Lands*

Act, Held by the Senate Committee on Interior and Insular Affairs, Pursuant to S. Res. 45, March 23, 1972, pp. 98–101.

4. *Ibid.*, p. 7.

5. *Ibid.*, Tables 53 and 54, pp. 63–65.

6. Commission on Marine Science, Engineering and Resources, *Panel Reports of the Commission on Marine Science, Engineering and Resources*, Vol. 3: *Marine Resources and Legal-Political Arrangements for Their Development* (Washington: Government Printing Office, 1969), p. VII–217.

7. National Academy of Engineering, Panel on Operational Safety in Offshore Resource Development, *Outer Continental Shelf Resource Development Safety: A Review of Technology and Regulating for the Systematic Minimization of Environmental Intrusion from Petroleum Products* (Washington: National Academy of Engineering, December, 1972), pp. 8-11.

8. Carl H. Savit, "Exploration Changes Radically," *Oil and Gas Journal*, 71 (May 21, 1973), p. 156.

9. S. J. Pirson, "Advantages and Limitations of Direct Oil-Finding Methods," *World Oil*, 176 (April, 1973), p. 63.

10. Outer Continental Shelf (OCS) Lands Act, Section 8.

11. OCS Lands Act, Section 5.

12. National Environmental Policy Act (NEPA).

13. U.S., Department of the Interior, Bureau of Land Management, "Oil and Gas Lease of Submerged Lands Under the Outer Continental Shelf Lands Act, Sec. 2."

14. OCS Lands Act, Section 8(b)(2).

15. Title 30, *Code of Federal Regulations*, Section 250. 33 (30 CFR 250. 33).

16. "Rigs Under Construction," *Offshore*, 32 (November, 1972), p. 136.

17. *Ibid.*

18. *Ibid.*, p. 131.

19. See L. M. Harris, *An Introduction to Deepwater Floating Drilling Operations* (Tulsa, Okla.: Petroleum Publishing Co., 1972), p. 31.

20. *Ibid.*

21. OCS Lands Act.

22. *Ibid.*

23. Federal Water Pollution Control Act (FWPCA) Amendments of 1972.

24. *Ibid.*

25. Occupational Safety and Health Act (OSHA).

26. 30 CFR 250. 34.

27. 30 CFR 250.34; 30 CFR 250.41; and 30 CFR 250.91.

28. OCS Order Number 2 for both the Gulf Coast and Pacific Areas.

29. 30 CFR 250.34.

30. Donald M. Taylor, "Shell Will Make a Seafloor Completion in 385-Foot Water," *Ocean Industry*, 7 (June, 1972), pp. 62–65.

31. 30 CFR 250. 15.

32. National Petroleum Council, Committee on U.S. Energy Outlook, Oil Subcommittee, *An Initial Appraisal by the Oil Supply Task Group 1971–1985* (Washington: NPC, 1972), pp. 35–37, 66, 73.

33. Morris K. Dyer, *et al.*, "Applicability of NASA Contract Quality Management and Failure Mode Effects Analysis Procedures Program" (unpublished report to USGS, November, 1971), p. 3.

34. *Ibid.*

35. OCS Order Number 8 for both the Gulf Coast and Pacific Areas.

36. *Offshore*, 32 (August, 1972), p. 54.

37. FWPCA Amendments of 1972.

38. U.S., Council on Environmental Quality, *National Oil and Hazardous Substances Pollution Contingency Plan*, August, 1971, Annex X, p. X-4.

39. Dillingham Corporation, *Systems Study of Oil Spill Cleanup Procedures* (2 vols.; LaJolla, Calif.: Dillingham Corporation, 1970).

40. Contingency Plan, p. X-4.

41. *Ibid.*, p. X-2.

42. *Ibid.*, p. X-4.

43. *Ibid.*

44. U.S., Department of the Interior, Geological Survey, "Incidents in the Outer Continental Shelf Resulting in Injury and Property or Environmental Damage" (unpublished U.S.G.S. data sheet). These data are included in Appendix B.

45. U.S., Congress, Senate, Committee on Interior and Insular Affairs, *Outer Continental Shelf Policy Issues, Hearings*, before the Committee Pursuant to S. Res. 45, A National Fuels and Energy Policy Study, 92nd Cong., 2d sess., on Oversight on Outer Continental Shelf Lands Act, March 23, 24, and April 11, 18, 1972, Pt. 3-Appendix, p. 1358.

46. Exploration, development, and production costs are those reported in Interior, *Questions and Policy Issues*, p. 86; transportation and lease purchase costs are those reported in U.S., Department of the Interior, Bureau of Land Management, *The Role of Petroleum and Natural Gas from the Outer Continental Shelf in the National Supply of Petroleum and Natural Gas*, Technical Bulletin 5 (Washington: Government Printing Office, 1970), p. 194.

47. For a brief but understandable discussion of production-price relationships see Alfred E. Kahn, "The Combined Effects of Prorationing, the Depletion Allowance and Import Quotas on the Price of Producing Crude Oil in the United States," *Natural Resources Journal*, 10 (January, 1970), pp. 53-61.

48. R. D. McCurdy, "Economics of Oil and Gas Operations Offshore, U.S.A.," an address to the Offshore Technology Conference, May, 1969.

49. J. K. McCarron, "Computer Simulation as a Tool for Evaluating Offshore Construction Alternatives," OTC 1359 in *1971 Offshore Technology Conference, April 19-21, Houston, Texas, Preprints*, Vol. 1, pp. 329-36.

50. E. L. Dougherty, R. D. Goodknight, and R. B. Oldaker, "A Comparative Study of the Economics of a Subsea and a Platform Oil-Producing System," *Oceanology International 1972*, Brighton, England, March 19-24, 1972.

IV. OCS Developers and Regulators

OUR PURPOSE in this chapter is to describe the industry that finds, produces, and transports OCS oil and gas resources and the governmental system that has been established to regulate that industry's activities. The descriptions of the two are intended to convey only a broad outline and general impressions.

THE PETROLEUM INDUSTRY: OCS DEVELOPERS

The petroleum industry is sometimes regarded as the world's largest fraternity. It views its history in romantic terms. It is an industry which sincerely believes that it has provided the base upon which our energy-intensive society has been built. And it views its role in meeting the ever-increasing energy demands of the world as an obligation.

This point of view clearly makes good business sense for the oil companies. It is also basically correct. A supply of low-cost petroleum products is an essential element of modern society and, unless we are willing to accept energy restrictions or energy-reducing social changes, the petroleum industry will be called upon to supply ever-increasing quantities of oil and gas. In meeting these demands, the industry will continue to expose itself to the risks associated with finding new sources of energy in increasingly hostile environments.

Over its lifetime, the petroleum industry has changed so that there is now less speculation and more concern with corporate stability. This change is nowhere more evident than on the OCS. The traditional patterns of onshore exploration and development have, in fact, been completely reversed in federal waters. Whereas independents have done most of the dry-land wildcatting and have found most of the gas and oil onshore,[1] a recent study by the Department of the Interior has shown that "federal offshore areas have been explored, developed and produced primarily by major oil companies because the capital requirements . . . exceed the capabilities of most independents."[2]

The pattern of leaseholds and development in state and federal waters is shown in Table 5. A total of 62 companies or groups produced oil and condensate from offshore United States in 1971. Only 22, those listed in the table, brought in more than a million barrels. The remaining 40 companies or groups, most of which were independents, together produced

93

Table 5. Offshore and OCS Oil Production

Producer	Gulf of Mexico Production, State and Federal, 1971[a] Oil and Condensate (Thousand bbls.)	Percent of Total Production	Corporate Income 1972[b] Gross Income (Million $)	Net Income (Million $)	Production in Federal Waters through 1968 Cumulative[c] Oil and Condensate (Thousand bbls.)	Bonus Paid (Million $)
Shell Oil Co.	105,496	17.1	4,591	245	221,500	284
Texaco, Inc.	96,959	15.7	7,529	904	16,800	407
Gulf Oil Corp.	95,428	15.5	5,940	561	162,800	271
Exxon Co., USA	73,719	11.9	18,700	1,466	244,900	519
Chevron Oil Co.	72,698	11.8	5,143	511	275,400	198
Continental Oil Co.	44,520	7.2	3,262	109	65,300	75
Signal Oil & Gas Co.	16,646	2.7	1,315	29	d	22
Placid Oil Co.	16,620	2.7	NA	NA	d	—
Kerr-McGee Corp.	15,131	2.5	603	51	7,108	—
Union Oil Co. of Calif.	14,367	2.3	1,873	115	50,000	81
Mobil Oil Corp.	12,596	2.0	8,243	541	38,600	188
Tenneco Oil Co.	10,902	1.8	2,841	184	23,400	105
Ocean Drlg. & Expl.	9,907	1.6	61	11	4,800	120
Lake Wash., Inc.	7,148	1.2	NA	NA	d	—
Amoco Prod. Co.	5,444	0.9	4,054	342	16,400	48
Atlantic Richfield Co.	3,897	0.6	3,658	199	40,000	85
Sun Oil Co.	3,414	0.6	1,939	152	d	16
Southern Nat. Gas. Co.	1,515	0.2	NA	NA	8,500	—
Superior Oil Co.	1,104	0.2	135	4	3,200	16
Phillips Petr. Co.	1,086	0.2	2,363	132	34,400	68
Skelly Oil Co.	1,031	0.2	555	38	d	24
Pennzoil Prod. Co.	1,020	0.2	731	33	d	—

NA—Not available.

[a] Clean Gulf Associates Oil Spill Contingency Agreement; Exhibit B. Percentage Participation of Members (July, 1972).

[b] Moody's Industrial Manual—1972, Moody's Investors Service, Inc. NY, NY.

[c] Offshore Petroleum Studies, Bureau of Mines Info. Circular—IC 8557.

[d] Not in top 20 Producers. Top 20 produced 97.7% of total.

just over one percent of the total offshore production of 618 million barrels.

In federal waters, only 18 companies have produced oil in significant quantities. Again, the majors predominate, accounting for approximately 91.8 percent of the total OCS production of 387 million barrels of oil and condensate produced in the Gulf of Mexico in 1971.[3]

The distinction between majors and independents, never entirely clear, has become even more blurred in recent years. The characteristic feature of a "major" has been its vertical integration. Through various divisions and departments, majors search for and produce crude petroleum reserves, convert them to salable products, and retail them through their own gasoline stations and other franchised dealers.

The most recent issue of the *U.S.A. Oil Industry Directory, 1972*, lists 32 "leading integrated oil companies . . . that engage in all branches of the petroleum industry."[4] It lists more than 700 large independent oil and gas producing companies, many of which engage in other industry activities as well. At least three of the independents are larger than some of the so-called majors.

Because of their size and marketing operations, the majors and their products have become household words. Exxon (formerly Standard Oil of New Jersey, Esso), Mobil, Texaco, Gulf, Chevron, Amoco, and Shell are as familiar as Ford, Chrysler, and General Motors. For the convenience of their customers, the integrated oil companies provide a wide range of services along with gasoline and oil, including consumer and business credit, maps and travel advice, clean rest rooms, and a variety of amusements and public service programs on radio and television. In a mobile society, they have become highly visible and an integral part of our daily lives.

This vertically integrated structure of the majors has a number of corporate advantages aside from the financial strength bestowed by sheer size. Most notable is the potential for distributing prices and costs between divisions in such a way as to minimize taxes and maximize profits. In its simplest form, this freedom insures that the highest profits are taken in those divisions with the best tax write-off privileges. Thus the refinery divisions may be called upon to "pay" a relatively high cost for crude, since the production division can apply the depletion allowance against profits or, alternatively, drill up the taxable income in new exploratory ventures.

Another distinction sometimes made between oil companies is the extent of their international operations. Until recently, the international oil industry has been completely dominated by a group of seven oil companies, sometimes known as the "Seven Sisters." The size ranking of these companies, based on sales, is: Exxon, Royal Dutch Shell (Shell), Mobil Oil (Mobil), Texaco, Inc. (Texaco), Gulf Oil (Gulf), Standard Oil of California (Chevron), and British Petroleum (BP).[5]

The sheer magnitude of the major oil company operations is indicated by the gross dollar volumes shown in Table 5. In the *Fortune* magazine list of the 500 top U.S. corporations, the major oil companies represent three of the top ten and twelve of the top forty.[6] Several privately-held majors, such as the Hunt Oil Company, are not included in the *Fortune* tabulation.

Table 6. Energy Diversification of Twenty-five Largest
Petroleum Companies as of Early 1970

Company	1971 Assets[a] ($000)	Energy Source						
		Gas	State Off-shore[b]	OCS[b]	Oil Shale	Coal	Uran-ium	Tar Sands
Exxon	20,314,249	x	x	x	x	x	x	x
Texaco	10,933,292	x	x	x	x	x	x	
Gulf	9,465,762	x	x	x	x	x	x	x
Mobil	8,552,273	x	x	x	x		x	
Standard Oil (Cal.)	7,513,190	x	x	x	x			
Standard Oil (Ind.)	5,650,724	x	x	x	x		x	x
Atlantic Richfield	4,704,105	x	x	x	x	x	x	x
Shell	4,646,282[c]	x	x	x	x	x	x	x
Tenneco	4,565,170	x	x	x				
Phillips	3,166,699	x	x	x	x		x	
Continental	3,048,709	x	x	x	x	x	x	
Sun	2,813,276	x	x	x	x	x	x	x
Occidental	2,580,028	x				x		
Union Oil of Cal.	2,564,770	x	x	x	x		x	
Cities Service	2,325,300	x	x		x		x	x
Getty	2,015,291	x	x		x		x	
Standard Oil (Ohio)	1,815,193	x			x	x	x	
Pennzoil	1,545,058	x	x				x	
Marathon	1,391,423	x	x	x	x	x	x	x
Amerada-Hess	1,328,205	x	x	x			x	
Signal	1,273,441	x	x	x				
Ashland	1,030,181	x	x		x	x	x	
Kerr-McGee	762,504	x	x	x		x	x	
Coastal States	661,686	x						
Superior Oil	540,753	x			x			

[a] *Fortune*, May, 1972, June, 1972.
[b] Oil and Gas.
[c] U.S. operations only.

Other measures of size and economic strength are equally impressive. In terms of cargo/tanker fleets, for example, both Royal Dutch Shell and Exxon own around ten million deadweight tons, each roughly equal to the combined fleets of Daniel K. Ludwig and Aristotle Onassis, the two largest independent ship operators.[7]

In a broader context, it is also significant that the major oil companies are carving out a place for themselves in the overall energy market through active programs of acquisition and diversification. Table 6 shows that, of the 25 largest oil companies, 18 had positions in oil shale, 11 had positions in coal, 18 were in uranium, and 7 in tar sands. In many ways, their move into oil shale and tar sands is a logical hedge against the depletion of domestic crude oil resources. Coal represents a future supplemental source for synthetic fuels, and the search for uranium is similar to the search for oil and gas, being founded on geology and geophysics.

Nevertheless, the new pattern of horizontal integration being superimposed on the traditional vertical integration of the major oil companies consolidates their broad power base and, at the same time, gives some reason for concern about the potential loss of competition among alternative energy sources.[8] These companies, according to Bruce C. Netschert, an energy economist, "tend to be dominant in their own submarkets and to bring substantial market power to each of the new fuel submarkets they are entering. The result is a tendency toward concentration and entrenched dominance."[9]

A second group of 20 or 30 smaller oil companies has entered the international oil industry in recent years, many of them U.S. firms such as Standard Oil of Indiana, Phillips Petroleum, Atlantic Richfield, and Union Oil of California. Although the new participants have been active in the Middle East and in new fields throughout the world, the "Seven Sisters" still account for the overwhelming majority of international crude oil operations.

The term "independents" covers a broad range of corporate size and diversity of operations. It includes such companies as Felmont Oil, which is in the business of exploration and production, most often as a partner in joint ventures. It includes, for example, Southern Natural Gas, which is primarily in the pipeline business, but which undertakes offshore production operations to insure an adequate supply of gas and oil to meet its contractual obligations. And it includes such companies as Ocean Drilling and Exploration (ODECO), whose major business is providing a variety of subcontractor services to the oil industry, but which also participates in offshore oil and gas production through farm-outs and group ventures.

Although a total of more than 40 independents have a piece of the offshore action, their contribution, in terms of lease purchases and petroleum production, is relatively modest. Table 7 compares independents and majors for all OCS lease sales through September 1971. It is clear that independents are the successful bidders on only a small percentage of the available tracts and that the tracts they do acquire are notably less productive than those of the majors.

This large-company dominance of OCS development has been of concern to various public-interest groups and has led to proposals for alternative OCS leasing procedures aimed at expanding the range of offshore producers. (Several leasing alternatives are discussed in Chapter IX.)

One significant development in this area is the trend toward joint ventures and consortia bidding. Although it has been common for smaller

Table 7. OCS Lease Acreage and Petroleum Production Through September, 1971

Lessee	Acreage (%)	Production (%)
Individual Majors	46	63
Groups of Majors	35	34
Individual Independents	2	1
Groups of Independents	17	2
Total	100	100

companies to join together in order to acquire and produce offshore tracts, the cost of OCS development has become so high that the majors themselves have also taken steps to spread the risk. One such consortium is CAGC, jointly owned by Conoco, Atlantic Richfield, Getty, and Cities Service. The CAGC Group was high bidder on 25 tracts in the Louisiana lease sale of December 19, 1972, for a total of $221.9 million. The SLAM Group (Signal, Louisiana Land and Exploration, Amerada Hess, and Marathon) won 10 bids for $132.3 million. The two consortia together acquired just under 30 percent of the 119 tracts on which bids were received.[10]

Aside from the diversification in the energy resource field, both the integrated and independent companies have taken strong positions in turbine engines and trucks, livestock and land management, ship building, insurance and banking, as well as in resource-related fields such as petrochemicals and fertilizer. Their high asset value and political strength make it possible for petroleum companies to undertake such activities on an international scale.

Finally, in speaking of the integrated majors, it would be misleading to imply that they are fully integrated in the sense of carrying out all functions on the OCS. They depend on a variety of subcontractors to carry out many of their offshore activities. From initial seismic surveys, through drilling and field development, to transporting and feeding offshore production crews, they rely either on low bidders or negotiated contracts with old corporate friends. The result has been a proliferation of specialty firms, many with headquarters in the Gulf Coast area, which are prepared to undertake a wide range of assignments up to and including complete field development.

The subcontractor-related low-bid system has been identified in discussions with individuals associated with regulatory agencies and the industry as one major cause of ecological damage in the past because of careless and inadequately supervised operations. In the absence of environmental criteria, it is not surprising that subcontractors faced with over-runs on optimistic bids should take a relaxed view toward ecological damage. At the same time, the contracting firm, being once removed from the offending activity, could rationalize nonintervention as good business judgment. In a less specific way, the tendency of many production corporations to develop long-term purchaser-vendor relationships with a single set of contractors may have lessened technological competition and thereby inhibited new developments. New federal regulations, however, and the clear accountability of the contracting firm for meeting the revised standards place a new emphasis on the quality of performance in offshore operations. Although there will continue to be differences in the zeal with which contractors and developers comply with the regulations, criteria have been established and minimum acceptable standards have been set for many OCS operations.

The reliance on subcontractors is part of an industry-wide pattern of cooperation on technical matters. In addition to contracting for at least a portion of all services, the oil companies share some geological information as members of bidding consortia. Their engineers and scientists exchange technical information at regional and national meetings. They have a tradition of patent sales and cross-licensing which insures that, for the most part, they all draw from a common pool of oil field technology. And, although the pace of technological development in the oil industry has been relatively slow, this pattern of patent sales and cross-licensing tends to make new technologies available throughout the industry.

A number of factors are moving the industry into broader areas of research and development (R&D) activity, chief among them being new environmental constraints and the move to worldwide and more diverse field locations. Nevertheless, the likelihood of major breakthroughs in technologies for discovering and producing OCS hydrocarbons is not high. The oil industry, as with most extractive industries, must deal with large quantities of material in a very direct way which does not lend itself to miniaturization (electronics), a more rapid or efficient expenditure of energy (air transportation), or the synthesis of new substances (medicine).

On balance, it must be said that the petroleum industry has developed a remarkably efficient system for finding and distributing energy resources. Its products have been freely, even excessively, available in all parts of the country at prices which have been relatively constant during a time of strong inflationary pressures. In the process, the industry has made a small number of people very rich and has enabled the small investor to participate in one of the fastest-growing parts of our economy. Together with the power companies, the automobile, and the airplane, it has transformed our society.

It remains now to see whether the corporate structures and incentives which have brought the industry to its present eminent position can deal successfully with the new realities of resource depletion, environmental concern, and social accountability.

THE GOVERNMENT-REGULATORY SYSTEM FOR THE OCS

Several federal statutes articulate policy objectives and collectively establish a legal/administrative system for managing and controlling the development of OCS oil and gas resources. The basic authority in this area is the OCS Lands Act which authorized the Secretary of the Interior to lease the submerged lands of the OCS in order to meet an "urgent need" for finding and developing oil and gas deposits.[11] While promoting the achievement of this objective, the Secretary must also provide for conservation and the prevention of waste.[12]

These remained the formally stated policy objectives for OCS development until passage of the National Environmental Policy Act (NEPA) in 1969. NEPA established a national policy for protecting and restoring the environment; the effect on OCS management has been to require that the OCS Lands Act be administered and interpreted in accordance with this new national environmental policy.

An increasing concern for the environment also accounts for provisions included in the Federal Water Pollution Control Act (FWPCA) Amendments of 1972 and the Marine Protection, Research, and Sanctuaries Act (Marine Sanctuaries Act). Section 311(b)(3) of the FWPCA Amendments of 1972 prohibits "the discharge of oil or hazardous substances into or upon the navigable waters . . . adjoining shorelines, or into or upon the waters of the contiguous zone in harmful quantities." This section also provides for a National Contingency Plan for responding to and removing spills of oil or hazardous substances.

The Marine Sanctuaries Act authorizes the Secretary of Commerce, after consultation with heads of other interested departments and agencies and with the approval of the President, to designate as marine sanctuaries areas extending as far seaward as the outer edge of the OCS. The Secretary may do this when he considers it necessary for the purpose of preserving or restoring the areas for their conservation, recreational, ecological, or esthetic values.[13]

Another social value, the safety and health of workers, led to the passage of the 1970 Occupational Safety and Health Act (OSHA). This legislation requires employers, including those engaged in OCS development activities, to provide a safe working environment for all employees.

The OCS Lands Act also assimilated state civil and criminal laws in effect at the time the Act was passed. These laws, when not in conflict with federal laws and regulations, are administered and enforced by appropriate federal officials and courts.

SPECIFIC AGENCY RESPONSIBILITIES

Department of the Interior: Of the departments and agencies with responsibilities in this area, the Department of the Interior clearly has the major role. The Secretary of the Interior is authorized to grant OCS oil and gas leases. He is responsible for administering these leases, including prescribing the necessary rules for regulating their development in a manner consistent with existing public policy objectives.

Within the Department of Interior, the Bureau of Land Management (BLM) administers the leasing provisions of the OCS Lands Act, in accordance with the Department's currently defined goals of: (1) orderly and timely resource development; (2) protection of the environment; and (3) receipt of fair market value. In carrying out these obligations, BLM:

1. receives nominations and selects tracts to be included in a lease sale;
2. prepares an environmental impact statement for each sale;
3. together with the U.S. Geological Survey (USGS), makes an economic, engineering, and geologic evaluation of tracts to be sold;
4. receives the bids and determines whether or not to award leases to the highest bidders on individual tracts;
5. receives revenues from lease sales; and
6. grants rights-of-way for pipelines to transport oil and gas from OCS leases to shore.

USGS has the primary responsibility within the Department of Interior for overseeing the development of a tract once it has been leased. In discharging the Secretary's OCS regulatory responsibilities, as specified in the *Code of Federal Regulations,* USGS:

1. through its Area Supervisors and in consultation with the petroleum industry, issues detailed regulations in the form of OCS orders and notices;
2. enforces OCS orders and notices;
3. issues geophysical and geological exploration permits;
4. approves post-lease exploration and development plans;
5. issues permits for both exploratory and development drilling;
6. approves pipelines as a part of field development; and
7. collects royalties.

The Department of the Interior is responsible for a variety of energy programs in addition to OCS oil and gas, and the Secretary recently established a departmental Energy Board to coordinate his overall energy responsibilities. The Board is chaired by the Secretary, and the Deputy Under Secretary for Energy serves as executive director.

Department of the Defense: The OCS Lands Act makes the Secretary of the Army responsible for preventing obstructions to navigation.[14] The Corps of Engineers, acting for the Secretary, requires that a permit be obtained before a structure may be placed on the OCS; this requirement has been applied to artificial islands, offshore platforms, and floating drilling rigs.

Department of Transportation: The Coast Guard, located within the Department of Transportation, has several OCS responsibilities. These include:

    1. insuring that structures on the OCS are properly marked to protect navigation;

    2. establishing and enforcing safety regulations for OCS structures;

    3. inspecting and certifying floating drilling rigs except for those which stand on the bottom during drilling; and

    4. maintaining surveillance for oil spilled or discharged into the waters over or immediately adjacent to the OCS.

The Office of Pipeline Safety (OPS), located in the Department of Transportation, has responsibilities for pipelines. Primarily, it supervises the safety of gas pipelines, including establishing design criteria.

Independent Regulatory Agencies: The Federal Power Commission (FPC) and the Interstate Commerce Commission (ICC) have jurisdiction over common carrier pipelines linked to interstate commerce. FPC has broad discretionary powers over the approval, design, and economics of common carrier gas pipelines, and it sets the wellhead price of OCS gas. ICC has no jurisdiction over pipelines for petroleum liquids until the line is actually constructed. However, once the line has been constructed, ICC requires the operator to be nondiscriminatory in accepting petroleum liquids for transport.

Other Agencies: A number of other agencies have some OCS responsibility. The FWPCA Amendments of 1972 call for the Federal Maritime Commission to determine the financial responsibility of oil shippers operating in the oceans adjacent to the U.S. Since most oil produced on the OCS is brought ashore by pipeline, this provision of the Act has limited application to OCS oil and gas operations.

The National Oceanic and Atmospheric Administration (NOAA), within the Department of Commerce, collects weather data used in platform design. And its responsibilities for commercial fisheries require that NOAA maintain a continuing interest in the environmental and multiple use impacts of OCS development.

The Environmental Protection Agency (EPA) is involved in the pre-lease sale environmental impact statement, in setting and enforcing discharge levels, and in oil spill contingency planning and implementation.

The Departments of Labor and Health, Education, and Welfare (HEW) have responsibilities under OSHA. HEW makes working-condition evaluations and provides technical assistance to employers; Labor is responsible for enforcing the rules established to provide all employees a safe working environment.

FEDERAL-STATE REGULATIONS

The OCS Lands Act assimilated state laws at the time it was enacted. In 1953, both Louisiana and Texas, the coastal states adjacent to the areas of the OCS which have been most productive, had laws which governed production. These laws set production limits for the adjacent OCS until 1970, when President Nixon withdrew OCS lands from state production controls. Limiting production on the basis of market demand is for the most part a dead issue since domestic demand now greatly exceeds domestic supply. It was this excess demand which led the President to withdraw the OCS from state production controls.

Since the submerged lands and the waters over them are a physical continuum, federal and state authorities have to interact on a regular basis so that oil and gas produced on the OCS can be transported to shore. State concern begins with exploration, and the procedures for granting federal exploration permits require that state interests in the protection and conservation of aquatic life be observed.

Federal-state cooperation and coordination are also required in bringing pipelines over the state's portion of the shelf to a shore facility located on state lands. Historically, the most intense federal-state controversies have been related to jurisdictional conflicts. Several of these disputes have now been resolved by the U.S. Supreme Court. However, the Court has not yet decided all the jurisdictional issues raised in the dispute between the federal government and the state of Louisiana, and the dispute over the Atlantic shelf is just beginning.

GOVERNMENT-INDUSTRY RELATIONS

Before the Santa Barbara blowout, government and the petroleum industry shared common goals for the development of OCS oil and gas. Their mutual objective was efficient development of OCS oil and gas resources while preventing waste and promoting conservation. The relationship was and continues to be close. In fact, many individuals move into and out of both government and industry, particularly at middle and upper levels of management in government usually filled by political appointees.

Both the government regulators and industry spokesmen acknowledged before the Santa Barbara blowout that it was the petroleum industry which possessed the detailed and expert knowledge needed to advance their mutual objective of efficient resource development. This promoted development of a regulatory philosophy of minimum regulation and maximum cooperation. Those regulations which were issued tended to be of a general nature. They did not specify design criteria or detailed technical standards; rather, they permitted operators wide discretionary judgment in achieving a stated objective.[15] Enforcement tended to be lax, owing in part to a lack of funds for enforcement activities and waivers were freely given, as, for example, to Union in the Santa Barbara Channel. (The waiver permitted Union to set casing to a shallower depth than that required by OCS Order Number 2.)

After the blowout at Santa Barbara, considerable pressure was generated to change government-industry relations. New environmental regulations required the Department of the Interior to broaden its responsibilities; and USGS, in consultation with industry, began to revise or replace old regulations and to write new ones. The move was toward more stringent regulations and strict enforcement. But perhaps most important of all, USGS's regulations became more specific and detailed, in some instances specifying what USGS determined to be the most satisfactory system.[16] In addition, there was recognition in both the Congress and the Department of the Interior that government needed to increase its internal technological capability for responsibly managing and controlling OCS petroleum resource development.

HOW WELL HAS GOVERNMENT PERFORMED ITS OVERSIGHT FUNCTIONS?

The overall picture which emerges from this brief examination of the governmental system for OCS development is one of fragmentation. Although the Department of the Interior has major responsibility for the OCS, the responsibility and authority for planning, policy-making, and administration have been and are decentralized. This results in a requirement for extensive inter- and intra-agency coordination and cooperation to avoid gaps and oversights, particularly in matters involving the relatively new concerns for the environment and safety, and places an enormous strain on the Department of the Interior if it attempts to be effective in meeting all of its responsibilities.

Our examination also points up the dual role assigned to the Secretary of the Interior. Not only is he responsible for promoting and regulating the development of OCS resources, but he has had to deal with the fact that one of the principal motives for development of these resources has been a demand for the additional governmental revenues which a lease sale would produce. Sales have sometimes been paced in response to this demand rather than as a step in some orderly scheme for OCS development. These demands for revenue have generally been generated externally, by the Office of Management and Budget and its predecessor, the Bureau of the Budget, rather than within the Department of the Interior or by the Secretary himself.

Largely because of the minimum regulation philosophy, information upon which to base planning, policy-making, and administration has been limited. Given this approach, not much information was needed; in fact, only short-term planning and policy-making have been attempted, and then only for the OCS itself rather than for the OCS as one source of needed oil and gas supplies. When something has gone wrong within this system—as, for example, at Santa Barbara—the fragmentation which has impeded coordinated planning, policy-making, and administration has also made it difficult to fix responsibility. And, of course, the closeness of government and industry and the commonality of their objectives have worked against development of a system of strict accountability.

1. U.S., Department of the Interior, Office of Oil and Gas, *An Appraisal of the Petroleum Industry of the United States* (Washington: Government Printing Office, 1965), pp. 41–42.

2. U.S., Department of the Interior, Bureau of Mines, *Offshore Petroleum Studies: Composition of the Offshore U.S. Petroleum Industry and Estimated Costs of Producing Petroleum in the Gulf of Mexico*, by L. K. Weaver, H. F. Pierce, and C. J. Jirik, Information Circular 8557 (Washington: Government Printing Office, 1972).

3. U.S., Department of the Interior, Geological Survey (Area Office, Metairie, La.), unpublished data sheet.

4. *U.S.A. Oil Industry Directory, 1973* (Tulsa: The Petroleum Publishing Co., 1973).

5. Michael Tanzer, *The Political Economy of International Oil and the Underdeveloped Countries* (Boston: Beacon Press, 1969), p. 190.

6. *Fortune*, 85 (May, 1972), p. 190.

7. Carol J. Loomis, "The Chinese Landlubber Who Came to Rule the Seas," *Fortune*, 87 (February, 1973), p. 92.

8. See, for example, Bruce C. Netschert, "The Energy Company: A Monopoly Trend in the Energy Markets," in *The Energy Crisis*, ed. by Richard S. Lewis and

Bernard I. Spinrad (Chicago: Educational Foundation for Nuclear Science, 1972), p. 75.

   9. *Ibid.*
   10. *World Oil,* 176 (January, 1973), p. 76.
   11. This is the language used in Section 8 of the OCS Lands Act.
   12. OCS Lands Act, Section 5.
   13. Marine Sanctuaries Act, Section 302.
   14. OCS Lands Act, Section 4.
   15. See the National Academy of Engineering report on *Outer Continental Shelf Resource Development Safety: A Review of Technology and Regulation for the Systematic Minimization of Environmental Intrusion from Petroleum Products* (Washington: National Academy of Engineering, December, 1972), especially Chapter 2, "Regulation and Inspection," pp. 51–65.
   16. On this change in philosophy and its implementation in OCS Orders 8 and 9 for the Gulf Coast Area, see W. E. Bleakley, "OCS Orders 8 and 9," *Oil and Gas Journal,* 70 (August 21, 1972), pp. 59–66.

V. Policy-Making for the OCS

MOST STUDENTS of our political system generally agree that in the United States public policy-making and administration in any substantive policy area usually involve only a few actors or participants on a continuing basis.[1] Continuing, direct participation is usually limited to those actors who have official responsibility plus those who have an unambiguous, obvious, and direct stake in what public policy in a particular policy area is and how it is administered. Typically these actors are highly organized and bureaucratized to promote their particular interests, as are the American Medical Association and the American Petroleum Institute, for example.

However, our political past also demonstrates that a variety of stimuli or factors can upset "policy-making as usual" in any area of public policy.[2] The attention of additional participants may be attracted by:

1. a catastrophic event such as a fire in the Coconut Grove night club in Boston or an oil spill in the Santa Barbara Channel;

2. a general change in values such as that which appears to have occurred recently toward environmental quality;

3. a shortage in the availability of petroleum products made visible by shutting down assembly lines, closing public schools, and limiting gas sales; or

4. an individual such as Rachel Carson or Ralph Nader.

In our political system, business is one of the best organized interests represented continuously in public policy-making. Not only is it among the best organized, it almost always possesses far more resources than do other participants. Other interests generally cannot compete effectively unless an event, a change in values, a change in conditions, or an extraordinary individual compensates for their lack of financial resources.

Other groups are also usually at a disadvantage because their goals are more finely focused than are those of business. Business groups such as the National Association of Manufacturers pursue comparatively general goals; businessmen can agree generally on the kinds of public policies that will benefit or be costly to them. In contrast, many competing interests are focused much more narrowly and become active only when their own narrow goal is affected. Groups promoting civil liberties, changes in our Southeast Asian policies, and prayer in public schools have demonstrated this on a continuing basis over the past several years. Groups promoting interests such as these tend to become active only when their concerns either have been adversely affected or are visibly threatened and their goals need to be advanced politically.

In the case of making and administering OCS policy, direct, continuous participation has been largely limited to the petroleum industry and government. Policies generally have been made gradually and, except for the OCS Lands and Submerged Lands Acts, tangentially. Since government and industry have had almost identical policy objectives, policy has been made and administered with extraordinary ease. When periodic battles have flared in Congress over special benefits, such as depletion allowances, tax benefits, and limited production, the oil states—and the industry—have been effectively represented by influential spokesmen. The result has been that the petroleum industry tends to be given special treatment. In addition to the depletion allowance and tax benefits, for example, the industry is singled out for special treatment in the Public Information Act of 1968. (The Public Information Act is discussed in Chapter VII.)

On the administrative side, one of the Secretary of the Interior's major sources of information and advice has been an officially established advisory board, the National Petroleum Council (NPC). This is an industry organization, and the studies which it conducts at the request of the Secretary are carried out by committees comprised mostly of industry people. Within the Department itself, many of the Secretary's advisors are either recruited from industry or are persons who have spent a part of their careers in industry.

At the operational level, detailed OCS orders regulating OCS development have been and are the product of a process of industry-government cooperation. In the Gulf Coast Area this involves the Area Supervisor, his staff, and the Offshore Operators Committee. The Committee is asked to review revisions and new orders before they are issued. It is the Area Supervisor, with the approval of the Chief of the Conservation Division of USGS, who decides what the order as finally issued will require.

Both at the departmental and area levels, the patterns of cooperative relationships are intended to give government access to industry expertise. At one level, the goal is to obtain data and information for informing policy-makers; at the other, it is to establish informed regulations which are enforceable. It is clear that the pattern of government-industry relationships which has been developed has produced a very closed system for making and administering OCS policies.

It is the closed character of this system which is being challenged at the present time. Given the generally increased concern for environmental quality and the impact of several specific events (such as the Santa Barbara catastrophe), new actors, representing new interests, have begun to demand a role in making and administering OCS oil and gas policy. Several of these new actors are performing as though they intend to participate directly and continuously in this policy area in the future.

Citizen groups interested in the environment or consumer protection have been organized on both a national and a local basis. At the national level, the Natural Resources Defense Council, Inc. (NRDC) exemplifies the potency of a well-organized environmentally concerned group. Acting in concert with the Sierra Club and Friends of the Earth, NRDC successfully enjoined a proposed OCS lease sale in December, 1971, and forestalled the sale until September, 1972.

Get Oil Out! (GOO!) is an example of a local environmental group. Organized after the Santa Barbara blowout, GOO! insists that there be no further development of petroleum resources in the Santa Barbara Channel. Although the organization is apparently unwilling to accept a consequent reduction in energy supply for the area, some of its spokesmen at least recognize a degree of incongruity in that position.

The Center for Law and Social Policy has been concerned with environmental quality and consumer protection on a wide-ranging national basis. And a Long Island group has proposed boycotts of all products of an oil company that engages in OCS operations without complying with OCS regulations.

Employing a variety of means, then, ranging from legal action to direct boycotts, citizen groups are attempting to achieve what they consider to be a higher order of responsibility on the part of industry and government in protecting the public interest. In particular, these groups focus their attention on bringing about changes in the policies under which OCS operations are to be conducted in the future. They intend to contribute data and insight beyond present governmental capabilities and to provide a broader overview of environmentally sensitive problem areas than has been possible under the old OCS policy-making system. Their goal, collectively, is to dilute and alleviate the commonality-of-interest relationship which has served to blur the line between the regulator-agency and the regulated-industry.

These new areas of awareness and the changes in values manifested in concerns for environmental quality have been recognized by both industry and governmental officials. In fact, they have acknowledged the loss of public confidence in their performance. For example, M. A. Wright, former Chairman of the Board of Humble (Exxon), told those attending the 1969 Offshore Technology Conference that

in significant measure, the freedom of operation we are allowed years from now may well depend upon our ability to convince the American public that we are capable of carrying out difficult, sophisticated technical operations deep in the ocean while maintaining the ability to conserve and protect the marine environment.[3]

And in 1972, V. E. McKelvey, Director of the U.S. Geological Survey (USGS), told an industry group meeting in Houston that, although it is the burden of industry to prove that it deserves to have the public's consent, "an important part of the proof . . . must come through the performance of state and federal regulatory organizations." He went on to explain that

> the public needs to know not only that a satisfactory technologic capability exists for safely carrying out a difficult and potentially dangerous operation, but it needs to be assured also that adequate regulatory supervision exists to see that the operation will indeed be conducted safely.[4]

A number of specific public policy issues have arisen as a consequence of the recognition of these changes from our political past. Changes are to be the hallmark of the future, for changes clearly will be required in the minimal standards that will be acceptable for industry performance and practice. Likewise the need for changes in governmental requirements has been recognized: that is, changes will be required in the social technologies if an improvement in performance and equipment standards required for optimal development of OCS resources is to be achieved.

Specific public policy issues which arise as a consequence of changes in how policy is to be made and administered for the OCS will be covered in Part III, which follows.

---

1. See, for example, Joyce M. and William C. Mitchell, "The Changing Politics of American Life," in Eleanor B. Sheldon and Wilbert E. Moore, eds., *Indicators of Social Change: Concepts and Measurements* (New York: Russell Sage Foundation, 1960), pp. 247–94. The abbreviated description here borrows from the Mitchells' analysis.

2. On this point see John M. Gaus' *Reflections on Public Administration* (University, Ala.: University of Alabama Press, 1947), especially his chapter on "The Ecology of Government," pp. 1–19.

3. Vincent E. McKelvey, "Petroleum Exploration and the Public Consent," *The Landman*, 17 (February, 1972), p. 8.

4. *Ibid.*, p. 9.

Part Three

Policy Issues Raised by OCS Development

Since government is responsible for managing and controlling the development of OCS oil and gas resources, promoting changes in practices and standards employed by the petroleum industry is ultimately a government responsibility. Chapter VI focuses on the adequacy of the technologies, standards, and operating procedures currently being employed by the petroleum industry on the OCS, and identifies changes which would enhance their adequacy. These changes require action to be taken by both industry and the governmental agencies responsible for overseeing OCS operations.

Chapters VII–IX concentrate on a second category of issues which arise in connection with OCS oil and gas development. These issues focus on the adequacy of the social technologies employed by the legal/administrative system which promotes and regulates OCS development. Changes proposed here are aimed at correcting deficiencies in these social technologies and the legal/administrative system that employs them.

VI. Adequacy of OCS Technologies

UNTIL RECENTLY, OCS technologies had to satisfy only the petroleum industry and the government agencies which regulate the development of OCS oil and gas resources. Now, however, environmental concerns have changed the criteria used in determining what is satisfactory. When evaluated on the basis of these new criteria, certain standards, procedures, and technologies being used on the OCS are found to be inadequate.

In a narrow sense, the problem of technological inadequacy can be related to the generally permissive nature of government regulation on the OCS. (This characterization results in large part from the lack of adequate resources to be a more active regulator.) As noted earlier, OCS orders are the product of industry-government cooperation. Furthermore, interactions between industry and agency personnel occur in a number of ways and at a variety of levels. Technology conferences, memberships on advisory boards, and the normal social interaction of people with similar backgrounds and interests insure that both the regulators and the regulated operate from a common background and within a well-defined framework. From both technical and administrative standpoints, the relationships are in no sense sinister. Nevertheless, the OCS regulations have always been well within the state of the art as practiced by the industry so that compliance has presented no serious technical challenge.

Improving the physical technologies, making them more reliable and less susceptible to human error, offers a major advantage as a response to public opposition to continued OCS development. Changing technologies to obtain a desirable objective can be less difficult than attempting to change human behavior, as past efforts in auto safety, for example, demonstrate. In this chapter, we identify several inadequacies in OCS technologies and suggest that some of these inadequacies can be remedied by changes in the physical technologies themselves. Some of the inadequacies, however, appear to be the result of the way in which the technologies have been managed and developed. For these inadequacies to be overcome, both the petroleum industry and the government agencies which regulate OCS operations must change their past patterns of behavior. We have divided our analysis of these inadequacies and the public policy issues which they raise into five categories: drilling and blowout control, production, transportation, accident response, and the development and management of technology.

113

DRILLING AND BLOWOUT CONTROL TECHNOLOGIES

Blowouts are a particularly visible type of accident and are often cited as being a major influence in the loss of public confidence in offshore oil and gas operations. The blowout rate has been approximately one for each 500 holes drilled on the OCS for the period from 1953 through 1971. According to USGS, during that period there were 19 blowout accidents which resulted in personnel injury and/or damage to property and the environment.[1] (A detailed analysis of accidents is presented in Appendix B.)

The magnitude of the spills and the damage associated with them are often in dispute. In this connection, it is important to make a distinction between oil and gas blowouts. Gas blowouts normally vent to the surface and are dissipated into the atmosphere. Oil blowouts are more serious. The released oil forms a slick on the surface of the water and, unless contained and cleaned up, can cause serious damage.

In the Union Oil spill in the Santa Barbara Channel, shoreline damage is well documented, as is the apparent recovery of most organisms. The magnitude of the spill, however, is widely disputed and the range of estimates is an indication of the doubtful nature of much OCS spill data. USGS reported a total spillage of 18,500 barrels from Platform A, 10,000 barrels initially and 8,500 from subsequent leakage. The President's Panel on Oil Spills estimated 24,000 to 71,000 barrels.[2] Allen estimated 79,300 barrels,[3] the Coast Guard 100,000 barrels,[4] and Foster, Charters and Neusel as much as 780,000 barrels.[5] Although the latter figure must be considered as being largely speculative, it is 40 times higher than the USGS estimate.

The number of kicks or near accidents which have been brought under control without serious consequences cannot be known. Although they may not have resulted in injury or damage, they represented a test of man or machine, or both, and their documentation could provide the data needed to evaluate equipment performance and procedures and thereby avoid or lessen future dangers. The importance of such analysis is due not only to the new emphasis on the environment, but also to new operating procedures, such as the trend toward multi-well platforms. Blowouts on multi-well platforms can have a great multiplier effect through mechanical damage to the other wellheads or, if followed by fire, through ignition or burning away of other structures. The Shell fire at Bay Marchand, for example, involved a total of eleven producing zones even though the loss of control initially took place during the workover of a single well.

Successful drilling involves a delicate balance between drilling mud weight and downhole pressures. Any sudden loss of mud, increase in downhole pressure, or sudden change in drilling rate is an indication of danger. Drilling wildcat wells into unknown geological formations can be particularly hazardous. Unexpected penetration into high-pressure zones can cause blowouts because of the difficulty of increasing the weight of the mud column rapidly enough to compensate for the increased pressure. A particularly vulnerable part of the drilling operation occurs during trips—moving the drill string into or out of the well bore—when the loss or gain of drilling mud is more difficult to monitor.

In response to these potential blowout situations, better measurement and monitoring equipment is needed. In particular, the ability to measure pressure at the bit face continuously would provide an early indication of danger. The industry has recognized the need for developing such instrumentation, but has not succeeded in doing so to date. For measuring mud quantities, equipment capable of identifying the loss or gain of one barrel of mud (about five cubic feet) is generally considered accurate enough to warn of a potentially dangerous kick. Although such equipment is available, its use is not universal.

When a potential blowout is indicated, the first response normally is to apply some combination of increased pumping rate and the addition of heavier mud. If this response is either impossible or does not work, the next action is to close any or all of the three hydraulically actuated blowout preventers attached to the top of the casing. On the blowout preventer (BOP) stack, which was described earlier, the top two preventers close around the drill pipe. If only these two are actuated, it is still possible for the well to blow out through the drill pipe if the kelley is not attached. Under these circumstances, it is necessary to close the third preventer, called a blind ram, which deforms or crimps the pipe and closes the hole. An alternative form of the third preventer is the shear ram, which shears off the drill pipe completely and allows it to drop into the hole. Since the loss of drill pipe makes it difficult to re-establish well control, the decision to use the blind ram is not made lightly. Another alternative, recently developed and not often used as yet, is an internal preventer to close off flow through the drill pipe.

Indications are that BOP stacks are reliable if properly maintained, tested, and operated by well-trained drilling crews. However, it has happened that pressure has increased or mud has been lost so rapidly that the preventers were not actuated in time to avoid loss of well control. Since many BOP stacks cannot be actuated from sufficiently distant or protected locations, the effectiveness of this otherwise reliable equipment may be of no practical value to the tool pusher faced with an emergency.

Although technological developments could contribute to more effective identification and control of kicks or mud loss, the industry identifies human error as *the* major problem. Specifically the problem is identified as inexperience, poorly trained personnel, or inadequate procedures.

The role that human error and procedures play in drilling accidents is suggested by a recent survey of 32 wells by John L. Kennedy, the drilling editor of the *Oil and Gas Journal*.[6] (The survey represented only a limited sampling.) Of the reported blowouts, 65 percent occurred during development drilling as opposed to exploratory drilling. Even though geological structures are better defined during the development phase and should therefore result in fewer surprises, Kennedy believed that the discrepancy was "easy enough to explain. Most [drillers] act with more caution on wildcat wells—carry a little extra mud weight, for example—so that potential problems . . . are offset by an extra margin of safety."[7]

Current efforts by both industry and USGS to respond to identified deficiencies in personnel training, procedures, or equipment are hampered by a lack of data. Although USGS has collected reports on drilling accidents, there is little incentive for drilling companies and their personnel to report loss-of-control difficulties, whatever their causes. There are, in fact, a variety of dis-incentives to candid accident reporting on the part of individuals and companies. The former can obviously suffer from the appearance of a poor performance record; the latter from increased surveillance by federal agencies or restrictions on their activities.

In this connection, it should be noted that there are significant differences in the quality of performance between the various companies operating on the OCS. A recognition of these differences has been evident in many of our discussions with industry people and groups. Acceptance of these differences is an integral part of most discussions of OCS drilling and USGS regulation. (A tabulation and discussion of major accidents by company is contained in Appendix B.)

When testifying before the Senate Interior Committee, R. C. Sharp, a retired engineering vice president for a drilling contractor, made the point that, "In my many years as a drilling contractor, I had the opportunity to work for most of the major oil companies and learned at first hand that they differ *widely* [author's emphasis] in their basic policies toward safety, adequate employee training, and protection of the environment."[8] It seems reasonable to assume that poor operators would have little desire to report their record to USGS. Even though USGS can require whatever procedures it considers necessary to insure drilling safety, present manpower and resource limitations make detailed review and inspection of each drilling operation impossible.

Many companies have tightened their drilling procedures for both economic and environmental reasons. Others have initiated training programs for drilling personnel, using either their own blowout simulators or training centers where non-producing wells provide realistic operating conditions. Apparently none of these programs is assessed systematically to determine effectiveness in decreasing drilling accidents. Nor have USGS or the companies established formal proficiency standards for drilling personnel.

The general picture, then, is one of gradual improvements in all phases of drilling and blowout control technology in response to the general pressure of public opinion and the more specific requirements of OCS orders. The recommendations of the recent National Aeronautics and Space Administration (NASA) study on quality management on the OCS have also played a part in accelerating change.

Assuming that present drilling procedures and technologies are used in the future, the rate of serious accidents will probably remain essentially constant with evolutionary improvements in equipment and procedures being balanced by a move into deeper water and more hostile environments. Based on the analysis of OCS accidents presented in Appendix B, an average of nearly two major drilling blowouts may be expected to occur on the OCS each year. This figure is based on a drilling accident rate of 0.19 percent and an average of 900 new wells being started each year. In addition, two major production accidents can be expected on the basis of a production accident rate of 0.034 percent and a total of 6,000 producing wells on the OCS. Any programs to increase present OCS leasing and production rates may be expected to result in proportional increases in major accidents.

Desirable Changes   OCS oil and gas operations are inherently hazardous and, as a practical matter, it will be impossible to guarantee that drilling and blowout accidents will not occur. Industry and regulatory agencies can only guarantee that every possible precaution will be taken to minimize the possibility of such accidents. Some of the possible changes or improvements in blowout and drilling technologies which could help to achieve this objective include the following:

1. Longer-lasting bits would tend to reduce the number of trips and thus the risk involved in this most hazardous part of the operation. Recent experience with special multi-purpose bits for the *Glomar Challenger*, for example, have been encouraging.

2. Improved downhole instrumentation could contribute to earlier identification of potential blowouts. Specifically the ability to measure pressure at the face of the bit would permit drilling personnel to react more quickly to potential blowouts.

3. Separation of wellheads and fail-safe design of multi-well platforms could reduce the likelihood of massive accidents as a result of single failure.

4. The installation of distant and protected control consoles for all BOP stacks would make it possible to actuate the BOP's after well control has been lost.

5. Requiring the use of a mud monitoring system that can measure the sudden gain or loss of quantities on the order of one barrel of mud could facilitate earlier detection of potential blowouts.

6. Improved training procedures using the latest simulation techniques and more follow-up would insure a high level of performance on the part of all operating personnel.

7. Continued development of automatic drilling technology could help to eliminate human error.

8. Developing survivable event recorders, similar in function to the crash recorders required for commercial aircraft, could provide a record of equipment malfunctions causing or contributing to an accident.

PRODUCTION TECHNOLOGIES

Judging by major accidents, the production record is considerably better than the drilling record. Each year, one in 3,000 producing wells is involved in a major accident. This compares with about one serious drilling accident for each 500 new wells started. The average amount of oil spilled in oil and gas operations on the OCS from 1954 to 1971 has been estimated by the Department of the Interior as approximately 1/8 barrel of oil for each 1,000 barrels produced. For 1971, when OCS production was 418 million barrels, this would have been about 52,000 barrels spilled. The actual spills for 1971 have been estimated at only 16,000 barrels; however, an estimated 93,000 barrels were spilled in 1970. The combined average for 1970 and 1971 corresponds very closely to the estimated spill rate from Interior data.

To place these numbers in perspective, we must consider that all offshore oil and gas operations, including drilling, account for no more than 4.0 percent of the oil discharged into the world's oceans. The OCS spills alone, if distributed uniformly, would amount to only a few barrels per cubic mile of water on the continental shelf. Nevertheless, such comparisons do not take into account local effects and are therefore treated with more than a little skepticism by most public interest groups. Where winds, tides, and other natural circumstances combine to concentrate or bring spills to shore, average distributions have little meaning.

The technologies associated with production safety and environmental issues may be divided into five categories:

1. housekeeping functions associated with normal operations;
2. platform design;

3. production systems and downhole safety devices;
4. servicing and workover; and
5. human factors.

The human-factors aspect of equipment design and operation is an integral part of each of the first four. As with drilling, the critical importance of human factors to safety is recognized by both industry and government.

HOUSEKEEPING AND NORMAL OPERATIONS

Chronic pollution from routine offshore oil and gas operations continues to be a problem. Estimated annual oil loss from normal operations into the world's waters in the 1969–1970 time period was approximately 700,000 barrels. This amounted to 2.0 percent of the total oil losses, as noted in Table 18 of Appendix B.[9]

In practice, chronic pollution has not generated widespread public concern or reaction. Furthermore, it is clear, as our discussion of background data will indicate, that the long-term effects of this type of pollution are not well understood. It is equally clear that it is well within the state-of-the-art to reduce existing chronic pollution by improvements in both technology and in routine housekeeping procedures. Some of these improvements—in the form of drip gutters, settling tanks, and the like—will be necessary to meet the new requirements for OCS dumping and the quality of waste water discharge.

Like drilling, housekeeping performance is variable within the industry, with performance varying considerably from platform to platform as well as from company to company. Improvement can be obtained only if the regulatory agencies require a consistent high level of performance from all operators on the OCS. To a large extent, new regulations and a greater sensitivity of producers to environmental concerns, combined with the ready availability of the necessary technology, make it possible for the routine housekeeping problem to be solved. In any case, no new technological initiatives seem to be required in this area.

PLATFORM DESIGN

The structural design of OCS platforms has reached a high level of competence. The major problems, which have to do with such matters as corrosion protection, soil stability, and the assumed characteristics of the waves used for design purposes, are the subject of active research programs. Of more immediate concern in this area is the trend to multi-well platforms noted before. Although multi-well platforms with multiple completions in each well have already become standard, there is a strong economic incentive to place even more wells on a single platform as operations move further from shore and into deeper water.

Recent fires in the Gulf illustrate the snowballing effect of single-well accidents on such platforms. A major problem is that existing designs do not adequately isolate fuel sources from ignition sources. Although technological innovation in fire walls may help, more care should be taken to isolate critical components and personnel. Some recent platform designs have placed crew quarters on separate platforms, thereby removing off-duty personnel from the areas of greatest danger. Further improvements in fail-safe design and redundancy are needed, along with more consideration for the ways in which the operator interacts with the platform functions and activities.

Another problem associated with multi-well fires is the difficulty in identifying which wells are on fire. This is a significant problem, particularly in the decision on where relief wells should be drilled. Other problems include inadequate fire control and communications systems. It is clear that substantial improvements can be obtained by an overall reassessment of platform design.

PRODUCTION SYSTEMS AND DOWNHOLE SAFETY DEVICES

On multi-well platforms, the Christmas tree is vulnerable to damage from adjacent wells. For this reason, it is generally recognized that the downhole safety device is the last line of defense against blowouts during production operations. The device formerly required by USGS and used by industry for many years has been a valve actuated by changes in velocity of the production stream. This device cannot be remotely controlled.

Although general statistics on the failure rate of the velocity actuated downhole safety valve are not available, their record seems poor. Of 42 completions, 10 failed to shut-in during Shell's Bay Marchand fire,* and 4 of 10 failed in Amoco's fire. One frequent explanation for their failure is that sand carried by the oil erodes the valve. Improper installation has also been a source of difficulty and, in fact, these devices have not always been installed because of their record of premature shut-ins and their failure to operate when needed. Such omission is in direct violation of USGS orders.

The general conclusion that the velocity actuated downhole safety device is unsatisfactory is reflected in the new requirement of OCS Order Number 5 for a remotely-actuated downhole safety device in the Gulf Coast Area. Since wells already producing need not be fitted with these devices until the tubing is pulled, many wells will not be equipped with

---

* Another source indicates 43 zone completions, 2 drilling wells, and 11 fires.

these surface actuated subsurface safety valves for a number of years, if ever. A new subsurface safety valve with surface actuating and fail-safe characteristics which could be substituted for the velocity actuated device on existing wells without pulling the tubing would be a major contribution to safety.

The present USGS program of inspecting downhole safety devices and levying fines against companies which do not have them installed or have devices installed which do not meet minimum standards is, at best, a stop-gap measure. A recent development aimed at improving inspection procedures for downhole safety devices involves installing a device known as a sand probe, which indicates when a given level of wear has occurred. At least one major company is now using these routinely.

SERVICING AND WORKOVER

Well re-entry for service and workover is a particularly hazardous part of normal production activity. In conventional wireline operations, the well must be opened and the downhole tools suspended and manipulated by a flexible line inserted through a collar at the top of the Christmas tree. Each insertion and removal of tools and the line itself represents a potential inadvertant loss of control. An alternative approach involves using a separate valve-protected circuit attached to the Christmas tree. This system provides for the tools to be inserted while the well is closed and then pumped down the bore hydraulically. The pump-down method is expected to be particularly valuable for subsea completions and has also been used recently for platform installations. Although it appears to be potentially less hazardous, the pump-down technique is not fully accepted by industry, and considerably fewer wells are equipped for pump-down tools than for wireline service at the present time.

HUMAN FACTORS

A majority of OCS accidents have been attributed to human error. In the recent Shell fire in the Gulf, for example, a workman failed to close a manual valve before leaving the wellhead. In the Continental accident of 1967, a workman turned the wrong handle in an attempt to actuate the safety system actuator valve. Despite the human errors, both accidents were due less to individual carelessness than to poor design from a human-factors standpoint.

The Shell platform valve had no open/close indicator; the only way to be certain that the valve was closed was to count the turns. The Continental emergency valves were similar to production valves and adjacent to them. Both were unmarked and, under the pressure of events, the workman actuated the wrong valve. In both the Shell and Continental accidents, the valves involved were standard configurations used widely throughout the industry.

Although it is impossible to avoid all human error, it is clearly possible to reduce it by applying human-factors concepts. Such application in new design has been accepted in most industrial and transportation activities, but is still used to only a limited extent by the oil industry.

Increased automation and fail-safe equipment can reduce human error. But until production operations are approached with a systems view rather than on a component-by-component basis, "human error" accidents will continue to be a major cause of difficulties on the OCS.

SUBSEA PRODUCTION SYSTEMS

As has been noted before, one of the most promising developments for off-shore production is the subsea production systems (SPS). Although SPS's are being developed largely for deepwater operations, they have fail-safe and redundancy characteristics which should prove useful for all types of production systems. Furthermore, the high cost of servicing subsea units has forced a trend toward automation which will reduce the likelihood of human-error accidents. Finally, the fact that SPS operations take place beneath the ocean surface reduces the threat of storm damage and conflict with surface uses such as fishing and shipping. It also avoids aesthetic objections, as has been demonstrated by a lack of public concern with the offshore Molino gas field west of Santa Barbara. This field is operated entirely with underwater equipment.

SUMMARY

Taking the broad view, the development of OCS production equipment has been characterized by a conservative approach to technological change. Despite the financial resources of most OCS producers and the complexity of the associated planning and management functions, the industry commitment to R&D programs seems modest. Technical improvements follow a pattern of incremental changes to existing components rather than a clean look at new approaches to basic problems. The significant improvements in the use of failure analysis, component redundancy, and system design which have taken place in other technical fields in the past twenty years have been applied only recently to the OCS oil industry. The industry has substituted a hit-or-miss program of operator training for a true human-factors approach to design and to the development of methods for measuring and displaying vital information to the tool pusher and production supervisor.

Industry representatives rightly point out that some recent wells have been drilled to record depths and in particularly adverse conditions using truly impressive equipment monitored through computer programs and embodying up-to-date fail-safe concepts. They point with pride to new training and failure-analysis programs and systematic approaches to new design. And they argue a strong case that the size and nature of their operations make it difficult, if not impossible, to respond quickly to new requirements and new technologies.

It is also true, however, that major improvements have found their way very slowly into the OCS production field and, all too often, under the pressure of government regulation. The recent USGS requirement for surface actuated subsurface valves on new wells is a case in point. Despite the long-time unsatisfactory record of velocity actuated valves, the industry by and large continued their use (or left them out entirely to avoid inadvertant shut-ins) until forced by regulation to install more modern and reliable subsurface valves. Old wells continue to be protected by erosion-susceptible storm chokes.

Desirable Changes Although long-term improvements in offshore operations may require time, technical invention, and some changes in attitude within the industry, there are several areas of production technology in which modifications or development are clearly indicated and could be expected to pay large dividends. They include:

1. Development and use of subsea production systems.

2. Increased attention to human-factors criteria during the design stage.

3. Increased emphasis on automatic and fail-safe features in the design of production components.

4. An overall review of platform systems design with particular attention given to safety and environmental criteria, including gas and flame detectors, fire containment, fire control equipment, and personnel escape systems.

5. Incorporation of methods for identifying which wells on a multi-well platform are out of control during a fire.

6. Development and installation of survivable event recorders.

7. Development of a reliable surface actuated subsurface safety valve which could be used to replace storm chokes in existing wells.

TRANSPORTATION TECHNOLOGIES

All gas and 97 percent of all oil produced in the Gulf of Mexico is pipelined to shore, as is all oil and gas produced offshore California. Generally this phase of offshore operations is believed to be relatively safe and accident free and, by comparison with barging and other surface transportation, its record is good.

According to USGS statistics, there have been four pipeline incidents on the OCS resulting in injury and property or environmental damage during the period 1953–1971.[10] These include two breaks caused by anchors being dragged across pipelines, one by overpressurization, and one for which the cause was not determined. One of the anchor accidents released 6,000 barrels and the other 160,000 barrels of oil. The 160,000 barrel spill, the largest ever recorded from OCS operations, was not detected for ten days.

The other two accidents released more than 8,000 barrels. One of these, caused by overpressurization as a result of human error, occurred in the Santa Barbara Channel.[11] This spill followed Union's blowout by about eleven months and released some 900 barrels of oil into the Channel waters.

Pipelines appear to be a major source of chronic pollution, although it is almost impossible to identify specific amounts of polluting oil released by them. Coast Guard data indicate that 1,267 "line leaks" released 9,062 barrels and 376 "pipe ruptures or leaks" released another 4,247 barrels of oil into U.S. waters in 1971.[12] Taken together, these two pollution sources account for 6 percent of the approximately 210,000 barrels introduced into U.S. waters in 1971 and represent about 84 percent of all oil introduced into U.S. waters from offshore facilities. The fact that pipelines are largely out of sight apparently explains a general lack of public concern with this phase of OCS operations.

Current techniques for detecting leaks include mass flow monitoring, pressure measurements, and visual surveys of rights-of-way. The first two techniques are adequate for detecting large leaks, but are not widely used. They are not sensitive enough to detect small leaks. Visual surveys are more successful with small leaks, but when an oil slick is spotted, it is difficult to identify the faulty pipeline. In fact, positive identification can only be accomplished by divers.

A major area of concern is the continuing integrity of old pipe. Pipelines can corrode both on the outside (from sea water and marine life) and on the inside (from water, sand, and sulphur compounds in the oil). At the present time, no satisfactory technique is available for identifying incipient pipeline failure as a guide to preventive maintenance.

Another area of continuing concern is at the shoreline where pipelines are brought ashore. At present, laying pipe in shallow water and marshlands involves extensive dredging and canal building. These pipelaying operations result in substantial alteration of coastal lands, and have been identified as having a critical environmental impact.

At the other end of the line, the capability for laying pipeline in deep water is an important consideration for future OCS leasing. Beyond 400- to 500-feet depths, pipelaying is currently limited to small diameters (12 inches or less). A related problem is the ability to repair pipelines in deep water. Current repair techniques are limited to about 400 feet and, although extensions below this depth can be expected, deep diving is hazardous and very costly.

Multi-phase pumping (simultaneously moving oil and gas in the line) could reduce duplication of gas and oil lines and, therefore, be economically advantageous. In particular, development of this capability could permit a reduction in the complexity of subsea production systems, eliminating the need for subsea separation and treatment facilities. The major technological problems with multi-phase pumping include minimizing friction and reducing pressure surges. Current efforts to resolve these problems include novel pump designs and coating the inner surface of the pipe. However, it is not certain that a satisfactory multi-phase pumping capability will be available within the next fifteen years.

If there are no major modifications in pipeline systems, the amount of oil spilled from pipelines will probably continue to contribute about the same proportion of the total oil spilled from offshore facilities, since improvements in the quality of the lines will probably be offset by leaks from aging lines.

Desirable Changes Although pipelines will probably not become a major source of public opposition, except where they are the cause of extensive environmental modifications in marshlands and estuaries, it appears that a few changes or improvements in technologies as well as some new developments would be beneficial. These include:

1. Development of a method for detecting weak points and flaws in long pipelines for the purpose of preventive maintenance.

2. Wider use of accurate mass flow monitoring systems which would automatically alert an operator or take remedial action when a major break occurs.

3. Development of efficient multi-phase pumps and pipelines.

4. Development of ways to bring pipelines ashore with minimum environmental disruption.

RESPONSE TECHNOLOGIES

The development of technologies for responding to oil spills on the OCS is largely a post-Santa Barbara phenomenon. Impetus for these developments results from recognition that, even with a maximum effort to prevent accidents, some spills will continue to occur. Accident response technologies can be grouped in three categories:

1. Re-establishing control over wells that have blown out.
2. Containing and cleaning up oil on water.
3. Salvaging marine life and birds and cleaning up beaches.

RE-ESTABLISHING WELL CONTROL

Technologies for re-establishing well control have been adapted from land to offshore operations. In a blowout without a fire, capping the well is a difficult and dangerous task, but the technique is well developed and straightforward.

In a blowout with a fire, capping is much more difficult. It requires bringing in equipment to spray large quantities of water on the fire to maintain structural integrity of the pipe and platform and to allow men to approach closely enough to be able to clear away debris. Once this is accomplished, an explosive charge can be used to blow out the fire and thus permit normal capping operations to proceed. (Although there is at the present time no work platform specifically designed to support fire fighting and capping efforts, the Red Adair organization has plans for such a vessel. It resembles a semi-submersible drilling rig and will be equipped to respond to a variety of serious platform accidents.)

If capping is not possible, the major alternative is to drill relief wells. This involves drilling a new well to intersect the well that is out of control. A combination of water, mud, and cement is then pumped in to plug the well. This technique is highly developed, but it involves bringing in a new drilling rig and may require months to accomplish.

If the well blowout produces oil, putting out the fire can result in large concentrations of oil on the water. To avoid this problem, some recent fires in the Gulf of Mexico were allowed to burn until killed with relief wells. In these fires, it was sometimes necessary to continue to spray water for months to maintain some degree of structural integrity in the remaining structure and pipe.

Various underwater shut-off systems have been proposed and tested, but none has been used yet in an offshore accident. One approach, shown in Figure 39, involves tapping into the tubing and crimping the pipe above the tap. Pellets or other suitable material can then be introduced to close off the well.

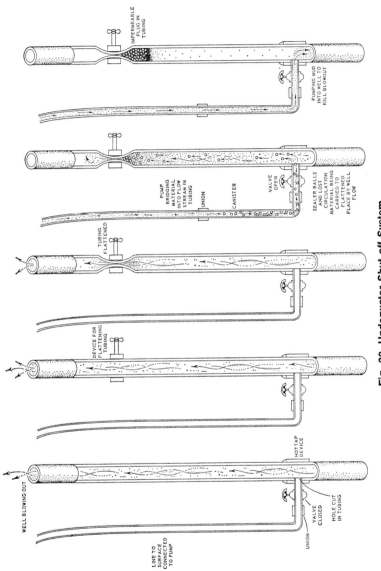

Fig. 39. Underwater Shut-off System

Source: Tenneco Oil Company. Used by permission.

CONTAINMENT

Neither industry nor government has an adequate capability to contain and clean up spills on the OCS. The effectiveness of existing containment and clean-up equipment is limited by wave height, wind velocity, and current. It is also limited by the relatively short period of time during which intensive boom development has been carried out. It is reasonable to expect that better systems will be developed, but it is also important to recognize that there is an upper limit on sea conditions beyond which oil containment is not practical. Fortunately, this situation is more likely to occur in deep water where the large volume of water and the distribution of the oil slick in the water column serve to disperse the oil.

CLEAN-UP

Mechanical clean-up devices generally have not been capable of performing to the predicted level. At present, these devices are suitable only for calm water and well-defined slicks. Although proponents of particular systems have claimed rough water capabilities, none has been proved effective so far and the prospects are not promising.

Sorbent materials are both effective and relatively cheap. Even though they must be handled twice and then disposed of by burning or burial, they will probably continue to be widely used, since the use of dispersants, sinking agents, and biological agents is sharply restricted by federal, state, and local regulations.

Beach clean-up has been relatively effective when a major effort has been expended. But both the extensive physical and chemical processes used to remove high proportions of oil from shorelines kill the plants and animals which inhabit them.[13] For this reason some beach clean-up operations have been limited to the use of sorbents such as straw, which are safer and less expensive, but do not produce a sterile environment.

The major study of the biological effects of the Santa Barbara spill[14] was complicated by the presence of other contaminants resulting from abnormally heavy rains and surface run-off. One investigator connected with that study found, however, that relatively few organisms were injured beyond recovery and that most of the affected populations had recovered or were on the way to recovery in the two-year interval between the spill and the study. (Some specific organisms were affected adversely by the Santa Barbara spill. See Chapter VII for a discussion of pollution effects.) This is not to say that beaches and shorelines can experience large spills without permanent damage: estuaries and marshlands, for example, would be more susceptible to injury from oil pollution than the sandy beaches and rocky shoreline of Santa Barbara.

Oily beaches, a sheen on the water, and oil-soaked birds have played a role in crystallizing public opposition to OCS development, but existing clean-up technologies, though primitive and inconvenient, are probably adequate for most spills. This does not mean that R&D on clean-up technologies should stop. Improvements can and should be developed particularly to meet the problem of tanker spills and oil spills in shallow, enclosed waters. But, in considering the allocation of resources for dealing with the specific problems of OCS production, the development of surface clean-up techniques does not appear to warrant a high priority. Research aimed at understanding oil-water interactions in a variety of wind, current, and wave conditions, on the other hand, should be encouraged. In essence, the prevention of spills rather than the clean-up procedures should be given major attention.

A serious environmental problem at the shoreline has been identified as chronic low-level pollution from small leaks and spills. Clean-up procedures are not effective against such pollution, and the only adequate response is to require offshore operators to meet high standards of housekeeping and waste disposal.

Enclosed waters and harbors present a more serious problem from the standpoint of oil concentration and lack of natural dissipative mechanisms. They are seldom threatened by OCS spills, however, and are more responsive to the limited capabilities of existing mechanical clean-up techniques because of the protected nature of the waters.

Desirable Changes On balance, the best strategy for dealing with OCS oil spills is to improve drilling and production equipment and operating techniques to minimize chronic spills and the likelihood of accidents. Significant improvements are possible in both areas and should be given first priority in the allocation of research and development. Well control and containment also deserve support, but the latter will probably require a better understanding of oil-water interaction under realistic conditions before significant improvements can be made. The following accident and pollution response technologies deserve emphasis:

1. Installation of emergency sub-mudline shut-off systems which are not likely to be compromised by surface damage.

2. Development of fast-response emergency equipment to support well control efforts.

3. Development and stockpiling of effective and rapidly deployable containment equipment.

4. Research into the behavior of oil in water to support containment R&D and to understand better the natural dissipative mechanisms.

5. Continuing development of containment and clean-up devices for moderately rough waters.

DEVELOPMENT AND MANAGEMENT OF TECHNOLOGIES

Certain issues are common to every phase of offshore operations where technological inadequacies have been identified. These relate to the way technologies are developed, maintained, and operated. As noted before, offshore technologies have generally been developed by incremental adaptation of onshore technologies. Standards of quality and performance have been enforced by competition. The assumption has been that the less efficient and reliable equipment would not be bought by the offshore operators.

The fact that this approach is not adequate to insure a high level of reliability can be deduced from a comparison with accident-prevention programs of other industries in which failures can be catastrophic. The aviation industry has, for example, been required to meet increasingly stringent performance criteria since the passage of the Air Commerce Act of 1926. The industry's review and certification process has been responsible to a large extent for the excellent safety record of the airlines, despite order-of-magnitude changes in the scope and nature of their operations as they progressed from Ford Tri-Motors carrying 10 passengers at 100 miles per hour to Boeing 747's carrying 400 passengers at 600 miles per hour.

A National Aeronautics and Space Administration (NASA) team examined OCS technologies for USGS and found that the lack of a systematic approach to equipment design and inadequate or non-existent quality assurance procedures are a major gap in industry's development and management of OCS technologies.[15] Although industry response to the NASA study has been generally favorable and has resulted in new programs being initiated, the major problems still exist. These fall into five categories:

1. Continued incremental and component-by-component development of technologies;
2. The lack of a formal system to identify and correct deficient technologies;
3. Weak inspection and quality-control systems;
4. Limitations associated with personnel training and procedures;
5. Limitations in the research and development system.

INCREMENTAL DEVELOPMENT OF TECHNOLOGIES

The incremental adaptation and linking of components has led to less redundancy in OCS technologies than seems justified by the risks involved and the consequences of failure. Greater emphasis on the systems design approach would have been more likely to lead to the establishment of performance standards and specifications for individual components as well as for the system itself. As it is, components meet only the minimum manufacturing standards and specifications developed by various industry and engineering societies, most of which do not reflect the unique characteristics of the offshore environment or require minimum levels of performance. Although the industry identifies human error as the major cause of accidents as indicated earlier, there is little evidence that equipment has been designed to minimize the likelihood of mistakes by the operating personnel. The acceptance of human factors criteria for new design has been promoted by the NASA report, but seems still to be viewed with some suspicion by individuals within the industry.

IDENTIFYING AND CORRECTING DEFICIENCIES

A knowledge of what went wrong last time is basic to any process for improving equipment or operations. As things now stand, when accidents or near accidents occur, the operator is required to file a report with USGS. In the case of large scale or significant accidents, USGS also prepares a report on its own findings. The results are based on a relatively informal system of investigation. Although some companies have been remarkably candid in publicly discussing major offshore blowouts, apparently neither this information nor available accident reports are adequate for systematically assessing and improving equipment and procedures. A reliability study of offshore technologies presently being carried out for the Environmental Protection Agency (EPA) may identify specific needs in this area.[16]

An accident investigation procedure similar to that provided by the National Transportation Safety Board (NTSB) for major aircraft accidents would be of great benefit to the industry, to USGS, and to the suppliers of mechanical components. Two investigations of recent platform accidents have been performed and published by the Department of Transportation.[17] Both were joint efforts of the U.S. Coast Guard Marine Board of Investigation and the NTSB and were carried out with the careful attention to detail for which the two Boards are noted. The documentation resulting from such inquiries could provide specific recommendations for improving the regulations, the equipment, and the procedures for OCS operations.

The authority to carry out such investigations by the NTSB is limited to circumstances in which Transportation or Coast Guard responsibilities are involved. Authorization for USGS to carry out such investigations in all cases of serious accidents, including the right of subpoena, would presumably require new legislation, since the present OCS Lands Act does not include sufficiently specific investigative powers.

Although the exercise of its obligations under such a system would require that USGS have access to *all* information pertinent to the lease, it would be possible to hold proprietary records confidential so long as such confidentiality is consistent with national policy and existing requirements for public disclosure.

Along the same line, the collection and analysis of malfunction and defect reports by USGS would provide an additional data base for the improvement of equipment and procedures. This function would be similar to that now exercised by the Federal Aviation Agency (FAA) for all aircraft and, more particularly, for scheduled commercial aircraft. When the results of failure can be catastrophic, the collection and analysis of detailed accident and near-accident information are justified from social considerations as well as from a cost/effectiveness standpoint.

QUALITY CONTROL AND INSPECTION

The general lack of quality assurance and performance standards for components has been noted before and is discussed in detail in the NASA report. Since quality-control procedures can only be based on clearly defined standards and specifications, the development of such criteria is of primary importance. Failure mode analysis and/or hazard analysis can be used to good effect. The former identifies the consequences of specific component and system failures. The latter, working backward from recognized hazards, defines the sequence of events which could lead up to the identified hazard. It thereby makes it possible to avoid or compensate for critical system or component malfunctions. These and other analytic techniques have been brought to a high degree of development in the aerospace industry and have demonstrated their worth in assuring the reliability of complex systems.

Once installed, equipment is subject to deterioration, misuse, and damage. A regular inspection procedure is therefore an essential element of overall quality assurance. At the present time, inspections are carried out by employees of the operator, by testing companies under contract to the operator, and by USGS inspectors. In the words of the NASA study, the OCS operators "contract for these services on a very informal basis and require neither evidence of personnel qualification nor standardization of test techniques."[18]

The frequency of USGS inspections varies with the region and the nature of past experience with the operator. In the Santa Barbara Channel, certain platforms are inspected daily, others weekly, and all offshore facilities are inspected at least once every six months. In the Gulf of Mexico, USGS inspections are conducted on a random basis, but each operation is inspected at least once every six months.

It is important to make a distinction between USGS inspections and the standardized and routine inspections required by an ongoing and adequate quality-assurance program. The former are concerned largely with checking for compliance with existing regulations and verifying the exercise of good general operating procedures. The latter go beyond the specific regulations and serve to document the performance of components and systems in a way which will be useful for improving existing equipment and setting standards for new design. Although the two inspection procedures are complementary, they are not a substitute for one another.

PERSONNEL TRAINING AND PROCEDURES

Even though the industry attributes most accidents to human error, training programs are not universal or consistent, nor do they incorporate follow-up investigations to determine effectiveness. The Coast Guard–NTSB investigation and report of the Chambers and Kennedy accident on May 28, 1970, noted that:

> Organization and assignment of responsibilities for the work were lacking. A number of the roustabouts were inexperienced and untrained, and their work assignments varied during the working day. . . . [They] did not know whom to go to for advice and orders. . . . All these factors coupled with hazardous work, resulted in an accident waiting to happen.[19]

Airlines, aircraft manufacturers, and the armed services, among others, have carried out extensive programs of investigation and development related to operator performance, work assignment, work station layout, and operating procedures. In addition, behavioral scientists have developed a large body of information on worker motivation and the learning process. More extensive use of these tested and available data would go a long way toward improving the training and performance of offshore crews and developing equipment. Robert C. Sharp testified before the Senate Interior Committee that blowouts had been estimated to have:

> . . . cost the oil industry over $200,000,000. This does not include the intangible costs to society of the attendant pollution of the environment. I firmly believe that a small percentage of the $200,000,000, perhaps only 5 percent, spent in the proper training of drilling personnel, could have prevented most of the blowouts.[20]

Along with better design and clearly defined responsibilities and assignments, such training is a necessary element of improved operator performance.

RESEARCH AND DEVELOPMENT

All major oil companies have research and development (R&D) organizations whose primary function is to solve immediate problems in the field. Some companies have large and highly sophisticated research organizations with clearly defined long-range objectives. Others appear to have little more R&D capability than that required to support field operations. Despite this variation, the NASA study uncovered no new problems which the operators had not already identified and were working on to one extent or another. Thus, the critical questions have less to do with an expanded shopping list of problems than they do with whether the overall R&D effort is adequate, whether the distribution of funds is reasonable, and—if more R&D is required—how best to encourage the necessary additional effort.

Although expenditures for OCS-related R&D cannot be isolated, some measure of overall petroleum extraction and refining R&D may be obtained by comparison with other industries. Table 8 shows the R&D expenditures for a variety of industries expressed as a percentage of new sales (the recorded dollar value for goods or services, excluding freight, taxes, and the like) and as a percentage of all industry expenditures for R&D. It can

Table 8. R&D Expenditures

Industry	% of Net Sales	% Total U.S. Company-Funded R&D
Food Products	.4	1.9
Paper and Allied Products	.7	1.0[a]
Primary Metals	.8	2.5
Petroleum Refining and Extraction	1.1	5.6
Fabricated Metal Products	1.2	1.8
Motor Vehicles	3.5	12.2
Chemicals and Allied Products	4.1	16.0
Electrical Equipment and Communications	7.5	20.4
Aircraft and Parts	18.3	11.0

Source: Adapted from Edward D. Goldberg, Convener, *Baseline Studies of Pollutants in the Marine Environment and Research Recommendations* (New York: IDOE Baseline Conference, May 24–26, 1972), pp. 20–21.

be seen that, by either measure, the oil industry's investment in R&D is relatively modest.

In 1970, the expenditures of the petroleum industry for R&D were $608 million, of which 95.5 percent was spent for applied research and development. The remaining $27 million was spent for basic research. Of the total, the federal government contributed only 7.1 percent, as compared with its support of 47 percent of all R&D performed by industry. In the fields of aerospace and electronics, the government contribution represents 80 percent of the total industry R&D budget.

Clearly, government-sponsored R&D plays a minor role in the development of petroleum technology. The situation appears to reflect the industry's desire to minimize government involvement and avoid the red tape associated with government contracts.

The fact that industry is spending only a relatively small part of its net sales on R&D does not necessarily mean that it is not spending as much as the situation justifies. When combined, however, with its relatively poor public image resulting from technology-related failures and the evidence of technical and operational inadequacies, the need for additional R&D activity seems evident.

There also appears to be considerable duplication of R&D effort and expenditures within the industry. For one thing, the individual companies view R&D as an important area of competition. For another, the petroleum companies perceive themselves as living constantly under the threat of anti-trust action by the government. These concerns extend into such non-competitive areas as safety and environmental protection. So long as the Congress or the Department of Justice does not specifically exempt the oil industry from the provisions of the anti-trust statutes in regard to these benign and essentially non-competitive technologies, industry cooperation to develop these kinds of technology will be more limited than is desirable.

To some extent, a broadening of the R&D base for OCS operations is already taking place through the entry of new companies and government organizations into the offshore field. The systems approach which Lockheed has brought to the development of subsea production systems and which NASA has brought to the study of equipment failure is likely to be beneficial by challenging past practices and introducing new methods. Since the aerospace industry has been subjected to very little cost constraint over the years, however, there is some danger that aerospace inputs may tend to overcomplicate both R&D and the solution to basic problems. The highly developed cost consciousness of the oil industry gives reasonable assurance that a satisfactory economic balance will be struck in responding to the conflicting requirements for new energy sources and environmental protection.

Desirable In summary, unless some modifications are made to pres-
Changes ent regulatory and R&D policies, it seems likely that
industry will continue to respond slowly to the recognized
needs for improved technology in OCS operations, that R&D efforts will
be duplicated beyond a reasonable degree of redundancy, and that the
public will continue to distrust the industry's ability to operate offshore
without an unacceptable risk to the environment.

A feasible alternative would be to establish the performance standards
for all OCS operations at *the best available technology economically achievable*. In order to achieve this standard, the following changes would be
desirable:

1. Establish equipment requirements in terms of the objectives to be
achieved and establish the inspection procedures necessary to assure that
those standards are met. While these requirements should include detailed performance standards for all pieces of equipment affecting safety
and environment, design specifications should not be allowed to act as
a deterrent to technological development. Both producers and suppliers
should be encouraged to establish quality-control organizations to assure
compliance.

2. Establish improved reporting procedures for failures, malfunctions,
and equipment defects, as well as for accidents and oil spills. To be
effective, the reports should be subjected to data analysis for the purpose
of preventing similar occurrences through modifications and additions
to performance and equipment standards.

3. Establish an investigation function for major accidents, similar to
that of the National Transportation Safety Board for aircraft, to determine and make public the accident cause(s). It should make appropriate
recommendations for changes or additions to procedures and equipment.

4. Develop procedures to insure that non-government personnel who
perform inspection and test functions are properly trained and certified
to uniform standards.

5. Encourage the oil and gas industry to undertake an expanded role
in offshore R&D related to safety and reliability for the purpose of bringing the technologies and procedures up to the best commercial level now
current in the U.S.

6. Establish improved training standards and procedures for operating personnel. The experience of organizations and individuals with
backgrounds in human behavior and performance should be sought out
and used.

7. Cognizant federal agencies should develop a program to identify
needs and contract for research, testing, and development as neces-

sary to insure optimal regulation of equipment and operations on the OCS. The effort should be aimed at filling in gaps and opening up new opportunities. So far as possible, contracts should be let to organizations outside the present petroleum industry R&D system.

8. An independent and representative body of experts should periodically review the state-of-the-art in OCS technologies and make recommendations to the appropriate agency in a public report, indicating where performance standards should be updated or revised.

9. Federal agencies should actively promote greater cooperation within industry on information exchange and R&D activities concerned with safety, accident prevention, and environmental protection. One lead agency should take the initiative for investigating the legal question of possible anti-trust violation as a result of such cooperation. In this connection, it could propose that the Anti-trust Division of the Department of Justice either establish guidelines for cooperative activities or offer written opinions on specific cooperative programs.

10. Establish a committee of OCS operators to define improved and standardized training and procedures for operating personnel. The inputs of outside organizations specializing in the training field should be encouraged.

1. U.S., Department of the Interior, Geological Survey, Conservation Division, "Incidents on the Outer Continental Shelf Resulting in Injury and Property or Environmental Damage (1953 to November 17, 1971)."

2. U.S., Executive Office of the President, Office of Science and Technology, *The Oil Spill Problem*, First Report of the President's Panel on Oil Spills (Washington: Government Printing Office, 1969), p. 4.

3. Allen A. Allen estimate, reported in Robert Easton, *Black Tide: The Santa Barbara Oil Spill and Its Consequences* (New York: Delacorte Press, 1972), p. 251.

4. U.S., Department of Transportation, Coast Guard, Office of Enforcement. Cited in Dillingham Corporation, *Systems Study of Oil Spill Cleanup Procedures*, Vol. 1: *Analysis of Oil Spills and Control Material* (La Jolla, Calif.: Dillingham Corp., February, 1970), p. A-28.

5. M. Foster, A. C. Charters, and M. Neusel, "The Santa Barbara Oil Spill and Distribution of Pollutant Crude Oil," *Environmental Pollution*, 2 (1971), p. 99.

6. John L. Kennedy, "Losing Control While Drilling: A 32-Well Look at Causes and Results," *Oil and Gas Journal*, 69 (September 20, 1971), pp. 121-28.

7. *Ibid.*

8. U.S., Congress, Senate, Committee on Interior and Insular Affairs, *Outer Continental Shelf Policy Issues, Hearings*, before the Committee, Pursuant to S. Res. 45, a National Fuels and Energy Policy Study, 92d Cong., 2d sess., on Oversight on Outer Continental Shelf Lands Act, March 23, 24, and April 11, 18, 1972, Pt. 2, p. 1141.

9. *Man's Impact on the Global Environment*, Report of the Study of Critical Environmental Problems (SCEP), sponsored by Massachusetts Institute of Technology (Cambridge, Mass: MIT Press, 1970).

10. Unpublished USGS data. See Appendix B.

11. Easton, *Black Tide*, p. 185.

12. U.S., Department of Transportation, Coast Guard, "Polluting Incidents in and around U.S. Waters, Calendar Year 1971."

13. C.F. Steinhart and J. S. Steinhart, *Blowout: A Case Study of the Santa Barbara Oil Spill* (North Scituate, Mass.: Duxbury Press, 1972).

14. Dale Straughan, "What Has Been the Effect of the Spill on the Ecology in the Santa Barbara Channel?" in *Biological and Oceanographical Survey of the Santa Barbara Channel Oil Spill, 1969–1970*, Vol. 1: *Biology and Bacteriology*, comp. by Dale Straughan (Los Angeles: Allen Hancock Foundation, University of Southern California, 1971), p. 417.

15. Morris K. Dyer, *et al.*, "Applicability of NASA Contract Quality Management and Failure Mode Effect Analysis Procedures to the USGS Outer Continental Shelf Oil and Gas Lease Management Program," report to USGS (November, 1971).

16. John E. Ritchie, Jr., and Henry D. Van Cleave, "A Reliability Study of Petroleum Systems and Prevention of Offshore Oil Spillage," OTC 1521 in *1972 Offshore Technology Conference, May 1–3, Houston Texas, Preprints*, Vol. 1, pp. 114–28.

17. U.S., Department of Transportation, *Marine Casualty Report, Continental Oil Rig 43—An Explosion and Fire With No Loss of Life, Gulf of Mexico, 24 October 1967* (Released 8 July 1969); and U.S., Department of Transportation, *Marine Casualty Report, Explosions and Fire on the Chambers and Kennedy Offshore Platform, Block 1890L and Fire on /MV Carryback in Gulf of Mexico, May 28, 1970* (Released 7 October 1971).

18. NASA, *Quality Management*, p. 23.

19. DOT, *Chambers and Kennedy*, p. 5.

20. Senate Interior Committee, *OCS Policy Issues, Pt. 2*, p. 1127.

VII. Information and Data

IN THIS CHAPTER we focus on issues which arise concerning the availability of scientific data to inform a broad range of OCS policy decisions. Analysis of these issues is divided into two sections: first, the adequacy of presently available background environmental data; and second, the adequacy of exploratory information available for managing and controlling OCS oil and gas development.

BACKGROUND DATA

The inadequacy of background data against which to assess environmental consequences has been cited by some opponents as a reason for slowing or stopping the development of OCS oil and gas resources. In this section we will examine current levels of understanding of the environmental effects of OCS activities in terms of: (1) chemical baseline information, (2) biological consequences, and (3) the impact of physical manipulations of the environment. An overview of current research efforts in this area is presented and guidelines are suggested for the acquisition of background data in the future, especially for acquiring data to assist those concerned with the environmental impact of OCS oil and gas operations.

ENVIRONMENTAL EFFECTS OF OCS OPERATIONS

There is little disagreement concerning the lack of background data. Not only scientists but responsible government and industry spokesmen as well are calling for increases in research to acquire these data. For example, participants in a recent conference held in connection with the International Decade for Ocean Exploration (IDOE) advocated a widespread, long-term research program to determine the quantities, fate, and effect of pollutants.[1] And a 1970 meeting of the Food and Agriculture Organization's (FAO) Technical Conference on Marine Pollution recommended "an immediate increase in research at national and international laboratories, to examine more closely the scientific problems associated with oil pollution and its effects on the marine environment."[2]

The American Petroleum Institute's (API) Committee for Air and Water Conservation has "recognized society's steadily growing concern for the quality of our environment," and supports its own research program which is performed by external research organizations.[3]

Federal agencies with oversight responsibilities for OCS resource development also have identified problems related to the inadequacy of the present state of knowledge. For example, in recent testimony before the Senate Committee on Interior and Insular Affairs, a Coast Guard representative noted that "the high costs associated with monitoring of natural systems have seriously restricted the knowledge available relative to the effect of toxicity of oil spills on fish and wildlife in the marine environment."[4]

These statements give some indication of the various perceptions of the adequacy of environmental data presently available. The efforts already being made to acquire these data can be grouped into four areas: (1) measurement of baseline levels of contaminants, (2) baseline faunal and floral studies, (3) studies of spills and experimental analysis of pollution effects, and (4) assessment of modifications due to ocean and shoreline construction. In the summary which follows, we point up several features of this current information: its apparent inconsistency, the level of professional disagreement on methods and conclusions, and the substantial biological impact or uncertainty in some areas which justify continued scientific concern. (Additional information, and a list of recent federal, state and industry research efforts are tabulated in Appendix D.)

Measurement of Baseline Levels of Contaminants

Information on the origin and present concentration of hydrocarbons in the marine environment is almost non-existent. NSF responded to this gap by sponsoring a year-long Baseline Data Acquisition Program.[5] Tentative

Table 9. Petroleum Hydrocarbon Levels in The Marine Environment

Location	Parts Per Million
West Falmouth, Massachusetts (in biota)	5–90
Narragansett Bay, Rhode Island (in biota)	3–16
Galveston Bay, Texas (in biota)	236
West Falmouth, Massachusetts (in sediments)	21–3,000
Louisiana Coast (in plankton)	100
Louisiana Coast (in water)	0.03
Santa Barbara, California (in sediments)[a]	0–13,000

Source: Adapted from Edward D. Goldberg, Convener, *Baseline Studies of Pollutants in the Marine Environment and Research Recommendations* (New York: IDOE Baseline Conference, May 24–26, 1972), pp. 20–21.

[a] Ronald L. Kolpack, James S. Mattson, Harry B. Mark, Jr. and Ta-Ching Yu, "Hydrocarbon Content of Santa Barbara Channel Sediments," in *Biological and Oceanographical Survey of the Santa Barbara Channel Oil Spill 1969–1970*, Vol. II: *Physical, Chemical and Geological Studies*, ed. by Ronald L. Kolpack (Los Angeles: Allan Hancock Foundation, University of Southern California, 1971), p. 293.

Table 10. Chemical Additions from Platforms

Substance	Source	Possible Biological Impact
Aluminum	Sacrificial anodes and drilling mud	Not significant, discharge continuous
Barite	Drilling mud	Impact not significant, discharge irregular
Brines	Produced fluids	Significant near out-fall on OCS, adverse effects near-shore
Chrome Lignosulfonate	Drilling mud	Impact unknown, discharge irregular
Lead	Sacrificial anodes	Impact not known discharge continuous
Mercury	Sacrificial anodes	Locally significant discharge continuous
PCB's[a]	Old heat exchangers, flushing or accidental loss	Locally significant, accident probability low

Source: Adapted in part from U.S., Department of the Interior, Bureau of Land Management, *Final Environmental Statement: Proposed* [*December*] *1972 Outer Continental Shelf Oil and Gas General Lease Sale, Offshore Louisiana*, pp. 70–78.

[a] Polychlorinated biphenyls.

information from the IDOE Baseline Conference group indicates that petroleum hydrocarbons are becoming incorporated into the tissues of marine organisms in a variety of marine localities, including the open ocean. Data in Table 9 indicate the wide variety of petroleum-derived hydrocarbon concentrations. The contribution of offshore operations to this pollution cannot be isolated, although in California the substantial hydrocarbon concentrations in Santa Barbara Channel sediments have been traced to the oil from the blowout on Union Oil Company's Platform A.[6]

This limited information on baseline data indicates that substantial concentrations of hydrocarbons exist in a variety of locations. The biological consequences of the concentrations have not been identified.

Offshore oil operations discharge a variety of materials in addition to crude oil. The sources and possible impact of some of these chemical additions are listed in Table 10.

Barite is occasionally discharged into the ocean when drilling mud is dumped, although most of this material is recovered and taken to shore for resale. The biological effects of water-based drilling-mud additives such as barite, aluminum stearate, and chrome lignosulfonate are not known.

Produced oil field waters vary in content, but in offshore Louisiana they may contain up to 27 percent dissolved "brine" solids. These contain iron, calcium, magnesium, sodium, bicarbonates, sulphate, and chloride. Total Louisiana OCS waste-water production is about 420,000 barrels per day.[7] The effects of these brines in marine environments have been largely ignored. However, John Mackin of Texas A&M University has documented a decrease in the number of bottom-living species in Galveston Bay in areas within one mile of platform brine discharges, and either an increase or normal species richness more distant from these outfall sites.[8]

Heavy metals are alloyed in corrosion-protection devices (sacrificial anodes), and it is estimated that significant quantities of mercury, for example, are discharged each year from anodes that are predominantly aluminum. Mercury pollution by man is confined to coastal waters, and neither augmented mercury levels nor deleterious effects have been documented in the open ocean.[9] In near shore areas, it is possible that resident members of the biota could concentrate mercury from sacrificial anodes, but this possibility has yet to be examined.

Polychlorinated biphenyls (PCB's) have been used in heat-exchangers to reduce the temperature of products as they leave the wellhead.[10] Although PCB concentration in ocean fish is a concern, the use of PCB's is being terminated and a USGS-approved substitute is now required.

Baseline Faunal and Floral Studies

Considerable data have been obtained through university research on the presence and absence of species on U.S. coastlines. However, data necessary to understand normal seasonal and long-term population fluctuations are generally unavailable. NSF and the National Institutes of Health (NIH) have sponsored much of the research in this area, primarily through support of faculty and graduate student research. In addition, the Gulf Universities Research Consortium, comprising a number of Gulf Coast universities and supported in part from petroleum industry sources, has outlined a ten-year environmental research program designed to gain an understanding of marine ecological processes and to develop predictive models.

Understanding the causes of population changes represents an effort in experimental systems ecology that is a step beyond simply gathering descriptive background data. This additional step is essential if the causes of environmental disruption are to be identified. But detailed population monitoring and studies of interactions within ecosystems are intensive long-term research efforts; and even the present "environmental crisis" has not stimulated the support necessary for mounting such an effort.

Studies of Pollution Effects

Surveys have been conducted following oil spills to attempt to document the consequences of a particular accident. Frequently only limited and well-hedged conclusions can be made, however, owing either to limited sampling capabilities or difficulty in interpreting the data. In the Santa Barbara Oil Spill Survey, conducted by the Allan Hancock Foundation of the University of Southern California, only limited effects were found in shallow waters. In deeper water, however, Kristian Fauchald, a participant in the Survey, found a well-documented many-fold reduction in the spoonworm *Listriolobus* and observed that certain other bottom-dwelling animals had completely disappeared.

Fauchald noted that "drilling in *Listriolobus* beds may be directly responsible for the damage, but the January, 1969 oil spill from Platform A may also have influenced the numbers of *Listriolobus* in the bed."[11] He goes on to say that "it is further recommended that a minimal program of exploitation be instituted on the Santa Barbara shelf. The *Listriolobus* beds are a completely unique biological environment, not known from any other area of the world; it is thus of great importance that they be preserved."[12] In contrast to these conclusions, Dale Straughan, who compiled the report of the Survey, believes that damage to the biota was not widespread, "but was limited to several species, and that the area is recovering."[13]

Both the procedures and conclusions of a study of Shell's Bay Marchand fire have been the subject of disagreement. Data from this survey were included in the *Draft Environmental Statement* for the December, 1972, General Lease Sale Offshore Louisiana. These data indicate a decrease of species abundance near the spill, as well as a loss of cells from fish gills. But following the submission by Shell of written testimony from three scientists, the material was not included in the *Final Environmental Statement*.[14]

Despite disagreement in some areas, certain possible effects of hydrocarbon pollution have been documented. Although this documentation is still incomplete, a listing of some findings on specific groups of organisms points to significant environmental problem areas; but for certain animals, such as seals and whales, for example, no biological problems have been identified.

Plants: In the Caspian Sea, chronic pollution, primarily from petroleum, in enclosed areas has resulted in a 50 percent reduction in plant species and an 80 percent reduction in their biomass during a seven-year period.[15] In contrast, open ocean and exposed coastal spills have shown no conclusive detrimental effect on phytoplankton and its productivity.[16] Some laboratory, bay, estuary, and fresh-water studies have documented growth retardation, growth abnormalities, and population decimation of phytoplankton as a result of oil pollution.[17]

Crude oil spills have killed and retarded growth in intertidal surf-grass and other flowering plants, as well as lichens and a variety of algae.[18] Species diversity of algae is substantially lower in areas of natural seeps.[19] There is some concern that crude oil spills may decimate vegetation in marsh areas, which would lead to erosion as well as to interference in primary marsh production. Accumulation of decomposing plants and oil may also lead to oxygen-depleted conditions.

Bottom-Dwelling Invertebrates: The ocean bottom receives oil from spill incidents and low-level, long-term petroleum discharge in both shallow and deep-water areas. Significant reduction of benthic fauna (from 50 percent to 90 percent) has been documented in major oil pollution areas (for example, the Caspian Sea and the Santa Barbara Channel), but distinguishing causal factors from other pollution sources in these areas is difficult.[20] Economically significant mollusc resources have been tainted in Louisiana, Oregon, Maine, Massachusetts, England, and Continental Europe.[21]

Swimming Invertebrates: Reproductive and juvenile stages of animals are usually those most susceptible to environmental limiting factors. Thus the impact on these planktonic stages of marine organisms may not be realized for several months or years, until a generation of adults is missing. Shallow-water near-shore areas are generally the "nursery ground" for many invertebrate and vertebrate resources. However, oil spills or chronic low-level pollution of waters have not been found to affect marine zooplankton, although some reports have documented mortality in several species of fresh-water zooplankton.[22]

Fin-Fish: A spill of 10,000 tons of crude oil in Puerto Rico killed small fishes, but larger fishes were more resistant.[23] Pelagic fishes escape most pollution. Specific fractions within crude oil, however, are acutely toxic to fish. Tumors have been reported in fish from polluted waters, but crude oil has not been definitely indicated in a causal relationship.[24]

Reptiles: Alligators have not been affected by oil developments in Louisiana coastal marshes, although it is possible that a major spill could have an impact on these crocodilians. Sea snakes have been killed by a 200,000 barrel oil spill following a platform blowout in the Persian Gulf.[25]

Birds: In some localities, birds offer a "convenient" yardstick for assessing the effects of oil spills. Birds succumb easily, are countable, and in many spill incidents thousands die. Tanker accidents and ship bilge cleaning are responsible for the vast majority of bird kills, and repeated spills in certain locations, such as the southern portion of England and on the Newfoundland Coast, have resulted in a great reduction in bird populations. Auks, puffins, and related species have been especially susceptible to spills. In the United States, species whose existence might be particularly threatened include the Whooping Crane in Texas, the Brown Pelican in Louisiana, the Cape Sable Seaside Sparrow in south Florida, Eider ducks in Maine, and Alcids in the Pacific Northwest.[26] (Appendix D lists those oil spills that have resulted in some documentation of bird kills.)

Mammals: Several groups of mammals are aquatic, semi-aquatic, or marsh dwellers. No pollution incident has resulted in documented detrimental effects on porpoises and whales. Whale death rates were normal during the 1969 spill after northward migration through the Santa Barbara Channel, and analysis of tissue from dead whales did not reveal the presence of crude oil. A detrimental effect of crude oil impinging on a rookery of Northern Elephant Seals and the California Sea Lion was difficult to determine although some premature births and infant deaths may have been due to crude oil.[27] Otters, rodents, and fur-bearing marsh animals could be affected by a spill. In certain localities these are an abundant and important resource, but detrimental effects on these mammals have not been reported.

The specific causes of mortality or decline in species for the above groups of organisms have not generally been ascertained. Specific causes may include smothering, tissue destruction, enzyme poisoning, and possible carcinogenesis. Smothering is the most understood process, whereas an understanding of the slower responses to toxicity will come only from needed research.

The carcinogenic effect of petroleum addition is one possible consequence of chronic low-level pollution that is perhaps least understood. Certain of the polynuclear aromatic hydrocarbons which cause cancer in laboratory tests are found in crude oil, but the origin of most of these compounds in the oceans is terrestrial or atmospheric.[28] Although tumors in fishes have been found in association with a spill in Puerto Rico, a direct link with oil pollution has not been made.[29] It has been suggested that continued beach pollution could pose a hazard to bathers, but the only present documentation of cancer from petroleum industry feedstocks or products has been in wax extractors whose skin was subject to a daily bath of solvent for at least seven years.[30] This issue still involves public concern, however, and the general problem of low-level toxicity is yet to be resolved.

The concentration of low-level doses of crude oil in the food chain is also identified as a significant consequence but, again, in an area characterized by an almost complete absence of critical data. Many scientists have suggested that an important fate of oil is decomposition by bacteria, yet the documentation of the specific compounds assimilated or the by-products of this assimilation have not been delineated. In the opinion of some scientists, many hydrocarbons simply accumulate, perhaps on the ocean floor. Pat Parker of the University of Texas has evidence of the concentration of hydrocarbons in certain plants in the Gulf of Mexico, and Max Blumer of the Woods Hole Oceanographic Institution has observed that hydrocarbons accumulate and persist in the lipid reserves of valuable mollusc species. But the actual concentration of these substances in long aquatic food chains remains to be documented.[31]

Modifications Due to Construction

The environmental impact of the construction activities of the offshore petroleum industry are now a matter of concern. Dredging and filling bays and estuaries was identified as a problem some time ago, but only more recently have scientists become concerned with the overall impact of such construction activities as building and placing platforms and laying pipelines. Marine structures have impacts on living resources both during and following construction. Although there has not been a systematic examination of biological effects of construction activities, there are some generally assumed effects, and the magnitude of these disturbances seems to be greater in nearshore or inland waters than in open ocean areas.

Platform installation and pipeline burial are recognized causes of local habitat disturbance and increased turbidity, which might be expected to decrease biological productivity. The magnitude of these problems has not been evaluated, although the current belief is that in most areas (except marshes) such disturbances do not produce persistent effects.[32]

Biologists with the Louisiana Department of Fish and Game have noted that the construction of pipelines in marshes requires canal excavation for laying equipment,[33] and that these wide canals can interrupt drainage patterns, although precautions such as bulkheads can minimize mass water movement. Such bulkheads, however, do not eliminate water seepage or salt intrusion. In areas such as Louisiana, new OCS activity will not substantially increase the area of marshlands cut by canals, but in Florida and Atlantic Coast areas, modified marsh hydrologic cycles could occur. In many cases, these shoreline modifications are less a product of offshore operations than from engineering projects for shipping, recreation, or general economic development.

Drill cuttings, discharged over the side of platforms, can form piles of sediment, smothering organisms. One such pile below the Standard-Humble platform in Summerland was studied by California Department of Fish and Game scientists. It "developed as a smooth-surfaced, silty pile without holes for shelter, so it did not attract fish, nor did it offer a suitable substrate for the attachment of plants or animals."[34]

Fixed platforms function as artificial reefs, affording places of attachment for benthic organisms, and providing spatial heterogeneity that permits the aggregation of a large number of fishes.[35] In California, these aggregations have been observed, and the increases in three species of perch were documented by California Department of Fish and Game divers.[36] But some biologists believe that the aggregation of sports fish, for example, around platforms has not been adequately documented, nor do they feel that this represents the total picture of biological consequences. Spokesmen for the Florida Audubon Society have responded adversely to industry's assertion that the platforms have a reef effect that could contribute to an increase in the total fish catch in the Gulf of Mexico. For commercial fishermen, these platforms act as an impediment to fishing operations.[37]

Although the impact of offshore activities occurs from a number of industrial activities, and impinges upon a great variety of marine species, the distinctive biological and climatic features result in geographically specific effects. In recognition of these distinctive environments, biotic provinces have been established which reflect different species composition.[38] These areas possess relatively unique climatic regimes and biological assemblages. Although less understood, the underlying food web that supports these marine communities may have distinct contrasts.

Some fundamental biological processes may thus differ among these areas, in addition to there being a different species composition. For example, Aleutian productivity is periodic, whereas Gulf of Mexico productivity continues throughout the year. Some areas have extensive detritus and bacterial metabolism (Gulf) whereas other areas have grazing food chains (Arctic). Some locations have extensive standing crops of algae whereas other localities have little. These fundamental contrasts imply that little generalization is possible in relating the effects of oil contamination from one area to another. (Certain distinctive features of these areas and their implication on pollution problems are summarized in Appendix D.) The important point is that when new OCS areas are developed both new surveys and field experimentation are required in order to anticipate the possible biological consequences.

SUMMARY AND POLICY IMPLICATIONS

This review underlines the point that data on the environmental effects of developing OCS oil and gas resources are limited and that—to the extent that these data are available at all—they may be contradictory. Current and programmed research (listed in Appendix D) promises to improve our present knowledge base, but acquiring a functional understanding of the coastal environment is an extremely long-term goal. There simply is no national commitment to undertake the kind of coordinated, intensive research effort which would be required to move significantly toward acquiring a systems understanding. At best, policy makers will have only selected, incomplete background data upon which to base OCS policy during the next fifteen years. While this may not be very satisfying to those who would like to have the certainty and security of a more complete knowledge, it does make it extremely important that the allocation of research resources be made keeping these limitations in mind. As a consequence, the basic issue is to determine how much additional research is needed to reduce environmental uncertainty to an acceptable level and to identify the ways in which this research could be coordinated and funded.

What Are the Alternatives?

Specific areas of research to be given emphasis can be ranked according to identifiable short- and long-term needs. In the long run, ecologists and oceanographers are agreed that the entire ocean ecosystem must be understood before they can thoroughly evaluate the consequences of environmental impacts such as those associated with developing OCS resources. But they also recognize that this long-term goal will have to be divided, and priorities set for the parts. The alternative research areas include:

A. Ecology-Oceanography
  1. Systems ecology
  2. Chemical, physical, and geological oceanography
  3. Microbiology and decomposition processes
  4. Ocean or shoreline engineering
  5. Fisheries biology
  6. Descriptive biotic surveys
B. Physiology-Toxicology
  1. Commercial species
  2. "Indicator" or other species

The question of who should fund the research is tied closely to the problem of credibility. Selection of the most satisfactory funding alternative should in part be based on which would produce the most widely accepted results. Alternative sources include private industry, private foundation, state government, and the federal government.

Alternative performers of this research include research scientists located within any of their institutional homes—industrial or government laboratories, government agencies, universities, or profit and non-profit private research institutes.

If we agree that research needs to be increased, the question becomes by how much? Alternatives include undertaking crash programs or somewhat more moderate increases.

Assessment of Alternatives

The two most essential needs at the present time appear to be more complete knowledge of background levels of hydrocarbons in the oceans and the physiological effects of acute and chronic toxicity on marine plants and animals. Knowledge of the fate of oil and of decomposition processes, for example, seems to be less pressing, as is the need to understand the broader effect of oil on the population dynamics of commercial fisheries and other specific biological populations, or possible synergistic effects.

Although a knowledge of the accumulation of hydrocarbons in the ocean would satisfy some of the information needs of conservationists and scientists, it is not likely that specific data would have any significant effect on public policy. Toxicity data, on the other hand, could be used in establishing discharge levels and other pollution requirements, as have toxicity studies of air contaminants, heavy metals, and carcinogens in the past.

To be most useful to public policy makers, research in these two areas, in addition to being scientifically competent and desirable, must be responsive to public concerns. For example, toxicity experiments with commercially significant species, such as lobster, abalone, clams, crabs, and certain fish, could be used to inform and influence public policy. However, on the basis of scientific criteria alone, other more sensitive organisms might be more suitable subjects for testing toxicity. Yet both interests could be served by a coordinated research program combining commercially significant as well as the more sensitive organisms; there is no reason to view public concerns and scientific values as being in conflict. Least pressing needs in terms of assessing the impact of offshore operations are further research in description of chemical, physical, and geological processes.

Who performs the research will also affect its credibility and thereby its usefulness to policy makers. In the view of many, it is difficult to separate the researcher from those who pay for the research. Frequently the tendency to distrust the findings of a particular study is based less on scientific grounds than on who did the research—and, by extension, who paid for it. The point is that environmental research conducted or funded by the petroleum industry is often immediately suspect. Response to a highly publicized study funded by an oil and gas association is a case in point. Although the study was conducted by competent scientists working out of a respected university, the published results appear generally to be treated with skepticism. In this case, skepticism is probably intensified by industry spokesmen who frequently cite the study when making their case for continued development of OCS oil and gas resources.

Research either sponsored or conducted by industry is also suspect because it has tended to focus on a relatively narrow range of topics, such as the origin and fate of oil from natural seeps, biodegradation of hydrocarbons, and widespread pollution surveys, rather than ecological experiments. In addition, industry spokesmen have often used the results of these studies to defend the industry against other scientific studies, thus giving the appearance of having either conducted or funded research for that specific purpose. The most extreme cases of this kind have involved the research efforts of persons within the industry. For example, a geologist with one of the companies operating offshore Louisiana became an amateur marine biologist and ultimately, under API sponsorship, a lecturer touring for the industry. His observations and pictures are related to fishing statistics for the Gulf to support the inference that offshore platforms are responsible for an increase in total catch. The lack of credibility of this kind of effort underlines the need for industry to consider its credibility problem when planning its environmental research program.

The same point applies to the other principals as well. However, environmental interest groups have no comparable research program; rather these groups tend to depend on ongoing research activities within universities. They also make effective use of a general lack of adequate knowledge.

Of course, there are no obviously unbiased institutional settings for environmental research. However, universities and, to a lesser extent, private research institutes and government are generally considered to be at least potentially less biased than is industry. Existing government agencies, particularly EPA, NOAA, and NSF, are in a position to formulate and fund a relatively unbiased environmental research program. Coordination among them might be difficult, but is necessary. Collectively these agencies could establish priorities employing a systems approach in formulating a long-range ecologically sound research program. Although universities and research institutions would probably do most of the research, this approach could provide for industry's active participation, both in funding and performing parts of the program. Agency supervision and review could legitimize industry's participation using such familiar mechanisms as the peer-review procedures employed by NSF and NIH, for example.

The point is that overall research needs are so great that funding from each of the available sources is needed, and a coordinated program offers an option for making funds from all these sources contribute to common short- and long-term goals.

As for level of funding, undertaking a crash program would be beneficial only if it promised to resolve existing environmental ambiguities in a generally acceptable way. Most scientists seem to agree that this is not possible in the short run. On the other hand, modest increases in funding for toxicity and hydrocarbon background studies, particularly for areas to be developed within the next decade or so, do seem warranted. However, considerable planning and coordinating should precede any large increases in funding for a long-term systems ecology effort.

The environmental impact statement required by NEPA might well prove to be a useful tool in setting environmental research priorities. The self-conscious review required by these statements focuses attention on gaps in our knowledge base that need to be filled if informed judgments are to be made on proposed actions. It is at this point that possessing or not possessing basic background data becomes most important for policy-making. Making energy policy, including policy for the development of the OCS, cannot await the acquisition of data which would be considered adequate by marine scientists for making scientific judgments. In the short run, policy is going to have to be made on inadequate data, and this will be less than satisfactory to everyone concerned. But the NEPA 102 statement is forcing the issue, and increasingly the statement requirement will generate pressures for industry and overseeing government agencies to provide better evidence rather than simply allege that, on balance, their proposed actions will benefit society.

Desirable Changes A single government agency could be assigned responsibility for coordinating and substantially funding research on the effects of oil and gas operations. Generally, more research should be funded by agencies with no responsibilities for oil and gas development. Research should be performed by government laboratories, universities, or independent research organizations. Substantive research priorities should be hydrocarbon background studies and toxicity studies to be carried out in selected geographic areas on commercially useful marine life and species sensitive to oil pollution. The steps could be as follows: (1) selection of geographic areas proposed for oil and gas operations (perhaps using BLM's five-year lease schedule) and continuous performance of hydrocarbon baseline studies on biological and physical environmental components; (2) continuous monitoring of sublethal physiological effects and toxicity of commercially useful species in all areas where oil and gas operations are carried out.

These desirable changes are not intended to eliminate studies which operating agencies and industry currently fund to acquire data essential for planning and performing their OCS activities.

EXPLORATORY INFORMATION

As the government official directly responsible for promoting and regulating the development of OCS natural resources, the Secretary of the Interior must attempt to achieve a number of policy objectives. These include conservation, the prevention of waste, and the protection of the environment. The Secretary and his deputies have limited geological and geophysical data upon which to base a number of important decisions such as tract value, land use plans, and environmental risk and safety. In particular, limited data curtail their ability to administer effectively the OCS leasing system. In this section, the problem of evaluating tract value, safety, and lease planning is defined; alternative information-acquisition procedures are analyzed and evaluated; and some desirable changes are suggested.

INFORMATION NEEDS

In advance of a lease sale, BLM and USGS are required to make economic, engineering, and geologic evaluations of each tract being considered for sale. The quality of decisions based on these evaluations is related directly to knowledge of the area being considered. According to the Department of the Interior, "in geologically well-known areas, the resources in a province or lease area can be estimated within an order of magnitude, using previous history and projections of trend and environment."[39] (For a detailed discussion of reserve and resource information, refer to Appendix C.)

As lessees, companies are required by the *Code of Federal Regulations* to furnish well logs, cores, core analyses, paleosamples, well tests, production information, and geophysical surveys to USGS.[40] But this information is available only for tracts already leased and being developed. Thus, Interior can only make relatively well-informed decisions on sales involving drainage tracts. (Drainage tracts are tracts from which oil and gas is being drained by production on adjacent tracts.) Industry is not required to share its exploratory information on unleased tracts with USGS; consequently, government data for these tracts is limited to what government has either gathered itself or purchased from industry.

Determining the value of individual tracts on the basis of inadequate data may be less a problem than evaluation of the safety risk of developing the lease. The competitive bonus bid system provides a market mechanism for pitting bidders with good exploratory data and highly refined interpretative capabilities against each other, but there is no similar built-in method for insuring safety without having adequate exploratory data. (The bonus bid system is discussed at length in Chapter IX.)

The principal vehicle for assessing whether a tract can be developed safely is now the environmental impact statement. (Most industry spokesmen do not believe there is a safety problem, but USGS lists safety as one of the reasons it needs exploration data.) As indicated previously, OCS lease sales are considered to be major federal actions with significant impact on the human environment. Consequently, every tract is evaluated to determine what effects its development might have on the environment.

At the present time, the impact statement evaluation does not include an analysis of geologic characteristics which might increase the probability of a development accident—such as Union's blowout at Santa Barbara or the collapse of a Shell platform in the Gulf. In part, this omission may be due to Interior's lack of data from other than industry sources; but it is also due to Interior's policy of treating industry data, whether obtained from lessees or purchased, as proprietary information which can only be disclosed with specific approval of the area supervisor.[41] This means that these data cannot be made public, not even to meet the environmental protection objectives of NEPA. One effect of this may well be to inhibit the effectiveness of the public review process.

The overall effect of this lack of adequate data for making important decisions for OCS development seems to be that Interior reacts to industry initiative rather than acting on the basis of its own "systematic and efficient plan of geologic study, resource appraisal and leasing of the OCS."[42] Interior itself says that "the current pattern is dependent primarily on industry preference."[43] One effect of this pattern is a conclusion on the part of some observers that Interior and the industry work too closely together. This, of course, can be costly in terms of further undermining public confidence in Interior as a vigorous promoter and protector of the public interest.

Under the present system, industry does nominate tracts to be included in the lease sales, but it nominates tracts within an area specified by BLM in its call for nominations. So long as bonus income continues to be a primary motive for holding lease sales, it will be difficult to employ a tract selection system that doesn't call for some initiative on the part of the potential bidders.

WHAT ARE THE ALTERNATIVES?

Two major variables have to be taken into account in considering alternatives to the present system: the first is the procedure for information acquisition; the second is the timetable. We will discuss four procedures that provide information before the lease sale and one procedure that makes information available following the lease sale:

1. Having the federal government, presumably USGS, collect its own data by contract surveys or with its own ships and equipment;
2. Requiring companies to submit their exploratory data and assessments to USGS on a confidential basis;
3. Having USGS collect some of its own data and continue to purchase some data from industry as it does at the present time;
4. Requiring companies to submit all raw seismic data to USGS on a non-proprietary basis in order to be issued an exploration permit and making all data furnished by lessees non-proprietary; and
5. Following the lease sale, the lease could be retracted and the bonus bid returned if, on the basis of information submitted after the sale, it is determined that the risk of developing the tract is considered to be publicly unacceptable.

ASSESSMENT OF THE ALTERNATIVES

Interior has reviewed the first three of these alternatives in its response to a series of questions it was asked to answer as a part of the energy policy study being conducted by the Senate Interior and Insular Affairs Committee.

Have Government Collect Its Own Data: In brief, the department saw a number of advantages in having the federal government collect its own data, including:

a. These data could be publicly disclosed in publications, impact statements, and for other public purposes;
b. The Department of the Interior could operate on the basis of a systematic and efficient plan of geologic study, resource appraisal, and leasing program; and
c. "A program of regional geologic study of all of the OCS could be planned and carried out on a systematic time basis for the preparation of geologic and resource analysis maps and topical reports."[44]

The sole disadvantage mentioned by Interior was cost. The estimate given for close-spaced seismic data purchased as a part of a small group was $50–$75 per mile. Under existing procedures, however, this data could only be made public if the government were the sole purchaser, so that the cost of non-proprietary data is substantially higher.

But there might well be some adverse effect on the service companies that conduct and sell seismic data as well as on the competitive bonus bid system itself. If close-spaced raw data were publicly disclosed, there would be no reason to pay for it any more. Making the data publicly available in advance of the sale might adversely affect competition. However, at the present time most bidders have access to similar exploratory data, and it is the difference in companies' ability to enhance, display, and interpret the raw data that accounts for real competition.

Under this alternative the data available to Interior would be much improved both for safety and effective management; however, it should also be pointed out that, with the best seismic data currently available, resource estimates are still not very accurate. Holes would still have to be drilled to determine the actual value of the lease.

Have Companies Submit Data and Assessments: According to Interior's assessment, there are two major advantages to the alternative requiring companies to submit their exploratory data and assessments to the government on a confidential basis. First, the data would be available for the cost of reproducing it; second, "to the extent that individual companies surveyed and appraised the same areas, the sum of their observations and interpretations would represent a broader spectrum of expert opinion than could be provided by a single organization."[45] But these data still could not be publicly disclosed, although Interior suggests that a possible additional requirement might be to place these data in the public domain after some set time.

A Combination of Government and Industry Data: The advantage of having government supplement data acquired from industry with data it collects on its own is that some of the data could be publicly disclosed. This alternative could also give Interior an opportunity to be more systematic with at least a part of its data-acquisition program.

Have Companies Submit Their Pre-Lease Raw Data: The alternative requiring companies to submit all raw seismic data and treating it and all data subsequently furnished by lessees as non-proprietary is the most far reaching of these alternatives. The Public Information Act of 1968 requiring that government agency records be made available for public inspection might have to be amended for this to be an available alternative. Section 552(b) of the Act exempts several categories, including "geological and geophysical information and data, including maps, concerning wells." The Act does not require that these records be withheld, but present Interior policy, as stated in the *Code of Federal Regulations*, restricts their use:

> geological and geophysical interpretations, maps, and data required to be submitted under this part shall not be available for public inspection without the consent of the lessee so long as the lease remains in effect or until such time as the supervisor determines that release of such information is required and necessary for the proper development of the field or area.[46]

This restrictive information policy enables the leaseholder to have an information advantage over competitors when bidding on adjacent tracts and limits public disclosure of data used in evaluating tracts.

The specific effect of public disclosure in this case depends, as it does in the first alternative, on when the raw data are to be made public. If disclosure is before the lease sale, in the impact statement, it could affect the competitive bonus bid system. However, if we are accurate in our impression that interpretation rather than raw data is the real point of competition, the effect on lease sales would be minimal.

Treating information submitted to USGS by lessees as non-proprietary would be a major change in policy and surely would generate an energetic negative response from industry. In one sense, the basic question is what rights did the leaseholder purchase? It is clear that he purchased a right to find, produce, and transport oil and gas. It is not clear that he also purchased an exclusive proprietary right to the information which he obtains in the process of exercising his other rights—although it might be argued that this has become a customary right.

Have Companies Submit Data After the Lease Sale: The final alternative, requiring the submission of exploratory information by the successful bidder after the lease sale and before development, is similar to the present requirement for submission of structural interpretations of geological and geophysical data for USGS approval of permits to drill. Although this data would support a review process to assess risk, the timing of the review could introduce uncertainty and bias into the possibility of subsequently rejecting a bid. Importantly, this alternative would neither meet information needs for a public review of the lease sale and other government decisions in managing and controlling OCS development nor satisfy information needs for land use and energy planning.

SUMMARY AND POLICY IMPLICATIONS

We have chosen to discuss these five alternatives either because they have been considered by Interior or they raise important issues. Many other combinations could have been discussed. However, our purpose has been to indicate that adopting any of these five alternatives (or an alternative involving combinations or variations of these same component parts) could produce numerous second-order consequences. We have noted only a few of these, such as possible effects on the seismic services industry, competitive bidding, and the level of confidence the public has in Interior and the industry. This is a complex system in which any change, such as having government collect its own data or establishing new rules concerning public disclosure, will produce changes in other parts of the system as well.

Some of the changes, such as publicly disclosing raw seismic data in advance of a lease sale, apparently should not affect the competitive bonus bid leasing system since it appears that every company can obtain raw data of comparable quality. If this is correct, logically raw data could be disclosed and competition could continue on the basis of differing capabilities to enhance, display, and interpret data. But this fails to take into account the symbolic importance which the petroleum industry attaches to this aspect of the competitive system. Decision makers, both public and private, have to be aware that this is the case. But if they are to act responsibly, they have to make their decisions on the basis of a broader set of energy-environment issues.

Desirable It would be desirable to supplement present exploration
Changes information collection procedures in two ways:

a. In order to acquire exploratory information for regional land use planning for offshore and onshore facilities, the government should contract its own seismic survey.

b. Before each lease sale, the government should contract for both seismic and subsoil surveys to provide adequate data for assuring that development can be carried out safely. These data should be public information, and as necessary, both the data and analyses should be included in the environmental impact statement.

1. Edward D. Goldberg, Convener, *Baseline Studies of Pollutants in the Marine Environment and Research Recommendations* (New York: IDOE Baseline Conference, May 24–26, 1972), p. ii.

2. Food and Agriculture Organization, *Report of the FAO Technical Conference on Marine Pollution and Its Effects on Living Resources and Fishing,* FAO Fisheries Reports No. 99 (Rome: FAO, 1971), p. 7.

3. American Petroleum Institute, Committee for Air and Water Conservation and Committee on Public Affairs, *Environmental Research: A Status Report* (Washington: API, 1972) pp. 1–2.

4. U.S., Department of Transportation, Coast Guard, *Answers to Policy Issues Related to Overview Hearings on the Outer Continental Shelf Lands Act, Before the Senate Committee on Interior and Insular Affairs, on S. Res. 45, March 23, 1972,* p. 48.

5. Goldberg, *Baseline Studies of Pollutants,* p. 14.

6. Ronald L. Kolpack, James S. Mattson, Harry B. Mark, Jr., and Ta-Ching Yu, "Hydrocarbon Content of Santa Barbara Channel Sediments," in *Biological and Oceanographical Survey of the Santa Barbara Channel Oil Spill, 1969–1970,* Vol. 2: *Physical, Chemical and Geological Studies,* ed. by Ronald L. Kolpack (Los Angeles: Allan Hancock Foundation, University of Southern California, 1971), p. 294.

7. U.S., Department of Interior, Bureau of Land Management, *Final Environmental Statement: Proposed [December] 1972 Outer Continental Shelf Oil and Gas General Lease Sale Offshore Louisiana,* p. 76.

8. John G. Mackin, "Environmental Effects of Petroleum Production on Marine Communities," a paper presented to the Interstate Oil Compact Commission, Biloxi, Mississippi, December, 1972, p. 7.

9. Goldberg, *Baseline Studies of Pollutants,* p. 4.

10. BLM, *Final Environmental Statement: [December] 1972 OCS General Louisiana,* p. 71.

11. Kristian Fauchald, "The Benthic Fauna in the Santa Barbara Channel Following the January, 1969, Oil Spill," in *Biological and Oceanographical Survey of the Santa Barbara Channel Oil Spill, 1969–1970,* Vol. I: *Biology and Bacteriology,* comp. by Dale Straughan (Los Angeles: Allan Hancock Foundation, University of Southern California, 1971), p. 76.

12. *Ibid.,* p. 77.

13. Dale Straughan, "What Has Been the Effect of the Spill on the Ecology in the Santa Barbara Channel," in *Biological and Oceanographical Survey of the Santa Barbara Spill,* Vol. I, p. 417.

14. BLM, *Final Environmental Statement: [December] 1972 OCS General Louisiana,* p. 112.

15. A. G. Kasymov, "Industry and the Productivity of the Caspian Sea," *Marine Pollution Bulletin,* I (July, 1970), p. 101.

16. M. Oguri and R. Kanter, "Primary Productivity in the Santa Barbara Channel," in *Biological and Oceanographical Survey of the Santa Barbara Spill, Vol. I,* p. 24.

17. Battelle Memorial Institute, "Biological and Ecological Effects of Oil Pollution," in *Oil Spillage Study: Literature Search and Critical Evaluation for Selection of Promising Techniques to Control and Prevent Damage* (Richland, Wash.: Battelle-Northwest, 1968), p. 64.

18. D. S. Ranwell, "Extent of Damage Due to the *Torrey Canyon* Incident," in *The Biological Effects of Oil Pollution on Littoral Communities,* ed. by J. D. Carthy and D. R. Arthur, Field Studies Supplement Number 2 (London: Field Studies Council, 1968), p. 2.

19. Nancy L. Nicholson and Robert L. Cimberg, "The Santa Barbara Oil Spills of 1969: A Post-Spill Survey of the Rocky Intertidal," in *Biological and Oceanographical Survey of the Santa Barbara Spill,* Vol. I, p. 400.

20. Fauchald, "Benthic Fauna of the Santa Barbara Channel," in *Biological and Oceanographical Survey of the Santa Barbara Spill,* Vol. I, p. 76.

21. Battelle, "Biological and Ecological Effects," pp. 15–19.

22. *Ibid.,* p. 82.

23. M. J. Cerame-Vivas, *The Ocean Eagle Oil Spill,* Special Report to Office of Naval Research (Washington: ONR, Ocean Biology Program, 1968), p. 4.

24. Battelle, "Biological and Ecological Effects," p. 8.

25. U.S., Department of the Interior, *Statement, Questions and Policy Issues Related to Oversight Hearings on the Administration of the Outer Continental Shelf Lands*

Act, Held by the Senate Committee on Interior and Insular Affairs, Pursuant to S. Res. 45, Mar. 23, 1972, p. 102.

26. Dillingham Corporation, *Systems Study of Oil Spill Cleanup Procedures*, Vol. 1: *Analysis of Oil Spills and Control Materials* (La Jolla, Calif.: Dillingham Corporaation, 1970), p. 48.

27. Robert L. Brownell, Jr., and Burney J. Le Boeuf, "California Sea Lion Mortality: Natural or Artifact?" in *Biological and Oceanographical Survey of the Santa Barbara Spill*, Vol. 1, p. 300.

28. Claude E. Zobell, "Sources and Biodegradation of Carcinogenic Hydrocarbons," in *Proceedings of Joint Conference on Prevention and Control of Oil Spills*, June 15–17, 1971, Washington, D.C., sponsored by American Petroleum Institute, Environmental Protection Agency and U.S. Coast Guard (Washington: API, 1971), p. 441.

29. Cerame-Vivas, *The Ocean Eagle Oil Spill*, p. 4.

30. Robert E. Eckardt, "Cancer Prevention in the Petroleum Industry," *International Journal of Cancer*, 2 (1967), p. 657.

31. P. L. Parker, J. K. Winters, and J. Morgan, "A Baseline Study of Petroleum in the Gulf of Mexico," in *Baseline Studies of Pollutants in the Marine Environment*, (Background Papers for a Workshop Sponsored by the National Science Foundation, Brookhaven National Laboratory, 24–26 May, 1972), p. 565; and M. Blumer, J. Sass, G. Souza, H. Sanders, F. Grassle, and G. Hampson, *The West Falmouth Oil Spill: Persistence of the Pollution Eight Months After the Accident* (Woods Hole, Mass: Woods Hole Oceanographic Institution, Reference No. 70–44, November, 1970), p. 26.

32. BLM, *Final Environmental Statement: [December] 1972 OCS General Louisiana*, p. 83.

33. Lyle S. St. Amant, "Impacts of Oil on the Gulf Coast," in *Transactions of the 36th North American Wildlife and Natural Resources Conference*, March 7-10, 1971 (Washington: Wildlife Management Institute, 1971), p. 211.

34. California, Resources Agency, Department of Fish and Game, *Artificial Habitat in the Marine Environment*, by J. B. Carlisle, Jr., C. H. Turner, and E. E. Ebert, Fish Bulletin 124 (Sacramento; Calif.: Office of State Printing, 1964), p. 43.

35. St. Amant, "Impacts of Oil," p. 213.

36. California, Dept. of Fish and Game, *Artificial Habitat*, p. 47.

37. St. Amant, "Impacts of Oil," p. 213.

38. Joel W. Hedgpeth, "Marine Biogeography," in *Treatise in Marine Ecology and Paleoecology*, Geological Society of America, Memoir 67, ed. by Joel W. Hedgpeth, Vol. I: *Ecology* (New York: Geological Society of America, 1957), p. 360.

39. Interior, *Questions and Policy Issues*, p. 72.

40. Title 30, *Code of Federal Regulations*, Section 250 (30 CFR 250).

41. OCS Order Number 12, Gulf Coast Area.

42. Interior, *Questions and Policy Issues*, p. 73.

43. *Ibid.*

44. *Ibid.*, pp. 73–74.

45. *Ibid.*, p. 74.

46. 30 CFR 250. 97.

VIII. Environmental Quality

PRESERVATION and improvement of environmental quality are the major concerns which must be accommodated if the public is to be persuaded that OCS oil and gas resources can be developed at an acceptable risk level. Developing these resources is a hazardous undertaking that has involved and will continue to involve some risk of damage to the environment. Environmentally damaging accidents can occur during any of the four major phases of finding, developing, producing, and transporting OCS oil and gas.

Although there is a tendency to think of environmental impact only in terms of oil spills, there are, in fact, several other kinds of positive and negative impacts as well. For example, the Department of the Interior identifies eight "impact producing factors," including, in addition to oil spills: debris, platforms, pipeline construction, storage facilities, support services, labor force, and production.[1] Interior also identifies ten "impact sustaining factors": refuges, estuaries, marshlands, beaches, national parks, commercial fisheries, sport fisheries, recreation, shipping, and the regional economy.[2] These particular lists can be modified, extended, or contracted, but the point is that both impact-producing and sustaining factors and their interactions now have to be taken into account in planning for OCS development. This requirement is a consequence of widespread adverse reaction to evidence of environmental degradation, including undesirable impacts resulting from large oil spills offshore, such as the Barracuda Company's *Torrey Canyon* tanker grounding, and from OCS drilling accidents, such as the one that occurred on Union Oil's Platform A in the Santa Barbara Channel.

Actually there have been two major responses to these threats to the environment. The federal government developed a Pollution Contingency Plan to provide for an organized response should spills similar to the *Torrey Canyon* accident occur offshore U.S. And in early 1969, less than a month after the Santa Barbara blowout, bills on environmental protection were introduced into the Congress; the resulting National Environmental Policy Act of 1969 (NEPA) was signed into law by President Nixon on January 1, 1970. NEPA established a national policy for protecting and restoring the environment.

160

NATIONAL ENVIRONMENTAL POLICY ACT

In practice, the section of NEPA that has had the greatest impact in implementing a policy favoring protecting and restoring the environment has been 102(2)(C). This section requires agencies to "include in every recommendation or report on proposals for legislation and other major Federal actions significantly affecting the quality of the human environment, a detailed statement by the responsible official on" what the environmental impacts will be.[3]

OCS lease sales are considered to be major federal actions having a significant environmental impact and 102 statements have been written for each separate OCS sale. At present, no further statement is required for normal field development. However, in March, 1972, the U.S. Geological Survey (USGS) published a new directive on the preparation of environmental impact statements.[4] Three categories of agency actions are described in this directive, those definitely requiring, those that may require, and those generally not requiring an impact statement. Extensive new exploratory drilling in environmentally sensitive areas on federal lands was cited as an example of an action that would require a statement. It can be assumed that this would include further development in the Santa Barbara Channel. Using explosives in geological and geophysical exploration on the OCS and drilling exploratory oil and gas and geothermal wells on onshore federal lands are examples of actions that may require statements. And development drilling, secondary recovery projects, and pressure maintenance projects on federal leases are among the examples of actions generally not requiring one.

Under rules presently in effect, USGS has thirty days within which to determine whether approval of a requested action would constitute a major federal action significantly affecting the quality of the human environment. During this time period, responsible officials are required to assess the potential environmental consequences of their proposed actions. There is no question about the lease sale, however, and within Interior the Bureau of Land Management (BLM) has the responsibility for preparing a statement for each OCS lease sale. BLM depends on USGS and other bureaus within Interior for assistance, and both BLM and USGS have assigned personnel specific data-collection and analysis responsibilities.

BLM proceeds by requesting comments on the proposed sale before drafting the statement. These requests are circulated among federal departments and agencies and a notice is published in the *Federal Register*. The Council on Environmental Quality's (CEQ) Guidelines for the preparation of environmental impact statements make it clear that the comment process is to include private organizations and individuals as well as governmental agencies at the federal, state, and local levels.[5] Comments from such agencies are to accompany the proposal "through the existing agency review processes" and are to be made public with the 102 statement.[6]

After the draft statement is prepared, it is to be circulated to other agencies and made available to all interested parties at least 90 days before the proposed action. Agencies may also hold public hearings on the draft statement, as BLM now does before each OCS sale. The draft statement has to be made available at least 15 days before the hearing is held.

According to CEQ's guidelines, "the agency must consider the comments it receives and change its proposal and the statement as appropriate. The agency must then make the final statement and comments public at least 30 days before taking action."[7]

A major impact of NEPA has been to open up decision-making to greater public scrutiny; and the review and comments provisions have provided a mechanism for the public to participate in governmental decision-making to an unprecedented extent. To date the overall effect of these changes has been to delay OCS development. In large part, this seems to have been a consequence of having to reach some mutual understanding among participants on just what the new requirements actually mean. For example, although Section 102 enumerates five points that must be included in environmental statements, BLM along with other agencies, particularly the Atomic Energy Commission (AEC), has had problems in determining what the specific content requirements are. In fact, both Interior and AEC have been challenged on this point by public interest groups.

One challenge has been to question the adequacy of treatment of one or more of the five points that section 102(2)(C) requires to be included in the statements. For example, in *Natural Resources Defense Council, Inc. (NRDC) v. Morton*,[8] NRDC contended that Interior's discussion of alternatives to the proposed lease sale was inadequate. The Court of Appeals for the District of Columbia agreed, giving in its decision some better indication of the required scope of such a discussion. The Court emphasized CEQ's guidelines which require not only a "rigorous exploration" and description of alternative courses of action but also "an analysis . . . of their costs and impact on the environment."[9]

The Court observed that "the impact statement provides a basis for (a) evaluation of the benefits of the proposed project in light of its environmental risks, and (b) comparison of the net balance for the proposed project with the environmental risks presented by alternative courses of action."[10]

Duplication is another problem which is becoming apparent as the 102 requirement is implemented. Many of the statements seem to repeat much of what has been included in previous statements. This is particularly true in the case of statements for successive OCS sales, but it is also evident in statements prepared for other energy alternatives, oil shale, for example.[11]

Fragmented responsibility also has been a problem. Each agency must prepare statements required in connection with its own programs, but many programs either overlap or are multi-agency programs. As a consequence, responsibilities are not always clear-cut. For the present this problem has been dealt with by adopting a lead agency concept. According to CEQ's guidelines, "the lead agency is the Federal agency which has primary authority for committing the Federal Government to a course of action with significant environmental impact."[12]

In its *Third Annual Report*, CEQ states that there are at least three factors involved in picking the lead agency: "which agency became involved in the project first, which has the heaviest involvement, and which is most expert with respect to the project's environmental effects."[13]

On the basis of these criteria, the lead agency in discussing alternative energy sources has been Interior. It is possible, however, that AEC might be required to take the lead agency role in connection with statements prepared in the future for fast breeder and fusion reactors.

The practice of requiring the agency proposing an action to prepare an environmental impact statement has also been identified as a problem. The concern is that the agency will become an advocate seeking to justify its own proposed actions. Several critics allege that this happened with the first draft statements for OCS lease sales as well as in the case of the trans-Alaskan pipeline. In this latter instance, critics quote from Interior's own multi-volume impact statement to show that Secretary Morton disregarded his Department's findings when he announced that he intended to issue the required permit. However, in both cases, the federal courts have provided a means for challenging the agency's advocacy.

These are all problems which have been encountered in implementing the requirements of NEPA, and collectively they have delayed OCS development to some extent. But the really major problem for NEPA in terms of OCS development has been a tendency to substitute Section 102 requirements for energy and land use policies. NEPA has focused attention on the need for an explicit policy correlating future energy requirements, uses, and availability. It has also highlighted the need to establish procedures for resolving conflicts among the multiple present and potential uses for public lands. The alleged inadequacy of Interior's discussion of alternatives or its 102 statements seems, at least in large part, to be directed at the lack of a national energy policy; and many of the objections to the development of specific OCS tracts seem to be focused on land use questions rather than on any general objection to OCS development. But NEPA as presently used is an inadequate substitute for either or both policies, and attempting to use it in their stead will likely continue to prove extremely frustrating and unsatisfying.

On the other hand, however, if the 102 statement is restricted in its use to insuring that environmental impacts of major federal actions are explicitly taken into account before a decision is made, NEPA can become an effective mechanism for building confidence in industry and regulatory agencies—when they deserve it. Given this more limited goal, the implementation problems encountered to date can probably be corrected without much difficulty.

Desirable Of the problems which we have identified with NEPA,
Changes the problem of what is to be contained in a statement has largely been worked out now, as has the question of which agency should take the lead when programs overlap. And the courts seem to provide a check on an agency's tendency to become an advocate. It would be desirable, however, to have an environmental impact statement prepared covering more than a single sale. This could either be a programmatic statement covering OCS leasing plans for a fixed time period of up to ten years or a series of regional statements for the same time period. In lieu of national energy and land use policies, regional programmatic impact statements could be a vehicle for integrating essential environmental, land use, and energy planning.

These programmatic statements, of necessity, would be general planning documents and therefore less specific than those written for individual lease sales. For this reason, they could be viewed as the apex of a hierarchy with the individual lease sale statements supplementing and amending the programmatic statements as well as determining the specific impacts of the individual sale. To insure that the lease sale statements are both adequate and consistent with the regional plan, a requirement could be established providing for a review by a specially constituted committee. These reviews could be made public and thereby provide another means for guarding against any tendency an agency might have to become an advocate.

FWPCA

Section 402 of the Federal Water Pollution Control Act (FWPCA) Amendments of 1972 establishes a permit system for discharges into the navigable waters of the U.S. Navigable waters are defined by the Amendments as the "waters of the United States, including the territorial sea." Section 403, "Ocean Discharge Criteria," extends the Section 402 permit system to the contiguous zone and the oceans. The Environmental Protection Agency (EPA) is required by Section 403 to set standards under which a permit can be issued. Before issuing such a permit, the Administrator of EPA is required, within 180 days after enactment of the Amendments, to establish guidelines on the effect of disposal of pollutants on human health and welfare, on marine life, and on recreational and economic values, together with guidelines for determining the persistence of the pollutant and other possible locations for its disposal.[14]

It is likely that a substantial amount of new information will be required before such sweeping guidelines can be established. Thus it is particularly significant that Section 403 also provides that, "in any event where insufficient information exists on any proposed discharge to make a reasonable judgment on any of the guidelines established pursuant to this subsection no permit shall be issued under section 402 of this Act."[15]

Applicability of the general performance standards established by the Amendments may be limited to three miles because of the Amendments definition of "navigable waters." Owing to this restricted definition, performance standards provided for in the Amendments to alleviate polluting discharges into navigable waters may not be applicable seaward beyond the three-mile limit. (At least one OCS operator interprets the Amendments as being applicable on the OCS and has submitted descriptions of its platform discharges to EPA.) Specifically, requirements for the use of "best practicable control technology" by 1977 and "best available technology" by 1983, as well as the national goal of eliminating all polluting discharges by 1985, may not be applicable to the waters above the OCS.

Together, these limitations may lead the Administrator of EPA to utilize the "no permit shall be issued" provision of Section 403(c)(2), in which case discharges into OCS waters would continue to be controlled exclusively by OCS orders.[16]

The oil and hazardous substance liability provisions of Section 311 of the Amendments are basically the same as the prior law on this subject. However, there is one important modification. Liability has been added for the removal of any hazardous material discharged into the navigable waters and the contiguous zone, the latter being defined as "the entire zone established or to be established by the United States under Article 24 of the Convention on the Territorial Sea and the Contiguous Zone."[17] (The Convention established a maximum limit of 12 miles for contiguous zones.)

However, since Section 311 defines an "offshore facility" as one that is located within the "navigable waters" of the United States, the provisions for the control of pollution from hazardous substances are inapplicable to offshore facilities located seaward of the three-mile limit. And further, notwithstanding its broad definition of "discharge," the provisions of Section

311 are not intended to apply to the discharge of oil from any offshore facility if the discharge is not in harmful quantities and is pursuant to, and not in violation of, a permit issued for the facility under Section 402 of the Amendments.

Desirable Changes Although the Amendments have only recently been enacted and have not been tested, it would be desirable to incorporate at least two changes: (1) extend the jurisdictional scope of the Amendments to include the contiguous zone in order to make oil and hazardous substances provisions clearly applicable to those offshore facilities located seaward of the territorial sea; and (2) extend the 1977 and 1983 performance standards and the 1985 national goal to eliminate all types of polluting discharges into waters of the United States by redefining "navigable waters" to include at least the contiguous zone.

NATIONAL CONTINGENCY PLAN

The National Oil and Hazardous Substances Pollution Contingency Plan[18] was developed in compliance with the Water Quality Improvement Act of 1970, and incorporated into the FWPCA Amendments of 1972. The Plan's objectives are to provide for efficient, coordinated, and effective action to minimize damage from oil and hazardous substance discharges, including containment, dispersal, and removal. The Plan, including the Annexes and regional plans, provides for:

(a) assignment of duties and responsibilities, (b) establishment and identification of strike forces and emergency task forces, (c) a system of modification, surveillance and reporting, (d) establishment of a National Center to coordinate and direct operations in carrying out this Plan, (e) a schedule of dispersants and other chemicals to treat oil spills, (f) enforcement and investigative procedures to be followed, (g) directions on public information releases and (h) instructions covering on-scene coordination.[19]

In all its aspects, then, the Plan creates a structure for a coordinated, integrated response by those federal agencies with assigned responsibilities under the Plan. This includes advance preparation as well as actual implementation, the primary goal being to be prepared to respond whenever and wherever a spill might occur.

The Plan established both national and regional response structures. The person immediately responsible for responding to an OCS spill is the On-Scene Coordinator. The Coordinator for offshore oil spills is a Coast Guard officer, predesignated for each coastal region and subregion of the U.S. His immediate responsibility when a spill occurs is to insure that the person responsible for the spill is aware of his responsibility for containing, cleaning up, and disposing of the polluting oil, and to ascertain that this person is taking the necessary action to meet his responsibility. If the responsible person is taking adequate action, the Coordinator observes, monitors progress, and provides advice and counsel as may be appropriate. If the responsible person cannot be identified, does not act promptly, or does not adequately respond (to contain, clean up, and dispose of the polluting oil), the Coordinator takes over. Either the government's own resources are employed or private resources are contracted for. If the responsible party is known, he is billed for the costs incurred; if he cannot be identified, the costs are paid from the revolving fund established by Section 311 of the FWPCA Amendments of 1972. This section also requires that the Plan include a system whereby the state or states affected by a discharge of oil or hazardous substance may act to remove the discharge and be reimbursed for reasonable costs.

The Plan provides for establishing strike forces to be trained to provide the necessary containment, clean-up, and disposal services. The nucleus of a national strike force is presently available. There are also to be local strike force teams made up of trained personnel drawn from local operating agencies. Local teams are expected to be able to deal with minor spills —less than 240 barrels (10,000 gallons)—on their own; they are expected to be merged with other local strike forces and/or supplement the national strike force for medium spills—up to 2,400 barrels (100,000 gallons)—and major spills—over 2,400 barrels.

In addition to government response teams, industry has established a number of response cooperatives, and most companies apparently have formulated their own contingency plans. Two of the major cooperatives are Clean Seas on the West Coast and Clean Gulf Associates on the Gulf Coast. These are primarily equipment and training cooperatives: that is, the cooperative purchases and maintains containment, clean-up, and disposal equipment and will train personnel in how to use it. Members of the cooperative draw on the equipment as needed, using their own personnel to operate it. Permanent staffs are expected to be small. Clean Gulf Associates, for example, now employs three marine supervisors and one research engineer full time.

A major lack, both for government and for industry, is adequate specialized equipment for dealing with an oil spill. Despite the best efforts of either the responsible party or the Coordinator, if a major spill should occur at this time, it is not likely to be contained and cleaned up unless it occurs in ideal conditions: close to a clean-up cooperative, on a calm day, with wave heights under three feet.

But response problems are not limited to the availability and capability of equipment; there are also organizational and managerial problems. At every level throughout the response structure, primary and advisory agencies are represented as appropriate. Four primary—Interior, Transportation, Defense, and EPA—and five advisory agencies—Commerce; Health, Education, and Welfare; Justice; State; and the now defunct Office of Emergency Preparedness—are designated by the Plan.[20] This multiplicity of agencies is necessary since relevant responsibilities are fragmented among these agencies. But this fragmentation can be expected to give rise to problems in coordination and continuity. It already has in terms of gaps in response capability due, at least in part, to a lack of a coordinated research and development (R&D) effort. This effort is supposed to be coordinated by the National Response Team through a multi-agency R&D committee.

The rather complex organizational structure appears to be cumbersome and unwieldy. But, except for regional responses to Santa Barbara and the three Gulf accidents, it really has not been tested at the level of a national emergency. The On-Scene Coordinators have been tested, but there were complaints that they lacked the expertise needed to perform their assigned responsibilities. The rationale for assigning the Coast Guard On-Scene Coordinator responsibilities offshore seems to be based primarily on the expectation that a Coast Guard officer will be familiar with tankers, containment, and clean-up. It is not because Coast Guard officers are expected to be familiar with OCS oil operations; and this seems to have been the basis for most of the criticism. In response to these complaints, a memorandum of understanding was signed by Interior and Transportation. It authorizes a representative of USGS to exercise exclusive authority over measures to abate the source of pollution when it is an oil or gas well.[21]

Desirable Changes   Under the Plan for coordinating containment, clean-up, and disposal R&D, the present arrangement needs to be implemented rather than revised. So long as responsibilities remain fragmented, little is to be gained by proposing an alternative coordinating mechanism. It would be a desirable change for EPA, in carrying out its responsibilities for coordinating R&D, to consider setting up a licensing arrangement under which industry licensees' efforts could be coordinated with governmental R&D activities relating to containment, clean-up, and disposal needs.

1. U.S., Department of the Interior, Bureau of Land Management, *Final Environmental Statement: Proposed [December] 1972 Outer Continental Shelf Oil and Gas General Lease Sale Offshore Louisiana*, p. 21.

2. *Ibid.*

3. NEPA, Section 102(2)(C).

4. *Federal Register*, 37 (March 11, 1972), p. 5263.

5. U.S., Executive Office of the President, Council on Environmental Quality, "Guidelines for Statements on Proposed Actions Affecting the Environment," *Federal Register, 36* (April 23, 1971), p. 7724.

6. NEPA, Section 102(2)(C).

7. CEQ, "Guidelines," p. 7726.

8. 458 F. 2d 827, 3 ERC 1558, 2 ELR 20029 (D. C., Cir. 1972).

9. 458 F. 2d at 833n. 12, 3 ERC at 1561n. 12, 3 ELR 20032n. 12, (D. C., Cir. 1972), quoting CEQ, "Guidelines," p. 7725.

10. 458 F. 2d at 833, 3 ERC at 1561, 2 ELR at 20032 (D. C., Cir. 1972).

11. U.S., Department of the Interior, *Environmental Impact Statement: "Prototype" Oil Shale Leasing Program for the States of Colorado, Utah and Wyoming* (Draft, July 1, 1971); and U.S., Department of the Interior, *Environmental Impact Statement, Geothermal Leasing Program* (Draft, October 6, 1971; Supplemental Draft, May 8, 1972).

12. CEQ, "Guidelines," pp. 7724–25.

13. U.S., Executive Office of the President, Council on Environmental Quality, *Environmental Quality, Third Annual Report* (Washington: Government Printing Office, 1972) Chapter 7, pp. 234–35.

14. FWPCA Amendments of 1972, Section 403.

15. *Ibid.*, Section 403(c)(2).

16. See, for example, OCS Order No. 7, August 28, 1969, for the Gulf Coast Area.

17. FWPCA Amendments of 1972, Section 502(9).

18. Council on Environmental Quality, "National Oil and Hazardous Substances Pollution Contingency Plan," *Federal Register,* 36 (August 20, 1971), p. 16215.

19. *Ibid.*, p. 16215.

20. *Ibid.*, p. 16216.

21. U.S., Departments of the Interior and Transportation, "Memorandum of Understanding," No. 1. 18, 1, August 10, 1971.

IX. Government Management

THREE major problem areas warrant special attention in our analysis of government management of OCS oil and gas resource development. These are leasing, planning, and cooperation and coordination. In this chapter we identify and analyze public policy issues in each of these three problem areas.

LEASING

The leasing problem has two principal aspects, the leasing system and how it is administered. Possible changes in the administration of the present OCS lease system are somewhat limited by the amount of geophysical data available to BLM and lack of a clear policy relating OCS production to national energy requirements. Until more data are available and a comprehensive OCS policy is developed, BLM will likely continue to be a relatively passive manager. But BLM need not be limited to scheduling lease sales. It could be a more active manager, attempting to insure that: (1) OCS production play its proper part as a source of energy for the nation; (2) government receive fair value for the OCS resources allocated to the private sector; and (3) OCS operations are supervised to the extent necessary to see that resource development is achieved through economically efficient means, with appropriate conservation of the resources, while allowing for adequate advanced planning and orderly development by the industry.

As for the leasing system itself, the Outer Continental Shelf Lands Act makes the Secretary of the Interior responsible for administering a system for leasing OCS lands. Within Interior, this responsibility is assigned to the Director of BLM. Before offering tracts for leasing, a call for nominations is published in the *Federal Register*. The call specifies the location and limits within which nominations will be received. Nominations may be made by private parties and by the Secretary on the recommendation of USGS. BLM and USGS are responsible for selecting the tracts to be included in the sale. (Step-by-step leasing procedures are listed in Appendix F.)

After tracts have been selected and NEPA requirements for environmental protection met, leases are let on the basis of competitive bidding:

... (1) by sealed bids, and (2) at the discretion of the Secretary, on the basis of a cash bonus with a royalty fixed by the Secretary at not less than $12\frac{1}{2}$ per centum in amount of value of the production, saved, removed or sold, or on the basis of royalty, but at not less than the per centum above mentioned, with a cash bonus fixed by the Secretary.[1]

Said more simply, the Secretary has the alternative of designating either royalty or cash bonus as the bidding variable. All sales up to June, 1973, have been cash bonus sales with a fixed $16\frac{2}{3}$ percent royalty.

In administering the system, the Secretary is charged with achieving several specific policy objectives, including meeting "the urgent need for further exploration and development of the oil and gas deposits of the submerged lands of the outer Continental Shelf," providing "for the prevention of waste and conservation of the natural resources of the outer Continental Shelf,"[2] and insuring receipt of fair market value for leased resources.[3] Passage of the National Environmental Policy Act (NEPA) in 1969 added another responsibility and objective, protection and restoration of the environment.

Successive Secretaries of the Interior have pursued a policy of pacing the development of OCS oil and gas resources, with leases being parcelled out at a rate that has kept the offshore industry hungry and bonuses high. Conservation and waste seem to have been treated as antonyms. (The implications of this treatment are discussed later in this chapter.) It has been assumed that waste is to be prevented and conservation promoted by developing resources in such a way as to optimize ultimate recovery of the resource. This view follows from a definition of conservation calling for the optimal use of resources—as with nondepletable resources such as water. This interpretation has made it possible for the Secretary to reconcile potential conflict between the objectives spelled out in the OCS Lands Act. Passage of NEPA changed this. Most criticisms of the present leasing system focus either on this conflict or on the tensions between simultaneous demands for more energy and greater concern for protecting the environment. Basic questions are raised about how effective the present OCS leasing system is in providing for the fair, safe, and orderly development of OCS oil and gas resources.

The fairness issue involves two principal questions: (1) Does the public receive fair value for the rights which are leased? and (2) Does the system provide adequate opportunities for independents to participate?

There is no simple, straightforward way to determine whether the public is receiving fair value for tracts leased under the present system. Under this system, 8.1 million acres were leased between the first sale held in October, 1954, and the December, 1972 sale.[4] Cash bonuses from these lease sales totaled $6.8 billion, an average of approximately $840 per acre.[5] As of December 31, 1971, royalty and rental income from these tracts had produced another $1.9 billion.[6] (A more detailed analysis of the economics of OCS development is presented in Chapter III.)

According to Interior, the cumulative value of oil, gas, and condensates produced on the OCS through 1971, was $11 billion. Total cumulative revenue to the federal government was $6.5 billion, leaving a return to operators of $4.6 billion.[7] On the basis of experience in both state and OCS lands between 1951 and 1965, T. D. Barrow, former president of Exxon, expected return to operators would be at an investor's interest rate of 7 percent.[8] R. W. Bybee, also of Exxon, says that,

> contrary to popular opinion, the offshore oil and gas business has not paid out its large investment. Economic studies by my company indicate that Industry's average return on investment for continental shelf lease sales will be low. Our current estimates indicate that the average return on investment for Industry from all Federal sales will be approximately 6 percent, providing no further changes in oil price and effective tax rate occur. Individual sales have ranged from outright losses to a high of almost 10 percent. The average payout period for these sales is over 13 years. Currently, Industry has a deficit of $4.1 billion for all offshore leases acquired in Federal sales. A total of $3.4 billion has been spent for Federal lease bonuses and another $8.5 billion has been or will be spent to explore, develop and produce the offshore oil and gas reserves of these sale tracts.[9]

BLM estimates a 5.6 percent rate of return from Gulf of Mexico operations as compared to 6.2 percent for onshore operations in South Louisiana and 4.0 percent from other continental U.S. operations.[10] (BLM used a discounted cash flow method to arrive at these percentages.)

Using competitive bidding models, rather than historical data, some analysts argue that the government is receiving *more* than its fair share—that overall the industry has paid too much for offshore tracts and that this is why the industry's economic performance so far has been relatively poor. The argument goes like this: suppose that Company A's geologists and engineers estimate the value of 50 tracts in advance of a sale. When they bid they will underestimate on some tracts and will overestimate on others. If they are "good" at their job, we can assume that their average estimates of value will coincide with the tracts' average true value. However, since the winner is the high bidder, a company will *tend* to win only on those tracts whose value its geologists and engineers have overestimated. This leads some analysts to conclude that, in general, winning bids are "optimistic" and that the federal government tends to receive *more* than fair value for the lease.[11]

Competitiveness is another aspect of the fair value question. There have been striking differences in bids for the same tracts, presumably reflecting differing assessments of a tract's petroleum potential and a bidder's overall estimate of his competitive position. Per acre bids have differed by as much as tens of thousands of dollars and by as little as a dollar or less. In the June, 1967, sale, for example, the most expensive tract was sold for $32.5 million, a bid of $14.8 million ($2,960 per acre) above the next highest bid for the same tract.[12] And in the September, 1972, sale the most expensive tract was let for $77.4 million, which was $44.0 million ($8,800 per acre) more than the next highest bid. In this same sale, the winning and next highest bids on one tract differed by only $0.90 per acre. Altogether, the September, 1972, sale produced $280.7 million in overbids: that is, winning bidders paid this much more than next highest bidders would have paid.[13]

In terms of numbers of bids per tract, *Oil and Gas Journal* described the September, 1972, sale by saying that, "as usual, the bulk of the acreage drew a small number of bidders—15 tracts drew single bids, 12 tracts had only two bidders, and 48 had four or less. Twenty-three, however, drew six or more, and two highly-sought parcels drew 15 bidders each."[14]

In its analysis of sales between 1954 and April 1, 1968, the Public Land Law Review Commission study found that, for all tracts offered, the average was 1.6 bids per tract. The per tract bid average for the Louisiana area, the area of greatest activity was 1.8.[15]

On the basis of the competitive character of the present system, the range of bids received, the revenues generated, and the apparently modest return bidders expect to receive, proponents of the system conclude that the present system protects the public as well as it can be protected.[16]

It is evident, however, that the present system does require a large initial capital expenditure for what amounts to a hunting license: that is, a large bonus is paid to obtain the right to drill holes where the bidder's assessment of geologic and geophysical data has led him to believe hydrocarbons are accumulated. Critics argue that this capital could better serve the public interest if it were invested in further exploration and development instead. At base, the argument is that development of needed energy resources is being delayed in part because of unnecessary capital tie-ups. Of course, this argument assumes that what would otherwise be spent for bonuses *would be* spent on exploration and development.[17]

The capital required to win and develop a tract does seem to affect participation; the present system is biased in favor of the major oil companies. As was noted in Chapter IV, individual majors hold 46 percent of OCS acreage and produce 63 percent of all OCS oil and gas; groups of majors hold 35 percent and produce 34 percent. Individual independents hold only two percent of the acreage and produce only one percent of OCS oil and gas; and groups of independents hold 17 percent and produce two percent.[18] Overall, then, majors individually or in combination hold 81 percent of OCS acreage and produce 97 percent of all oil and gas produced on the OCS while independents control only 19 percent of the acreage and produce only three percent of all OCS oil and gas. However, it is not clear how much of this is due to the bonus bid system. Even if the initial capital requirements caused by bonus bids were removed, OCS activities still necessitate large financial commitments made with a relatively high degree of risk. The argument can be made, with some justification, that companies that cannot afford the financial risks associated with bonus bidding are not likely to be able to afford the financial risks associated with developing and producing OCS oil and gas.[19] These risks and costs will become even greater as development and production activities move into deeper water.

One aspect of the risk involved is the lessee's unlimited liability. F. Allen Calvert, chairman of an Independent Petroleum Association of America committee concerned with increasing independents' participation in OCS development, identified unlimited liability for oil spills as "a goblin that just spooks you."[20]

But there is a way for independents to participate at the present time. Companies lacking sufficient capital or wishing to spread risks and opportunities can participate in joint ventures. There were 62 group and 65 individual bids in the December, 1970, sale. In September, 1972, group bids outnumbered individual bids 43 to 31, and Shell, the largest offshore operator in the Gulf of Mexico, participated in group bidding for the first time.[21]

Another aspect of the capital/rate of development issue was covered by *Offshore* in its November, 1972, issue when it compared development of the North Sea and the Gulf of Mexico. *Offshore* points out that more reserves have already been discovered in the North Sea than have been found to date on federal lands in the Gulf.[22] This is attributed to the concession system, under which a large aggregate amount of acreage has been offered and leased within the past eight years. Leases cover 55 percent of all North Sea acreage. Acreage was made available in single blocks ranging up to 130,000 acres off Norway. In contrast, single block size is limited to 5,000 acres or less in the Gulf, where only 15 percent of all federal acreage (to a water depth of 600 feet) has been leased in almost 19 years. Also, in contrast to the bonus bid system employed in the Gulf, the governments of the North Sea nations have used an administrative system for evaluating minimum work programs submitted by operators. One consequence has been that fees and rentals are nominal.

While explicitly leaving the question open, in effect, *Offshore* uses these comparisons with the North Sea to argue for making much more extensive acreage available in the Gulf. But the magazine also acknowledges that until the Ekofisk Field was discovered and the size of the discovery became

444

public knowledge, operators were, in fact, pulling rigs out of the North Sea. It seems that positive indications of commercial accumulations of petroleum are the critical variable, and there is ample evidence that petroleum is present in the Gulf. Capital requirements and tract size have not lessened industry's interest in the Gulf. They know that petroleum is there, and they want to have increased opportunities to find and produce it.

In contrast to the question of fairness, questions concerning safe and orderly development generally do not concern the bonus bid system itself but, rather, its administration. Over much of the time since 1954, lease sales have been scheduled only sporadically. Interior did not announce a formal future leasing plan until June, 1971, almost 18 years after the first OCS sale. In June, 1971, the announcement indicated plans for the next five years. Areas were specified by coastal region, as were the month and year when the sale would take place. The plan is supposed to be updated annually in order to maintain a five-year projection.

The schedule has been caught up in the energy-environment conflict. As a consequence, two sales scheduled for the Gulf of Mexico between November, 1971, and September, 1972, were not held on time; and the entire schedule is in doubt since there is organized resistance to proposed sales for the Atlantic and for Florida's west coast. Environmental interest groups have been successful in delaying sales, but, as has been indicated, the stop-and-go character of the system is not entirely attributable to the intervention of these groups. However, the lack of stability within the leasing system also results in large part from the lack of predictable certainty in scheduling of lease offerings.

Critics of the high degree of uncertainty associated with the present system point out that OCS development requires long-range planning with regard to such things as financing, contracting, equipping, and fabricating.[23] Subcontractors and equipment suppliers, as well as the operators, are affected by the instability of the present system. Individual human costs can be high, particularly in terms of job security. Proficiency and, thereby, safety also can be affected.

Another lease management issue, raised by Counsel for NRDC, concerns overdrilling and unitization.[24] As has been indicated in Chapter VII, only limited exploratory information is available to BLM and USGS prior to lease sales. This limitation coupled with the block system used for leasing tracts can result in two or more tracts overlaying a single reservoir. On land this problem has generally been resolved by requiring fields to be developed as a unit regardless of how many leaseholders there are. This practice, which is known as unitization, is a means for insuring efficient development and eliminating unnecessary drilling. Title 30, Part 250.50 of the *Code of Federal Regulations* authorizes the Director of USGS either to require or permit unitization on the OCS. Practice in the Gulf Coast area has been to permit rather than require unitization; however, changes to OCS Order Number 11 now being processed establish much tighter controls over reservoir management. The effect of these changes, whose promulgation is pending, will be to prevent overdrilling.[25]

In terms of performance, the present system has promoted the development of offshore resources, federal and state, to the point that 10 percent of all oil and gas produced domestically in 1970 came from the OCS.[26] Of the tracts sold, those that have been developed had, by the end of 1971, produced 2.5 billion barrels of oil and condensate and 14.5 trillion cubic feet of natural gas.[27] Since there has been no overall national energy policy, there are no obvious criteria against which this performance can be measured.

In evaluating the overall performance of the present system, proponents argue that allocating leases by competitive bidding substitutes market forces for administrative judgment. Under competitive bidding, in addition to being inexpensive to administer, it is assumed that the more efficient producers can afford to pay a larger cash bonus. In the long run, therefore, the competitive bidding system acts to select the most efficient, safest operators. Thus, it is argued that not only does the public receive fair value, but marginal, possibly unsafe (or less safe) operators are less likely to be able to participate.

If present policies are continued, questions of fairness will continue to arise both in terms of fair return for the resources and in terms of the bias of the system toward the majors. The most telling cost of continuing the present system, however, is in terms of the great uncertainty which will continue to be associated with the start-and-stop character of the present system at least until: (1) the role of OCS petroleum is related specifically to national energy needs, and (2) an accommodation of energy-environment interests is achieved.

WHAT ARE THE ALTERNATIVES?

Goals and objectives must be established before the advantages and disadvantages of competing leasing systems can be evaluated. In part, different countries have different types of offshore leasing systems because they have different goals and objectives. Around the world these include maximizing government revenue, maintaining low prices, reducing dependence on imports, and promoting national economic development.[28] On the basis of explicit and implicit goals and objectives established for any U.S. leasing system, the following criteria or factors have to be taken into account:

1. Will the government receive a "fair share" of the value of the resources? (And how will this be determined?)

2. Does the system favor certain potential developers over others?

3. Does the system take into account environmental protection concerns?

4. Does the system provide for the prevention of waste and conservation of the natural resource?

5. Does the system provide for orderly development within a stable long-range plan taking into account the role of OCS resources in meeting national energy needs?

6. Are there inherent difficulties in administering the system?

Alternative lease allocation methods involve combinations of several variables or factors. If it is assumed that a competitive system is desired, these include:

1. Is bidding to be open or closed? And are the bidding variables to be limited to bonus, royalty, or work program, or to some combination of the three?

2. Is the fixed variable to be established by a floor percentage or a dollar amount with respect to the fixed bonus or royalty?

3. What is to be the timing of payments to the government?

We have chosen to discuss only six of the many possible alternative lease allocation methods. These six alternatives are responsive to the major criticisms made of the present system and have the merit of being sufficiently feasible to warrant consideration.

One alternative to the present system is to change the combination of bidding and fixed variables. Three possibilities, none of which would require legislation, are:

1. A variable royalty bidding system. In this system the bid variable would be royalty rather than bonus. A cash bonus would be fixed (as the $16\frac{2}{3}$ percent royalty is now). The principal benefit claimed for this system is that it reduces the large initial capital required under the present system. Two consequences expected are: making more capital available for immediate exploration and development, and allowing participation by smaller companies.

2. Retention of the bonus bid system with an increased fixed royalty rate. This offers a possible means for forcing the bonus bids down, thereby reducing to some extent the initial capital requirements.

3. Sliding royalty rate system. Under this system the present bonus bid and fixed royalty would be retained. However, the royalty would be

gradually reduced according to some formula, to assure optimal ultimate recovery. If present royalty rates were to be increased, a sliding-scale royalty rate would become more important.

Three alternatives requiring new legislation include:

4. Staggered bonus system. The bonus would be paid in stages rather than all at once as required now. One possibility would be to have ⅓ of the total bonus bid paid at the time of the sale, another ⅓ when commercial deposits are discovered, and the final ⅓ when production commenced. The advantage of this system is that the amount of capital tied up would be decreased. If no commercial deposits were found the lease could be relinquished with only ⅓ of the initial bid being paid.

5. Apportioned development between majors and independents. There are several alternative ways to give independents a larger role in OCS development. Competitive bidding could be used to establish value and then independents could be allowed to bid on some set of specified tracts at or near the known winning bids. This would give them a chance to develop a portion of OCS acreage without having to risk large amounts of capital by bidding blind against the majors.[29] Alternatively some tracts could be set aside to be bid on only by independents.

6. A performance system. Companies would apply for areas, and the lease would be granted to the company offering the most ambitious work program. This can be interpreted as a competitive system; however, the decision to award a tract would be made on administrative rather than economic grounds.

ASSESSMENT OF ALTERNATIVES

Variable Royalty System: This is one of the alternatives proposed most frequently as a replacement for the present system; and such a system could be implemented at the discretion of the Secretary of the Interior. According to William A. Vogely, Director of Interior's Office of Economic Analysis, an experimental royalty-bid plan has been designed for use in some future lease sale.[30] However, details of the plan have not been made public.

Within this plan, the combination of fixed bonus and variable royalty can presumably be adjusted to assure a desired level of government income. When testifying before the Senate Interior Committee in June, 1972, Harrison Loesch, then Assistant Secretary of the Interior for Public Land Management, indicated that revenues from variable royalty were expected to be the same as from the bonus bid system; the government would simply have to collect its income over a longer time period.[31]

As we have seen, the present system has produced an average per acre bonus of $840. This experience provides some basis for establishing the amount of a fixed bonus—but it contributes nothing toward clarification of what the overall effect would be on "fair value." According to Vogely, a 70 percent royalty rate would be required for the government to receive as much income between 1954 and 1985 as it would receive during the same time period from the bonus bid system.[32] There has been no indication of how fixed bonus would be specified.

Loesch, in his testimony before the Interior Committee, also pointed out that royalty bidding would give a more equal opportunity to bidders. No type of bidder would be favored over any other type, one consequence being to give independents a chance for a larger role on the OCS. But Loesch went on to testify that there were drawbacks associated with lowering the admission price.[33] Limited capital requirements might result in participation by irresponsible, marginal, and/or speculative operators. Environmental problems might be increased as a consequence. OCS orders do specify minimum operating standards, but in practice USGS lacks the resources required to look over the shoulder of every operator all the time.

Even if the large initial capital requirement of the bonus-bid system were eliminated, the capital requirements for development and production are substantial and are invested with considerable risk. In fact, development and production costs are increasing as a consequence of an emphasis on safety and environmental protection. For example, a recent *Oil and Gas Journal* report estimated that it has cost the industry $50 million per year to meet new standards imposed when OCS Orders 8 and 9 were revised in October, 1970.[34]

Increasing participation opportunities by means of the royalty bid may be something of a false issue in any case. Ample opportunities already exist by means of joint ventures, and in many ways this is preferable since risks and opportunities can be spread.

The charge that the bonus bid system is slowing OCS development because of the large capital requirements seems unfounded at the present time. In fact, there is industry pressure to step up the pace of leasing, an indication that capital is not a real constraint. (In his 1973 Energy Message, President Nixon announced that he had directed the Secretary of the Interior to triple the annual OCS acreage leased by 1979 beginning with expanded sales in the Gulf in 1974.)

Historically the industry has been able to generate up to 90 percent of its capital needs, but the trend is toward greater dependence on outside sources of capital. According to the *Oil and Gas Journal*, a recent Standard and Poor's analysis showed that internal funding declined from 90 percent in 1966 to 70 percent in 1970.[35] New lease sales involve large capital outlays that do not generate revenues for at least three to five years after they are made. Therefore, if the pace of making OCS lands available were stepped up, apparently so would the industry's dependence on outside capital sources.

Another concern is the effect the royalty bid has on conservation. The bonus bid represents a "sunk" cost, and therefore the size of the bonus does not ordinarily enter into the decision on whether or not to produce a field once it is discovered. The bonus has been paid and is not returned if the field is not developed. The decision to produce or not is based on whether the field can be produced at a cost which provides for some minimum rate of return (not counting the "sunk" bonus cost). As long as oil or gas can be sold for more than it costs to produce it, the field should be produced. In contrast, a high royalty bid may lead to abandoning a field early in its life, or not developing it at all. Since production rates decline over time, operating costs per barrel increase. A field can be produced profitably only so long as income per barrel exceeds production costs per barrel, but the royalty directly affects the operator's income per barrel produced. As a consequence, high royalty bids will cause fields to be shut-in and abandoned much earlier than they would have been under the bonus-bid system.

A related drawback of the variable royalty bid system is that companies might overbid only to find that their bid was too high for commercial development. It is possible for a reduction in royalties or rentals to be granted by the Director of USGS if he finds "it necessary to promote development or finds a lease cannot be successfully operated under the terms provided therein."[36] To make a particular tract attractive to develop might require lowering the rate of royalty to be paid. However, this presents a number of difficult administrative problems with the royalty bid system. If renegotiation were permitted, bidders would, in effect, be encouraged to overbid; if renegotiation were not permitted, otherwise producible reservoirs would not be produced.

Overall, then, the variable royalty bid system appears to offer few advantages and numerous disadvantages compared to the present bonus bid system. The royalty bid system apparently would decrease initial capital requirements and, thereby, increase opportunities for participation. But whether this is a desirable goal when balanced against safety and environmental concerns is at least somewhat questionable, and joint ventures already provide an alternative means for rather broad participation. Moreover, it appears that administering the royalty bid system would be considerably more difficult than administering the bonus bid system. For example, it would be a real challenge to find some means for promoting conservation while not encouraging excessive per acre bids.

Increase the Fixed Royalty Rate: As with the variable royalty bid system, the Secretary of the Interior could, at his discretion, fix a royalty rate higher than the present 16⅔ percent. The only statutory requirement is that the rate not be set lower than 12½ percent.

It is assumed that if the royalty rate were raised, bonus bids would decrease. If this is true, initial capital requirements would be reduced and broader participation in the OCS development could result. The extent to which bonus bids would be lowered is in doubt. Several analysts suggest a bidding model which states that: *The sealed bonus bid = A factor based on probability of finding oil or gas and the estimated total value of oil and gas × 1 — The royalty rate.*[37] Thus, everything else being equal, the sealed bonus bid might be expected to drop by 20 percent if the royalty rate were raised from ⅙ to ⅓. If this is so, raising the royalty rate will not do much to decrease the initial capital requirement.

As was mentioned earlier, a stepped-up pace of offering OCS lands for lease could possibly result in lowered bonus bids. Increasing the royalty rate is a means for avoiding the resulting reduction in government revenues. However, the conservation problem identified in our analysis of the royalty bid system would also be a problem. Generally, increasing the royalty rate decreases the income per barrel, and this leads to an earlier abandonment of the field.

Sliding Royalty Rate System: Another option currently available to the Secretary is to have a sliding scale for royalty rates. This would, in effect, combine aspects of the bonus bid and royalty-bid systems. Both bonus and/or royalty could be bidding variables. But the most important feature of the system is recognition of the effect that bonus-royalty costs have on development.

One alternative would be to continue to use bonus as the bidding variable and to fix the initial royalty rate at something higher than the present 16⅔ percent, but subsequently the royalty rate could be scaled down based on reservoir size and age. Other combinations of bonus and royalty could be used, and all of these could be designed to produce a desired level of government income and to promote the development of all reservoirs that could be economically developed given that level of investment.

The Public Land Law Review Commission reported that California has used a variation of royalty bidding (known as royalty factor bidding) in which the lease provides for a sliding-scale royalty that increases when production reaches specified quantities with the lease being awarded to the bidder offering the highest multiple to be applied to the scale. Further, the Commission pointed out that the California system might be improved upon by providing a royalty slide to zero or very low rates as wells approach exhaustion or abandonment.[38] It is noteworthy that California has used both sliding royalty and royalty factor bidding despite the increased administrative difficulties inherent in these types of royalty arrangements.

Staggered Bonus System: A strict interpretation of the OCS Lands Act makes it appear that an amendment to the Act would be required before a staggered bonus system could be adopted. However, the Interior's Office of the Solicitor is considering this question and has yet to issue an opinion.[39]

The key provision of a staggered bonus system would serve to decrease the gamble involved in bonus-bidding. Instead of having to pay the full amount even if no commercial accumulation of oil or gas were found, the bidder would have to pay only a portion of the bonus initially. At each stage in the development of the field, the bidder would have to decide whether to go ahead. To go ahead would be to pay another portion of the bonus, but each decision could be based on much more complete information than is ever available at the pre-lease stage. Since the risk of losing this investment would be lessened, presumably more participants would be able to take the initial risk.

If government revenues were to be maintained at their present level, the average bid per acre would have to increase. This would be required in order to make up for the bonus income lost when some tracts are not developed. Alternatively, a higher fixed royalty rate could be used as a means of generating income to make up for these losses.

As with any system that reduces initial capital requirements, it could lead to speculation and possibly unsafe, irresponsible operations. However, since the bonus would be the bidding variable, the system should discourage purely speculative bids much more than the variable royalty system.

In terms of conservation, the staggered bonus system has one disadvantage (compared to the current bonus bid system). Since only one-third of the bid represents a "sunk cost" and the other two-thirds enters the decision on whether the field is economical or not, the staggered bonus system would require larger field sizes (as does the variable royalty system). However, once the decision is made to produce the field, this system should yield the same maximum total recovery as the current bonus system—if the royalty rate remains the same. (However, an industry spokesman suggests that one effect of this system might well be that companies would make their decision to produce at a later time than they do under the current leasing system.)

This system would not introduce any additional administrative or regulatory problems, since the renegotiation of royalty rates should be the same under this system as under the current bonus bid system.

One person has criticized this system by saying that it raises the question "on what's a giveaway, which can cause serious public repercussions."[40] But bids might generally be expected to go up since only one-third of the bid is subject to the "dry" tract risk. This would mean that government income would increase on producible tracts. For the dry tracts, it is unlikely that someone would accuse the government of a "giveaway" for selling a worthless tract for several million dollars.

Apportion Development Between Majors and Independents: Adopting any system for apportioning OCS development between majors and independents would apparently require new legislation or substantially amending the OCS Lands Act. There are a number of alternative means for apportioning development opportunities.

George Mitchell, President of the Texas Independent Producers and Royalty Owners Association, has proposed a system patterned after that used by the Department of Defense in buying its fuels. The Defense Supply Agency sets aside a certain percentage of its requirement to be procured from independent petroleum refiners. In applying this principle offshore, Mitchell proposed that the present bonus bid system be used to establish the value to be placed on specific tracts. Certain of these tracts would then be withdrawn rather than being awarded to the high bidders. These tracts would be offered to independents on a competitive basis, the assumption being that the independents, knowing the value of the tracts and bidding only among themselves, could purchase the tracts at or near the winning bid established in the original bonus bid sale. This system would reduce the risk for independents and also insure that they would be allowed to develop a certain portion of the OCS.[41]

The fairness of this proposal has to be questioned, and it seems that it does nothing to lower total capital requirements. An alternative that is somewhat more appealing might be to set aside specific tracts on which initial bidding is restricted to independents. Or perhaps tracts that are rejected in a regular bonus bid sale could be offered to independents—which on the surface would hardly seem an enticing proposal since the initial bid is assumed to have been based on an expert assessment of the potential for commercial accumulations of hydrocarbons. However, an analysis of tracts for which initial high bids were rejected but that were subsequently reoffered reveals that on the reoffer generally there is more bidding activity and the high bids are greater. In fact, in its study of the OCS, the Public Land Law Review Commission found that the average bid on reoffered tracts was $411.38 per acre, whereas the average for all other OCS oil and gas leases had been $403.24 per acre.[42]

Performance System: Another approach toward the same objective is to establish a performance or work program system. At base this system substitutes administrative evaluation for the competitive market place. As a consequence, this system would involve much more administration than does the bonus bid system.

The British use the proposed work program as a principal criterion in selecting from among applicants. Applicants indicate how much money they intend to invest within what time period to perform what specific development tasks. Other performance criteria that can be taken into account include previous records for efficiency, safety, and environmental protection, for example.

The major advantage of a performance system is to build in criteria other than a willingness to gamble as the basis for assigning tracts for development. And the system could be administered to meet whatever standards of fairness were desired; independents supposedly would be able to compete on more nearly equal terms with the majors. Of course, the major disadvantage of such a system is the inherent administrative difficulties in trying to justify a decision on who should win a particular tract and in trying to determine a method by which the government will receive a fair share of the revenue.

Overall, any scheme designed to provide for greater participation of independents carries some risks with it. As was discussed in the analysis of the variable royalty system, it is not clear that several important public interests, including safety and environmental protection, are served by giving small operators an opportunity to be the sole lessee and operator.

SUMMARY

A number of other possible alternatives have not been discussed. We have singled out these six because in some ways they include either all or most of the variables which will have to be incorporated into any system. Consequently, these alternatives have provided an opportunity to demonstrate the interaction of these variables and some of the problems associated with their various combinations.

We have not discussed concession systems beyond mentioning the use of performance criteria such as minimum work programs. We assume that it is not now politically feasible to opt for a noncompetitive system in the U.S. And we assume that the desire to continue having the government receive substantial income from its OCS leases also militates against a concession leasing system.

A more extended treatment of alternatives may be found in the Public Land Law Review Commission's "Study of Outer Continental Shelf Lands of the United States."[43] And Richard Corrigan has reviewed a range of alternatives in a recent issue of the *National Journal*.[44]

Given the objectives identified for any system for leasing OCS lands, the bonus bid system has much to recommend it. It does require a large initial capital investment, but capital does not appear to have been nor does it appear likely to be a constraint on OCS development. Several of the alternatives aimed at reducing capital requirements carry with them risks to the environment and potentially adverse effects on conservation. The environmental risks presumably could be dealt with administratively, but this would require considerably more administrative capability than is presently available.

The staggered bonus system would seem to answer the major criticism of the present system, namely a reduction in the amount of the high risk bonus. At the same time it does not create major additional problems, as does the variable royalty system. It would not encourage outright speculation, nor would it reduce total recovery. However, it would require larger reservoir sizes, given present prices.

Neither of the six alternatives discussed provides for unitization. Except for systems which call for variable royalties, each of the alternatives would be compatible with a requirement that all reservoirs be developed as units. Such a requirement could create administrative difficulties if the tracts to be unitized were sold at different royalty rates. However, soon to be promulgated OCS Order Number 11 accomplishes the same goals as unitization by means of detailed reservoir management requirements.

Desirable Changes   Whichever system is used, the orderly development of the OCS depends on establishing policies which set forth the role OCS resources are to play over what time period in meeting energy demand. Only then can a schedule be formulated to meet the requirements of that policy.

1. In order to allow for advanced planning and orderly development of OCS resources, BLM should:

a. prepare a longer range leasing plan for up to 10 years designating general areas to be leased, Offshore Louisiana, Gulf of Alaska, and Northern Atlantic OCS, for example;

b. designate more precisely those areas included on BLM's present five-year lease schedule;

c. select specific tracts for inclusion in the draft impact statement well in advance of a scheduled sale; and

2. In the immediate future BLM should continue with the bonus bid system and not even experiment with the variable royalty-bid system.

However, BLM should give consideration to the staggered bonus system, including possible selective experimentation.

PLANNING

A related government management issue is planning, explicit regularized procedures for bringing together and coordinating diverse, often overlapping energy and land use programs. Officials responsible for developing OCS oil and gas resources have not had national policies to guide their planning and policy-making. For both energy and land use, policies which have existed have usually been partial (incomplete), short range, and disjointed primarily as a consequence of programs in these areas being fragmented among a number of departments and agencies.[45] Those responsible have tended to promote their own particular programs and respond primarily to the interests and demands of their agency's clients. Even if a single department or agency has been responsible for more than one program, it has usually assigned particular programs to different internal divisions or bureaus, thereby contributing to a pervasive overall pattern of fragmentation.

In this section, several planning problems, two of which have been identified earlier, will be analyzed. These include: environmental impact statement requirements; the questionable adequacy of data on energy requirements, sources, availability, and uses; and the multiple uses of the OCS and coastal zone. Following these analyses, the changes either already instituted or being proposed by the President and the Departments of Commerce and Interior will be examined and a number of desirable changes to the present system proposed.

ENVIRONMENTAL IMPACT STATEMENTS

Implementation of the NEPA requirement for environmental impact statements has been revealing. (For the discussion of NEPA, see Chapter VIII.) It reveals, notably, some of the costs associated with fragmentation of planning responsibilities and underlines the critical need for some general statement of overall energy and land use policies to provide guidelines for those responsible for specific programs. In several cases, the courts have been asked, for example, to determine whether certain actions required an impact statement to be written[46] or whether alternatives to the proposed action have been analyzed adequately.[47] In each case, the court has had to apply a national policy of protecting and restoring the environment in an area in which responsibilities are fragmented among a number of agencies.

In the *NRDC v. Morton* case, for example, the government's attorneys took the position that the only alternatives that the Department of the Interior was required to discuss in connection with an OCS lease sale were those which could be adopted and put into effect by the Department itself. The court was unwilling to accept this position.

In its decision, the court said that, "it is the essence and thrust of NEPA that the pertinent statement serve to gather in one place a discussion of the relative environmental impact of alternatives" *available to the government as a whole.*[48] What NEPA requires, the court decided, is "information sufficient to permit a reasoned choice of alternatives so far as environmental aspects are concerned."[49]

ADEQUACY OF DATA

The practical problem for the Department of the Interior in responding to the court is that many of the alternatives to OCS development are outside its province. Even if the President's 1971 and 1973 Energy Messages could be interpreted as overall energy plans, meeting the court's demand for sufficient information requires almost unprecedented coordination and cooperation among a number of departments and agencies. And within Interior itself, it is doubtful whether adequate planning data on long-term energy requirements, uses, availability, and sources are available for satisfying the court's admonition. (See the discussion on background data and exploratory information in Chapter VII.) Interior's capability to analyze and assess the land use impacts of the various energy alternatives is probably even more limited, since the Department of Commerce has major responsibilities for overall offshore land use policies and programs.

The House and Senate Committees on Interior and Insular Affairs recently reviewed a number of energy requirement studies. Both Committees found these studies to be of limited use. After its review, the House Committee found that:

> ... most of the studies are fundamentally deficient for their failure to deal with an exact energy concept, their analyses are usually only loosely structured to address some vague notion of energy demand, and little attention is given to a correct interpretation of the forecasts. The crucial issues of price and supply limitations are usually all but ignored. Perhaps most important of all, many studies seem to suggest that their forecasts can be used by policy makers as target levels for future energy consumption. They do so, however, without justifying their implied GNP growth rate objectives and without considering the relative costs and benefits of providing various levels of energy consumption in the future.[50]

Data on energy reserves and resources are equally deficient. In 1972, USGS published its most recent estimates based generally "on geologic projections of favorable rocks and anticipated frequency of the energy resource in the favorable rocks."[51] For the resources that have been identified and are economically recoverable with available technologies, the accuracy of these estimates is in the range of 20 to 50 percent; for resources that have not yet been discovered and which are neither technologically nor economically feasible to extract and utilize at the present time, these estimates are accurate only within an order of magnitude.

In short, available energy demand projections and resource estimates are of doubtful accuracy and reliability. Even when these data are available, they are an inadequate basis for comprehensive planning and policy-making. Individual departments and agencies, in addition to being limited by the lack of overall energy and land use policies and plans, are potentially handicapped by these quality and quantity limitations in the data.

In practice, the Department of the Interior has not been appreciably handicapped by the lack and quality of these data, primarily because it has not attempted to plan for the systematic development of OCS resources. The only obvious plan which it has formulated is a five-year lease sale schedule, which was not published until 1971. In fact, there seems to be ample evidence that the pace of OCS leasing has been determined more by a desire for revenue than on the basis of an assessment of the portion of total energy requirements that it is desirable to obtain from the OCS. Furthermore, there is no indication of any formalized procedure for coordinating leasing with land and other multiple uses before the opposition developed to the proposed lease sale of OCS tracts in the Santa Barbara Channel.

MULTIPLE USE

A general belief does appear to be developing in this country that more conscious attention must be given to land use planning. Pressures on our land resources have become more obvious as our population has increased, both in terms of competition for space and in terms of our increased needs for natural resources. With these pressures has come recognition of some of the environmental impacts which flow from the ways in which these resources have been treated and used in the past.

The most direct effects on OCS development have come from demands that: (1) certain areas be set aside as sanctuaries; and (2) before any OCS tract is sold, the impact that its development will have on other users be evaluated. Sanctuaries became a practical problem for the Department of the Interior for the first time when it announced plans for leasing tracts in the Santa Barbara Channel. Now, however, the Marine Protection, Research, and Sanctuaries Act, enacted by the 92nd Congress, gives to the Secretary of Commerce authority, after consultation with other departments and agencies and with the approval of the President, to designate marine sanctuaries which may extend from the coast to the outer limit of the shelf area under federal jurisdiction. The 92nd Congress also amended the Marine Resources and Engineering Development Act (sometimes referred to as the Coastal Zone Management Act) to include a title on management of the coastal zone. Since the coastal zone is defined as extending only to the outer limit of the three-mile territorial sea, the provisions do not affect the OCS itself. However, since OCS activities are linked to the shore, OCS oil and gas development will obviously be affected, particularly in siting pipelines, terminals, and onshore facilities. Some construction of all these types of facilities is now being delayed by local or state governments or blocked by suits brought under NEPA.[52]

Passage of these two acts has served to underline the interrelatedness of energy and land use policies for the OCS and the coastal zone. Planning for either land use or development of energy resources clearly cannot be an independent activity if the goals established for both programs are to be achieved. At some point the two must be brought together.

THE ALTERNATIVES

It seems that the ideal solution would be to develop a detailed overall integrated national energy and land use policy which would include details concerning the OCS and coastal zone. This is impractical and cannot be expected. It is more reasonable to expect that a general overall plan for the OCS for a specified time period can be developed. Since responsibilities and authority are decentralized, this would require either taking some step toward centralization or developing some mechanism for effective coordination and joint planning. And since data presently available are apparently inadequate, some effort would have to be made to provide a more adequate data base to inform the planners.

With the exception of the proposed Department of Natural Resources, the alternatives initiated by the President and the Departments of Commerce and Interior have taken an organization-and-procedures approach to planning and policy-making. Instead of fundamental organizational restructuring, new centralizing mechanisms either were or are being added to facilitate communication, coordination, and joint planning. These initially included appointing a presidential counselor for natural resources, assigning a presidential counselor responsibility for oil policy, naming a special energy consultant, establishing a special committee on energy, and establishing new in-house coordinators in Commerce and Interior. More recently the President has reverted to a more decentralized system placing

greater reliance on department heads, particularly the Secretary of the
Interior.

ASSESSMENT OF ALTERNATIVES

Presidential Initiatives: In its report on executive reorganization, the President's Advisory Council on Executive Organization recommended that a
Department of Natural Resources be established. (The Council was
chaired by Roy Ash who is now serving as the Director of the Office of
Management and Budget.) Five components—land and recreation, water
resources, energy and mineral resources, marine resources and technology,
and geophysical science services—were to be brought together into a single
department as a means for correcting the existing fragmentation of responsibilities. The Council's stated objectives were to group together natural
resource programs which share broad common purposes and to make it
possible to achieve a coordinated natural resources management policy.[53]

President Nixon called for creation of such a department in both his
1970 and 1973 Energy Messages. However, in 1973, he changed the name
of the proposed department to Energy and Natural Resources.

In the absence of favorable Congressional action on his proposals, the
President has attempted to gain some of his reorganization goals by establishing a centralized policy organization of presidential counselors, committees, and councils. The counselor or "super cabinet" portion of the system he established was short lived. (Press Secretary Ziegler announced
the end of the system on May 10, 1973; Watergate and the departure of
H. R. Haldeman and John D. Ehrlichman from the White House are
the apparent reasons for the system's demise.) But other parts of the President's machinery for centralizing energy policy remain intact, at least for
the time being (May, 1973).

What remains is a three-member Council on Energy Policy and a National Energy Office, both in the Executive Office of the President, and an
Oil Policy Committee in the Department of the Treasury.[54] The Council,
which was approved by the Senate on May 10, 1973, is responsible for: data
collection and interpretation, coordination of federal agency activities, and
preparation of a long-range comprehensive plan for national energy resource management.[55] Two members of the Council as originally constituted continue to serve, national security advisor Henry A. Kissinger and
Treasury Secretary George P. Schultz; the third member, John D. Ehrlichman, has resigned from the White House staff and his temporary successor
as Chairman of the Domestic Council, Kenneth R. Cole, Jr., has not been
appointed to replace him on the Council on Energy Policy.

The National Energy Office is to develop " 'comprehensive plans and programs to insure the availability of adequate and dependable supplies of energy,' and to 'make recommendations to the Director of the Office of Management and Budget concerning proposed funding of energy programs and activities.' "[56]

When Charles J. DiBona, head of the Office, was initially appointed, he was identified as an energy consultant to the President and the Council on Energy Policy.[57] It now appears that his office will function primarily as a staff for the Council on Energy Policy.

When the Oil Policy Committee was transferred from the now defunct Office of Emergency Preparedness to his Department, Treasury Secretary George Schultz was assigned overall supervision of oil policy. (Although not officially designated as such, Schultz appears to be the Administration's energy policy coordinator.) His Deputy Secretary, William E. Simon, has been designated Chairman of the Committee. Implementing policies shaped by the Committee will be the responsibility of the Department of the Interior's Office of Oil and Gas.[58]

Although new and untested, these Presidential initiatives represent an effort to provide a mechanism for more effective, centralized coordination in making energy policy. This remains true despite elimination of the presidential counselor system. Unless or until energy activities and programs are brought together in a single department, the Council on Energy Policy will likely be the key organization for coordinating the making and administration of energy policy. (Personnel and titles are changing so rapidly in this area that descriptions are outdated almost as soon as they are written. Since this section was revised in May, the President appointed Colorado Governor John A. Love to be his chief energy advisor.)

Departmental Initiatives: During the period when the President was establishing his super cabinet, the Secretaries of Commerce and Interior took departmental actions aimed at providing for better intra-departmental coordination of energy activities and policy. The mechanism chosen by the Secretary of the Interior was an Energy Board to be headed by an executive director, the Deputy Under Secretary for Energy. The Board is to be chaired by the Secretary himself.

The Secretary of Commerce established an Office of Energy Programs. Located in the Bureau of Resources and Trade Assistance, the Office is to be particularly concerned with balance-of-trade problems and liquid natural gas (LNG) import projects. Stimulating domestic production, promoting the development of new energy sources, and long-range energy planning are also mentioned in the Departmental Order establishing the Office.[59]

In his 1973 Energy Message, the President announced that he had directed the Secretary of the Interior to strengthen Interior's organization of energy activities by: (1) expanding the responsibilities of a new Assistant Secretary for Energy and Minerals to incorporate all departmental energy activities, (2) developing a capacity for gathering and analyzing energy data, (3) establishing an office of energy conservation and, (4) strengthening the Department's capabilities for overseeing and coordinating a broader range of energy R&D.[60] The Secretary issued an order on May 7, 1973, creating Offices of Energy Data and Analysis (to collect and publish resource and consumption figures), Research and Development (to direct and finance the search for new fuel sources and pollution-free combustion), and Energy Conservation (to develop methods of conserving energy).[61] (The Secretary also ordered that Offices of Mine Safety and Health and Land Use and Water Planning be established.)

Like the President's initiatives, these departmental changes are new and untested. Given the President's announced retreat from a centralized super cabinet, the responsibilities of individual cabinet officers and their departments are expected to be enhanced. In particular, the Secretary of the Interior's energy policy role is likely to be enlarged over what it would have been had his only access to the President been through a presidential counselor. However, the Council on Energy Policy and the Oil Policy Committee may still limit the Secretary to primarily a staff and implementation rather than a policy-making role.

Desirable Changes The change most likely to produce the desired degree of coordination of national energy and land use policies is the establishment of a Department of Natural Resources (or Energy and Natural Resources) following the general guidelines of the President's Council recommendations on how to group, manage, and coordinate programs.

If this cannot be achieved, the next more desirable alternative is an add-on arrangement for coordinating planning. As a practical matter, it would seem preferable to have a top official of the federal government designated as energy coordinator. The coordinator should be designated on the basis of organizational location and program responsibilities.[62] Such an arrangement would probably provide for greater stability and continuity than one based on personal relationships.

Whatever the mechanism chosen to promote coordinated planning and policy-making, it is desirable to improve the data base available to the planners. And it is desirable that an overall plan for some specified time period be developed to guide those who must plan and administer individual energy programs such as the development of OCS oil and gas. At the present time, the environmental impact statements required by NEPA are forcing both the acquisition of better, more complete data and some planning, at least to the extent required to consider what the alternatives to OCS development are. While this is clearly not the most desirable means for obtaining data or planning, it is desirable, at least until some institutionalized mechanism is established, to use these statements as a means of achieving some degree of coordinated planning. A more direct means to achieve this objective would be to enact legislation requiring that an over-all OCS development plan be formulated and that the environmental impact statement (or some similar statement) include an explanation of how individual actions, such as an OCS lease sale, will fit into it.

COOPERATION AND COORDINATION

Problems of inter- and intra-departmental or agency cooperation and coordination extend beyond the problem of planning. Since the responsibility for aspects of OCS oil and gas development is divided among several departments and agencies and often further subdivided within departments and agencies, cooperation and coordination are difficult to achieve.

INTRA-DEPARTMENTAL COOPERATION AND COORDINATION

One of the most obvious conflicts of interest associated with OCS operations is the Department of the Interior's responsibility for both promotion and regulation. As indicated earlier, the Secretary is assigned a promotional responsibility by Section 8(a) of the OCS Lands Act. The Act states that, "in order to meet the urgent need for further exploration and development of the oil and gas deposits of the submerged lands of the outer Continental Shelf, the Secretary is authorized to grant . . . oil and gas leases on submerged lands of the outer Continental Shelf."

The authority for Interior's regulatory function comes from the OCS Lands Act, Section 5(a)(1): "the Secretary shall administer the provisions of this Act . . . in order to provide for the prevention of waste and conservation of the natural resources of the outer Continental Shelf." In an attempt to separate these two functions, BLM was given primary responsibility for promotion and USGS for regulation.

The potential conflict between these two responsibilities appears most clearly in providing for the prevention of waste and conservation. Interior has traditionally taken this to mean maximizing ultimate recovery of oil and gas. An important ingredient in this policy has been to limit current production to meet existing market demand. (Since December, 1970, OCS production has been set at the Maximum Efficient Rate (MER) by USGS.) This definition of conservation and Interior's policies for promoting it, however, are opposed by a number of conservation and environmentalist groups. Generally, in the view of these groups, to conserve is to husband petroleum resources. They are husbanded to enhance the possibility of prolonging their use by future generations, so that they are available when an emergency requires their development, or until they can be produced more safely.

Historically, the basic governmental policy for OCS petroleum resources has been to emphasize their development at a rate which would meet market demand. The ultimate goals of the industry and its regulator have been identical and no other public policy priority has seriously challenged their achievement. However, the situation has changed since events such as Union's Santa Barbara blowout expanded participation in OCS policy-making and administration. The new participants argue that there is a fundamental conflict between Interior's development policies and its conservation responsibilities. An example used to make the point is the practice of either venting or flaring oil-well-produced gas at or near the site of production platforms.

When oil is produced, often some gas, called associated gas, is also produced. Frequently the quantities of associated gas being produced cannot be economically compressed and transported to shore or to an existing gas pipeline. As a consequence, this gas is often vented to the atmosphere or flared. Although only relatively small quantities are vented or flared on any one platform, Interior has estimated that as much as 272 million cubic feet per day or 23 percent of all associated gas presently being produced on the OCS is being flared. This daily loss of gas is equivalent to about 3.4 percent of all OCS gas produced by both gas and oil wells.[63]

Critics point to the practice of venting or flaring natural gas as an illustration of how the conservation mandate is not being carried out by the Secretary. They maintain that a depletable resource is being lost because of the present emphasis on satisfying an urgent need for more oil. The practice also illustrates how FPC's policy of keeping prices down to protect the consumer can affect Interior's success in conserving gas: that is, a higher wellhead price for this gas might eliminate at least some of the venting and flaring, as might a USGS policy requiring that royalties be paid on vented and flared gas.

The Union blowout at Santa Barbara triggered a different criticism. In this case, at least one frequently cited writer has claimed that USGS did not divulge its geophysical information to BLM before leases were let in the Santa Barbara Channel in 1968.[64] The allegation is that such information would have permitted BLM to evaluate how safe it was to develop the Channel area—and presumably that BLM would have decided not to go forward with the sale. This is a tenuous presumption, and the Department of the Interior has explicitly denied that USGS withheld data from

BLM. An Interior order now formally defines the respective roles of BLM and USGS in making economic, engineering, and geologic evaluations of each tract before it is offered for sale.[65] Under the new order, USGS does not disclose to BLM data obtained from industry considered to be proprietary; however, USGS does use these data in meeting its own responsibilities for evaluating tracts.

THE ALTERNATIVES

In this instance, both the regulation and promotion functions could be combined, either within the Department of the Interior or in a Department of Natural Resources. Alternatively, one of the functions could be moved into another department or agency.

ASSESSMENT OF ALTERNATIVES

Combining the promoter and regulator roles would resolve the coordination and cooperation problems, but potentially at a cost. It is possible, perhaps probable, that one role would come to dominate the other. In fact, this is what some of the critics allege has happened in Interior, even with the separation of functions between USGS and BLM.

If the goal is to have the two functions compete, the most competitive situation would be afforded by having responsibility for the two functions located in different departments. However, this might well intensify the problem of cooperation and coordination. The organizational mechanisms to coordinate planning and policy-making which were discussed above, could prove useful in resolving this problem as well.

While the question is basically one of policy, it is important that the machinery for administering that policy be balanced. Once the policy objectives for conservation and environmental protection, for example, are defined, the design of the administrative machinery should insure that they are incorporated as criteria to be seriously considered when decisions are being made or implemented.

Desirable Changes It is desirable to continue the separation of the two functions; if changes are to be made, it should be to strengthen the competition between them.

INTER-DEPARTMENTAL COOPERATION AND COORDINATION: PIPELINES

A number of problems of inter-departmental cooperation and coordination arise in connection with transporting oil and gas from the OCS by pipeline to a shore facility. The agencies with responsibilities for pipelines,

Table 11. Summary of Federal Agency OCS Pipeline Jurisdiction and Regulation

Agency	Material	Jurisdiction			Regulation and Administration	
		Type	Pipeline Miles in Jurisdiction	Purpose	Inspection Function	General Role
BLM	Oil and gas	Common carrier and single custody transmission lines[a]	Total 3,672 (includes FPC and ICC lines plus 713 other lines[b])	Administration	None	Issues "right-of-way" permits, collects right-of-way rental fee
USGS	Oil and gas	Field gathering[c] and flowlines[d] (single custody only)	Flowlines = 2,345 (does not include gathering lines)[e]	Safety, administration, revenue collection	Field inspection capability	Approves easements, sets safety standards, measures flow and value, and commingling,[f] checks inspection and maintenance records, collects royalty
OPS	Oil and gas	Common carrier	2,959	Safety	No capability	Reviews accident reports, contracts engineering studies[g]
FPC	Gas	Common carrier	2,412	Rate regulation	None	Issues "certificates of public convenience and necessity" required for line construction, and facilities acquisition, regulates gas prices, purchases, and sales
ICC	Oil	Common carrier	547	Rate regulation	None	Oversees profit structure of oil line companies

a Transmission lines move oil and/or gas after final USGS metering, processing, and/or sale. FPC or Judicial hearings may be needed in specific cases to resolve this term.

b Other: Lines approved by BLM but not common carriers. They are used by the operator as flowlines moving products to a sales point.

c Field gathering lines: lines usually moving oil or gas from the well to a header system or storage tank.

d Flowlines: lines moving oil from a header system, tank platform, or other facilities to a point for final metering, processing, and/or sale.

e Number of miles of field gathering lines is not compiled by any agency. Estimates vary from 800 to 5,000 miles.

f Commingling is defined as bringing together the production from different wells, leases, pools, and fields, and with production from other operators (30 CFR 250.68).

g Statutory authority includes inspection and oversight of testing and maintenance. These functions are not performed at this time.

the extent of their jurisdiction, and their administrative/regulative functions are summarized in Table 11; in Table 12, gaps, overlaps, and ambiguities of this fragmented structure are summarized. Together, these tables indicate that:

1. two agencies grant rights-of-way permits;
2. there is some confusion as to who is responsible for pipeline safety standards; and
3. there are recurring questions on the definitions which are necessary to determine who has jurisdiction over a particular line.

The general problem appears to be that there are too many agencies, each concerned with its own particular aspect of the system, and often these various aspects are not well defined or separable.

In addition to these several gaps, overlaps, and ambiguities, there are inefficiencies because no one is concerned with "pipeline systems." (This point was discussed earlier in our analysis of the OCS leasing system.) It appears that, as a consequence of this, duplicative pipeline systems have been built on the OCS.

Although FPC appears to have sufficient authority to plan a system of OCS gas pipelines, no such plan has been developed. In general, FPC has actively exercised its authority to control pipeline investment in terms of the gas reserves necessary to amortize pipeline costs. The questions which arise here concern whether FPC has the information on gas reserves required for making sound judgments. In this connection, FPC apparently does not fully use the information and expertise which USGS makes available.

ICC is charged with regulating the rate schedule of common carrier oil pipelines, but it does little more than approve rate structures established by the pipeline owners themselves. During the past 12 years, no rate dispute cases involving OCS pipelines have come before ICC. Some concern has been expressed in the Congress that ICC approved rate structures favor large producers and discriminate against small independents. Problems associated with the method by which ICC approves rate structures and controls access to oil pipelines are apparently philosophical rather than a reflection on the lack of staff, facilities, or expertise. It should be noted that ICC does not have statutory authority to approve the construction of common carrier oil pipelines. Oil pipelines are considered to be adjuncts to refineries or a method to transport a raw material. Since these pipelines do not transport a product that is purchased by the general public, the ICC consumer-protection supervisory function is minimal as compared to FPC's control of the gas transmission industry. However, oil pipeline costs are eventually passed on to the consumer so that the lack of a "Certificate of

Table 12. OCS Pipeline Agency Overlaps, Gaps, and Ambiguities

Agency	Overlaps	Gaps	Ambiguous Areas
BLM	a. With USGS in issuing "rights-of-way" for transmission lines		a. Operators have choice of USGS or BLM for "rights-of-way" or easements
USGS	a. With BLM in issuing "rights-of-way" for flowlines b. With OPS in safety responsibility c. With ICC and FPC in measuring commingling		a. Resolving flowlines, field gathering lines, and transmission lines b. Safety design criteria for transmission lines c. Legal regime of flowlines
OPS	a. Safety responsibility of offshore pipelines (with USGS)	a. Limited safety design criteria b. No inspection capability c. No design approval, testing, or maintenance checks or criteria	
FPC	a. With USGS in geophysical and engineering capabilities	a. Little geophysical expertise b. Little field supervision	a. Liquid condensate transport b. Placing exploratory and field development costs on pipeline rate base c. Separation of gathering and transmission functions
ICC		a. No allocation supervision b. Limited rate schedule supervision c. No construction approval	

Public Convenience and Necessity" for a common carrier oil line is based in part upon philosophical, rather than economic, grounds.

A major gap in the control and management of OCS pipelines occurs because of limited implementation of the Natural Gas Pipeline Safety Act of 1968. In accordance with section 14 of that Act, an Office of Pipeline Safety (OPS) was established in 1968. Although "the OPS has jurisdiction over gas pipelines and interstate liquid pipeline systems in the Outer Continental Shelf," including "safety, inspection, maintenance, and construction," until recently the office has had no capability to meet most of its responsibilities.[66] Even now the capability is limited since the office has a total of only 27 staff positions, 24 in Washington and three in a field office in Houston.[67] Although several of OPS's responsibilities overlap with those of USGS, it is not clear that all of OPS's responsibilities are being covered by USGS.

THE ALTERNATIVES

The overall problem with the arrangements for overseeing OCS pipelines is the fragmentation of responsibilities and the gaps and ambiguities resulting from the assignment of similar responsibilities to different agencies. Alternatively responsibilities could be centralized into either a single agency or, at least, fewer agencies. Where there are now gaps and ambiguities, assignments of responsibilities can be clarified and duplications eliminated by giving responsibility to an agency with a capability for meeting its obligations. In all instances, formal coordination agreements could be used as a means for avoiding some of the present problems.

ASSESSMENT OF ALTERNATIVES

Since OPS is assigned specific responsibilities by the Natural Gas Pipeline Safety Act, it would require legislative action or an inter-agency agreement to effect a transfer of its OCS responsibilities. Under the latter arrangement, OPS would retain its statutory responsibilities but delegate their performance to some other agency, presumably USGS. Since USGS already has similar responsibilities, OPS functions could be integrated and performed by staff personnel in each area, seemingly without adding appreciably to their present workload.

Overlaps within Interior could be easily handled by giving USGS exclusive authority for granting "rights-of-way" and easements; alternatively BLM could issue rights-of-way only after consulting USGS; this arrangement and the procedures for their implementation could be formalized in an inter-agency agreement or a departmental order. This would keep USGS better informed on the total OCS pipeline system.

An inter-agency agreement could be used to give FPC access to USGS data in order to inform FPC's decisions on granting a certificate of public convenience and necessity. If the data required is proprietary, the agreement could provide for USGS to furnish confidential assessments of it.

Desirable Changes   It would be desirable to have USGS and BLM agree on some means for coordinating their responsibilities for easements or rights-of-way; FPC should seek access to and utilize USGS data when making decisions on pipeline investments. And since USGS already has a field inspection capability and possesses the expertise for establishing design criteria, it would be desirable to have USGS be responsible for establishing and overseeing safety, inspection, maintenance, and construction requirements for all OCS pipelines.

INTER-DEPARTMENTAL COOPERATION AND COORDINATION: SAFETY AND HEALTH

Implementation of the Occupational Safety and Health Act (OSHA) promises to pose several cooperation and coordination problems. The Departments of Health, Education, and Welfare, Interior, Labor, and Transportation all now have responsibilities for safety or health on OCS facilities. Within Interior, USGS has had responsibility for preventing accidents on platforms, including providing a safe working environment. OSHA assigns this responsibility to Labor and gives to HEW the responsibility for establishing standards to be enforced by Labor.

THE ALTERNATIVE

Responsibility for implementing OSHA on the OCS could be consolidated or the departments involved could negotiate inter-departmental agreements delegating these responsibilities to a single agency.

ASSESSMENT OF THE ALTERNATIVE

Since USGS already has an inspection responsibility and capability, USGS could easily be responsible for implementing and enforcing OSHA on the OCS. HEW could still establish the standards to be enforced by USGS. This approach would eliminate the duplication of effort and take advantage of USGS's knowledge and expertise. There would appear to be no particular advantage to be gained by having two agencies inspecting different aspects of safety and health. Nor is there any reason to believe that USGS would be any less effective in enforcing these new requirements.

Desirable Changes It would be desirable to have the Departments of Labor and Interior (or USGS) enter into an inter-agency agreement delegating OSHA inspection responsibilities to USGS.

1. OCS Lands Act, Section 8.
2. OCS Lands Act, Section 8 and 5.
3. U.S. Code 31, Section 403(2) and Bureau of the Budget Circular A-25.
4. U.S., Department of the Interior, *Statement, Questions and Policy Issues Related to Oversight Hearings on the Administration of the Outer Continental Shelf Lands Act, Held by the Senate Committee on Interior and Insular Affairs, Pursuant to S. Res. 45, March 23, 1972*, p. 13; *Oil and Gas Journal*, 70 (September 18, 1972), pp. 38–41; and *World Oil*, 176 (January, 1973), pp. 76–78.
5. *Ibid.*

6. Interior, *Questions and Policy Issues*, p. 32.

7. *Ibid.*

8. T. D. Barrow, "Economics of Offshore Development," in *Exploration and Economics of the Petroleum Industry*, Vol. 5: *New Ideas, New Methods, New Developments* (Houston: Gulf Publishing Co., 1967), pp. 133–46.

9. R. W. Bybee, "Petroleum Exploration and Production on the Nation's Continental Shelves—Economic Potential and Risk," (unpublished paper presented at the Annual Meeting of the Marine Technology Society in Washington, D.C., July 1, 1970), p. 3.

10. U.S., Department of the Interior, Bureau of Land Management, *The Role of Petroleum and Natural Gas from the Outer Continental Shelf in the National Supply of Petroleum and Natural Gas*, Technical Bulletin 5 (Washington: Government Printing Office, 1970), pp. 160–61.

11. For models of offshore bidding see, for example, E. C. Capen, R. W. Clapp, and W. M. Campbell, "Competitive Bidding in High-Risk Situations," *Journal of Petroleum Technology*, 23 (June, 1971), pp. 641–52.

12. Eldon Ball, "How Companies Fare in Offshore Bidding," *Offshore*, 31 (October, 1971), pp. 31–34.

13. *Oil and Gas Journal*, 70 (September 18, 1972), pp. 38–41.

14. *Ibid.*, p. 38.

15. U.S., Congress, Public Land Law Review Commission, *Study of Outer Continental Shelf Lands of the United States* (6 vols.; Springfield, Va.: Clearinghouse for Federal Scientific and Technical Information, 1969), Vol. 3, pp. 489–90, and Table 8–1, p. 463.

16. See Richard Corrigan, "Energy Report/Demand for More Oil and Gas Prompts Review of Offshore Leasing," *National Journal*, 4 (July 8, 1972), pp. 1109–16.

17. *Ibid.*, p. 1109.

18. Interior, *Questions and Policy Issues*, p. 8.

19. See Corrigan, " . . . Review of Offshore Leasing," p. 1115.

20. *Ibid.*, p. 1116.

21. *Offshore*, 31 (January, 1971), pp. 27–31; and *Oil and Gas Journal*, 70 (September 18, 1972, pp. 38–41.

22. *Offshore*, 32 (November, 1972), pp. 33–37.

23. Persons in industry repeatedly emphasized this point in interviews.

24. U.S., Department of the Interior, Bureau of Land Management, *Final Environmental Statement: Proposed [December] 1972 Outer Continental Shelf Oil and Gas General Lease Sale Offshore Louisiana*, p. 607.

25. Phone conversation with Robert F. Evans, USGS Conservation Manager for Gulf of Mexico OCS Operations, on May 25, 1973.

26. Interior, *Questions and Policy Issues*, p. 1.

27. *Ibid.*, pp. 63–64, Tables 53 and 54.

28. Alvin Kaufman, "International Offshore Leasing Practices," *Journal of Petroleum Technology*, 22 (March, 1970), pp. 247–52.

29. Corrigan, ". . . Review of Offshore Leasing," p. 1114.

30. Corrigan, ". . . Review of Offshore Leasing," p. 1112.

31. *Oil and Gas Journal*, 70 (June 26, 1972), p. 34.

32. Corrigan " . . . Review of Offshore Leasing," 1112.

33. *Oil and Gas Journal*, 70 (June 26, 1972), pp. 34–35.

34. *Oil and Gas Journal*, 70 (August 21, 1972), pp. 59–66.

35. "Fiction and Fact," *Oil and Gas Journal*, 70 (May 1, 1972), n.p.

36. Title 30, *Code of Federal Regulations,* Part 230.12(3).[30 CFR 250.12(e).]

37. See, for example, the bidding model discussion in Paul B. Crawford's "Texas Offshore Bidding Patterns," *Journal of Petroleum Technology,* 22 (March, 1970), pp. 283–89.

38. Public Land Law Review Commission, *OCS Lands,* Vol. 3, pp. 679–81.

39. Corrigan, ". . . Review of Offshore Leasing," p. 1116.

40. *Ibid.,* p. 1113.

41. *Ibid.,* p. 1114.

42. Public Land Law Review Commission, *OCS Lands,* Vol. 3, pp. 462–554.

43. *Ibid.*

44. Corrigan, ". . . Review of Offshore Leasing," pp. 1109–16.

45. See, for example, President's Advisory Council on Executive Organization, *Memorandum for the President: Establishment of a Department of Natural Resources Organization for Social and Economic Programs* (Washington: Executive Office of the President, May 12, 1970).

46. *Kalur v. Resor.* 335 F. Supp. 1 (D. C. 1971), 3 ER 1458, 1 ERL 20637, and *Sierra Club v. Sargent,* 3 ERC 1905, for example.

47. *NRDC v. Morton,* 458 F. 2d 827 (D. C., Cir. 1972). For an extensive review of court actions in connection with NEPA, see Robert S. Lynch, "Complying with NEPA: The Tortuous Path to an Adequate Environmental Impact Statement," *Arizona Law Review,* 14 (1972), pp. 717–45.

48. Cited by U.S., Executive Office of the President, Council on Environmental Quality, *Environmental Quality, Third Annual Report* (Washington: Government Printing Office, 1972), p. 7.

49. *Ibid.,* p. 244.

50. U.S., Congress, House of Representatives, Committee on Interior and Insular Affairs, *Energy "Demand" Studies: An Analysis and Appraisal,* Committee Print (Washington: Government Printing Office, 1972), p. 7.

51. U.S., Department of the Interior, Geological Survey, *Energy Resources of the United States,* by P. K. Theobald, S. P. Schweinfurth, and D. C. Duncan, Circular 650 (Washington: Government Printing Office, 1972), p. 1.

52. Siting of facilities of all kinds is widely viewed as a major problem. See for example: "U.S. Crude Imports Hit 1.6 Million B/D," *Oil and Gas Journal,* 70 (January 3, 1972), pp. 28–29; Howard M. Wilson, "West Coast Offshore: Oil in a Strait-jacket," *Oil and Gas Journal,* 70 (January 10, 1972), pp. 25–28; Gene Kinney, "Watching Washington," *Oil and Gas Journal,* 70 (November 27, 1972), p. 31; and James A. Noone, "Resources Report/New Federal Program Seeks to Aid States in Control of Coastal-Area Exploitation," *National Journal,* 4 (December 9, 1972), pp. 1889–98.

53. President's Advisory Council on Executive Organization, *Memorandum for the President . . ."*

54. See: Dom Bonafede and John K. Iglehart, "White House Report/End of Counselor System Enlarges Policy Forming Role of Cabinet," *National Journal,* 5 (May 19, 1973), pp. 726–29; and *Oil and Gas Journal,* 71 (May 21, 1973), p. 82.

55. *National Journal,* 5 (May 19, 1973), pp. 734, 737.

56. *Science and Government Report,* 3 (May 1, 1973), p. 6.

57. *Oil and Gas Journal,* 71 (March 5, 1973), pp. 44–45; and Gene Kinney, "Nixon Energy Team Ready, Awaits Final Policy Signal," *Oil and Gas Journal,* 71 (March 26, 1973), pp. 33–36.

58. Kinney, "Nixon Energy Team Ready," p. 35.

59. *Oil and Gas Journal*, 70 (November 27, 1972), pp. 38–39.

60. "President's Message on Energy," *Congressional Record*, 119 (April 18, 1973), p. S7697.

61. *National Journal*, 5 (May 19, 1973), p. 743.

62. See *Science*, 179 (January 26, 1973), pp. 358–59.

63. Interior, *Questions and Policy Issues*, p. 7.

64. Frederick deGroat Harlow, "The Oil Men and the Sea," *Arizona Law Review*, 11 (1969), pp. 677–730.

65. Interior, *Questions and Policy Issues*, p. 72. The order replaces an earlier BLM–USGS agreement.

66. The quoted portions of the text are based on a letter from Melvin A. Judah, Industry Programs Officer, OPS, dated November 22, 1972.

67. *Ibid*.

X. Jurisdiction

AT LEAST three kinds of jurisdictional questions arise concerning the OCS: gaps within federal jurisdiction, disputes between the states and the federal government, and the definition of the shelf area which is under national jurisdiction.

GAPS WITHIN FEDERAL JURISDICTION

There are three obvious gaps in federal jurisdiction on the OCS. These include a six-mile zone of ambiguous federal authority off the Gulf coasts of Florida and Texas, the non-applicability of some provisions of the Federal Water Pollution Control Act (FWPCA) Amendments of 1972 to the OCS, and the lack of inspection and certification requirements for some types of drilling rigs.

By virtue of decisions handed down by the U.S. Supreme Court in 1960, the states of Texas and Florida have jurisdiction over their Gulf coast submerged lands out to three marine leagues. This sets the shoreward limit of the OCS at this point or at roughly nine miles rather than at three miles as it is for all other coastal states. As interpreted by the Coast Guard, the authority of the Corps of Engineers and the Coast Guard for protecting navigation literally does not apply in the six-mile area between three and nine miles adjacent to these two states. The reason that the agencies do not have unambiguous authority in this area is that the Submerged Lands Act and the OCS Lands Act apply respectively to the navigable waters of the U.S.—the territorial sea which extends from the baseline seaward for three miles—and to the OCS, the portion of the shelf seaward from the outer edge of state jurisdiction to the outer limit allowed by the Continental Shelf Convention.

A similar gap exists with regard to the applicability of the FWPCA Amendments of 1972 to offshore facilities located on the OCS. The Act is generally limited in its application to offshore facilities, defined as being only those located within the navigable waters, apparently thereby excluding facilities on the OCS. (Navigable waters are defined by the FWPCA Amendments as the "waters of the United States, including the territorial sea." However, as noted earlier, at least one major operator interprets the Amendments as being applicable to its facilities on the OCS and submitted descriptions of platform discharges to EPA prior to the deadline date of April 16, 1973.)

205

The final gap, identified by the Coast Guard in their response to questions raised by the Senate Interior Committee, is the lack of certification and inspection requirements for certain types of drilling rigs.[1] Floating units are inspected and certificated as seagoing barges, but the Coast Guard interprets these requirements as being inapplicable to mobile bottom bearing units.

THE ALTERNATIVES

New legislation may be required to deal with the problem of ambiguity in the six-mile zone off Florida and Texas. In the case of the FWPCA Amendments of 1972, Congress may have excluded OCS facilities on purpose; in any event, new legislation would be required to extend coverage to include these facilities. As for mobile bottom standing drilling rigs, a change in the regulations issued by the Coast Guard or the Secretary of Transportation may be adequate for dealing with the problem.

ASSESSMENT OF ALTERNATIVES

If the gaps in the authority of the Corps and Coast Guard are unintended, the only reasonable alternative seems to be to fill them by amending the Submerged Lands and OCS Lands acts as necessary. The amendments could be written to include other areas which might become exceptions in future litigation between the federal government and the governments of coastal states.

The gap in the FWPCA Amendments of 1972 may be purposeful; if so, an alternative is to do nothing. However, to except OCS offshore facilities from the discharge requirements seems inconsistent with the general intent of the Act. There seems to be no reason why USGS could not enforce Environmental Protection Agency (EPA) equipment standards on the OCS, but this would require extending applicability of the Act.

The authority of the Coast Guard for inspecting and certificating floating drilling rigs is based on their being treated as vessels; it seems that the first step in extending these requirements to mobile bottom standing rigs should be to treat these rigs as vessels also. The Coast Guard has begun action to accomplish this by publishing a change to the applicable section of the *Code of Federal Regulations*. Should this means fail, new legislative authority can be requested.

Desirable Changes It would be desirable to clarify the ambiguities concerning the six-mile zone between the outer limit of the territorial sea and the beginning of OCS off the coasts of Florida and Texas. It seems likely that legislative action in the form of amendments to the Submerged Lands and OCS Lands Acts will be required.

It would also be desirable to apply the discharge provisions of the FWPCA Amendments of 1972 to offshore facilities on the OCS. While EPA would still establish discharge standards as provided for in the Amendments, it would be desirable to have USGS enforce these standards on OCS facilities.

It would be desirable to have the Coast Guard begin to apply inspection and certification requirements to mobile bottom standing drilling rigs. If this application is successfully challenged, legislative authority to apply these requirements should be enacted.

FEDERAL-STATE

Historically, there have been a number of problems concerning the seaward extent of state jurisdiction, the baseline onshore from which jurisdiction is measured, and the handling of leasing and development of areas where state and federal claims overlap. All of these have been submitted to the courts for resolution.

Several of these problems coalesced in the Gulf of Mexico in disputes between the federal government and Louisiana. While these were being resolved, development of mineral resources proceeded in the area of overlapping jurisdictional claims under an "Interim Agreement." This agreement provided security for the lessee-operator by establishing arrangements under which bonus, rental, and royalty monies were either placed in escrow or divided.

A different situation exists on the Atlantic Coast and in other unleased areas. Atlantic Coast states have no state agencies with the oil and gas expertise of those in California, Louisiana, and Texas. Thus a wider potential administrative latitude exists for establishing state–federal intergovernmental cooperation. However, anticipated jurisdictional problems along the Atlantic Coast may result in conflict and delay, possibly to the point of forestalling OCS petroleum resource development. This is a real possibility if these questions have to be resolved in the courts.

The possibility that the international boundary (the territorial sea) may be extended seaward nine additional miles raises the possibility that coastal states may reopen the jurisdictional dispute. However, there is little precedent to justify this larger claim, and the Submerged Lands Act clearly specifies the three-mile width of state jurisdiction, except where additional claims existed prior to the state entering the Union.

In addition to straightforward questions of jurisdiction over territory, jurisdictional questions arise concerning pipelines and environmental pro-

tection. Finding sites for onshore facilities is becoming increasingly difficult, and pressures are mounting for federal intervention. Land use legislation has been introduced into the Congress which would require the
states to develop a program "which protects the environment and assures
recreational opportunity, but at the same time provides for necessary social
services and essential economic activities."[2] Providing for reliable energy
systems is listed as a necessary social service and presumably would include
dealing with the siting problems.

There are also federal-state problems which arise because of the need to
route OCS pipelines across state lands. The major problem apparently
occurs when the route takes the line across marshlands or an estuary. But
whatever the route, the states retain jurisdiction over their shelf areas and
must grant rights-of-way before a pipeline can be placed. Except for
marshes and estuaries, there have been few problems to date. However,
environmental concerns may make this more of a problem in the future.

Some states have requirements more stringent than those of the federal
government. California, for example, has more stringent environmental
requirements. It has ceased holding lease sales until technologically adequate clean-up devices can be obtained. In this instance, the federal government has complied with state standards by not scheduling future OCS
lease sales adjacent to California. California also has stricter oil-water
separator discharge levels than those promulgated for the OCS, but these
differences have apparently not created demonstrable federal-state problems. California's requirement also is more broadly based than is the OCS
requirement and includes standards for heavy metal concentrations, par-
ticulates, and effects on dissolved oxygen levels.[3]

Both jurisdictional and environmental issues have special significance
for OCS development off states presently without offshore operations. In
OCS areas adjacent to a number of these states, new developments will
most likely proceed initially in federal waters since favorable petroleum
sediments are generally distant from shore. This is likely to lead to the
need for specific prior arrangements which will facilitate federal-state ac-
commodations and, in particular, arrangements which will satisfy state
concerns for the environment.

THE ALTERNATIVES

The question of which level of government has jurisdiction over what parts
of the shelf will have to be resolved either by the courts or by some kind
of non-judicial settlement. If the disputes are to be litigated, as is probable,
the two governments can negotiate an interim agreement to permit development to continue pending a final settlement.

For both land use and environmental protection, federal controls and jurisdiction could be extended to achieve the advantages of a single set of governing rules. However, in both areas, it seems more likely that federal guidelines could be enacted establishing minimum standards and requirements.

ASSESSMENT OF ALTERNATIVES

There appear to be advantages to be gained through implementation of either proposal for resolving ownership disputes. The major problem with non-judicial settlement would seem to be the difficulty of working out the agreements. This approach would require negotiation of several agreements, all of which might require legislative approval by at least two bodies. The principal advantage would be that the public, industry, and regulatory agencies could operate in a stable milieu.

An interim agreement would really be a temporary measure designed to build some stability into OCS activities. Even if final fixed boundaries were never determined, this proposal has the advantage that the administration and regulations governing a tract would not change during the lifetime of a lease. This alternative, of course, does not resolve jurisdictional disputes at all; it does, however, permit resource development. It is likely that difficulties in implementing other alternatives may result in further use of interim agreements, most of which can be implemented by executive decisions.

While a single, uniform set of rules for land use management in the coastal zone and for environmental protection would offer some advantages, such rules would require legislative action. Present legislation either assimilates state laws, establishes federal rules, or offers federal guidelines for the states to follow. Setting minimum standards for environmental protection would have the advantage of not cancelling out existing state regulations that are more stringent. The same is generally true for coastal zone management. However, there will have to be requirements such as those included in the present bill before the Congress which recognizes a need to take necessary social services and essential economic activities into account.

Desirable Changes   It would be desirable to have the federal government negotiate interim agreements with the governments of those coastal states which have claimed jurisdiction beyond the three miles provided in the Submerged Lands Act where OCS development is scheduled.

It would be desirable to have a federal land use law for the coastal zones providing for federal, state, and local coordination in preparing land use plans; the law should require that provisions be made for siting onshore facilities to serve OCS development.

It would be desirable to have compatible and consistent discharge standards for the OCS and the adjacent state. Standards could be based on criteria such as those used by California, including standards for heavy metals and dissolved oxygen content.

NATIONAL-INTERNATIONAL ISSUES

The U.S., together with many other coastal countries, is a party to the 1958 Geneva Convention which defines the continental shelf as

> . . . the seabed and subsoil of the submarine areas adjacent to the coast but outside the area of the territorial sea, to a depth of 200 meters [approximately 660 feet] or, beyond that limit, to where the depth of the superjacent water admits of exploitation of the natural resources of the said area.[4]

Within this area, the governments of coastal countries may exercise sovereign rights for exploring and exploiting natural resources.[5]

In the *North Sea Continental Shelf Cases*,[6] the International Court of Justice found that the definition written into the 1958 Convention does not apply to countries not parties to the Convention. The Court found instead that a coastal country has a right to the adjacent continental shelf as a natural prolongation of its land territory and that, by virtue of its sovereignty over its land mass, it also has sovereignty over the adjacent shelf.[7] However, the Court stopped short of elaborating clear-cut criteria for defining the outer limit of this natural prolongation of land territory.

The conventional definition is equally imprecise. The definition included in the Convention was a product of compromise, one arrived at because delegates to the 1958 Geneva Conference on the Law of the Sea (LOS) were unable to agree on either a geologic or a fixed-limit definition for the shelf area that could be claimed by coastal countries. They were able to agree on a technologically open-ended definition that seemed adequate at the time. However, conditions have changed significantly since 1958.

A rapid expansion of the international political system was already underway when the LOS Conference met; that expansion trend has continued, and the system is considerably more heterogeneous in 1973 than it was in 1958. Most of the newcomers are non-Western and less developed. Two issues preoccupy them: anti-colonialism and economic development. For them, the issues of developing subsea mineral resources and promoting the economic development of less developed countries are closely related.

The rate of scientific and technological change also was increasing rapidly by 1958, but technologies for exploiting subsea mineral resources at water depths greater than 200 meters (approximately 660 feet) have been developed much more rapidly than the LOS conferences anticipated. For example, the petroleum industry now possesses technologies capable of developing oil and gas resources in water depths of more than 600 meters (almost 2,000 feet) and is rapidly developing technologies which will make it feasible to develop commercial accumulations of oil and gas at virtually unlimited water depths. Hard minerals can also be mined from the deep seabed. In fact, entrepreneurs from Japan, the U.S., and West Germany are preparing to mine hard minerals experimentally with equipment designed to operate in water depths as great as 4,500–5,400 meters (roughly 15,000–18,000 feet).

Concern for the quality of the global environment also has increased since 1958. The 1958 Convention on the Continental Shelf did provide that coastal countries operating offshore installations such as oil wells were "obliged to undertake . . . all appropriate measures for the protection of the living resources of the sea from harmful agents" in a safety zone around the installation.[8] Since then, however, an intensified interest in problems of the human environment led the General Assembly of the United Nations to approve a resolution calling for an international Conference on the Human Environment. And this Conference, which met in Stockholm in June, 1972, focused attention on the environmental aspects of natural resources management.

Collectively, then, new governments, new technologies, and a recently intensified concern for protecting and restoring the global environment have combined to pose a fundamental challenge to the meaning and adequacy of the 1958 rules. Pressures for the international community to deal with international ocean problems led to a call for a UN-sponsored LOS conference to meet in Geneva in 1973 (and now rescheduled for 1974). Two major political issues identified with the long-range development of offshore oil and gas resources are to be given priority treatment there as integral parts of the seabed issue: who is to manage and control the development of seabed mineral resources beyond 200 meters, and who is to benefit from their development.

A major initiative for resolving these issues came from Malta's representative to the UN, Ambassador Arvid Pardo. In 1967 he presented a proposal to the General Assembly that would reserve the seabed beyond the limits of national jurisdiction to exclusive international control *and* earmark the benefits to be obtained from the seabed primarily to promote the economic development of the developing countries. He and the representatives of several other developing countries have argued that the benefits to be derived from the exploitation of these resources should be used

to benefit the entire international community, not just the developed
countries which possess the technology for exploiting them.

In his May 23, 1970, statement on Ocean Policy, President Nixon proposed

> ... that all nations adopt as soon as possible a treaty under which they would
> renounce all national claims over the natural resources of the seabed beyond
> the point where the high seas reach a depth of 200 meters . . . and would
> agree to regard these resources as the common heritage of mankind.[9]

Subsequently, the U.S. Representative to the United Nations introduced
into the General Assembly a draft seabed treaty "working paper" incorporating this provision. This draft treaty would also establish an International Seabed Authority (ISA) to manage and control development beyond the continental margin. The adjacent coastal country would act as
trustee for the international community in managing the development of
the continental slope and rise, the area between 200 meters and the outer
limit of the continental margin, a point at which the average water depth
is 4,000 meters (13,124 feet). (See Figure 40.)

At the same 1970 General Assembly session, a "Declaration of Prin-
ciples Governing the Sea-Bed and Ocean Floor, and the Subsoil Thereof,
beyond the Limits of National Jurisdiction" was adopted by a vote of 108
to 0 with 14 abstentions. The limits of national jurisdiction are not defined, but the Declaration does affirm that there is a limit and that the
area beyond it is to be established as an international regime.

The U.S. Congress appears to favor a policy different from that of the
Administration. There appears to be support in the Congress for a policy
which would extend national control beyond the 200 meter isobath. This
is a policy favored also by, among others, the National Petroleum Council,
the American Petroleum Institute, the American Bar Association, and the
American Branch of the International Law Association. In 1970, the Senate's Special Subcommittee on the Outer Continental Shelf adopted in its
entirety the wide-shelf interpretation agreed upon by the American Branch
of the International Law Association. This position holds that "rights
under the 1958 Geneva Convention on the Continental Shelf extend to
the limit of exploitability existing at any given time within an ultimate
limit of adjacency which would encompass the entire continental margin."[10]

A third approach is to extend national jurisdiction over adjacent *ocean
space* thereby amalgamating "the various aspects of control over surface,
water column, seabed and subsoil."[11] This approach was initially limited
to a few west coast Latin American governments which claimed exclusive
jurisdiction over adjacent ocean areas extending seaward as far as 200

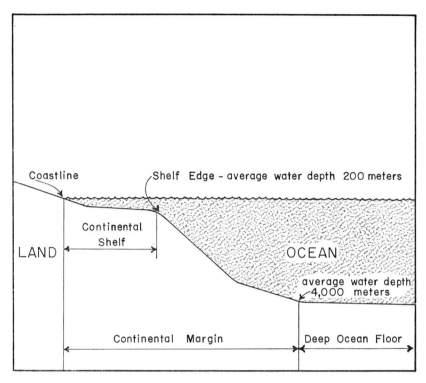

Fig. 40. Schematic Representation of Seabed and Ocean Floor

miles. But a growing number of coastal nations are now making these claims, in part it seems in response to the expanding seabed claims being made by technologically advanced countries. This led Malta to submit a draft ocean space treaty to the UN in 1971. This treaty would extend the jurisdiction of a coastal state to "a belt of ocean space adjacent to its coast, the breadth of which is 200 nautical miles."[12]

The UN has responded to the continuation of these unilateral claims by adopting, at the 1969 annual session of the General Assembly, a resolution calling for a moratorium on seabed and ocean floor exploitation. Governments were admonished to refrain from exploiting the resources of the seabed beyond the limits of national jurisdiction until an international regime is established to manage and control the development of these resources.

As the 1971 Malta ocean space draft treaty indicates, the seabed issues are only a part of a larger set of interrelated ocean issues, almost all of which involve the extent to which national jurisdiction can be extended to areas formerly considered beyond national jurisdiction. These issues are now so pressing that, as mentioned earlier, a UN-sponsored LOS Conference was scheduled for 1973 (now rescheduled for 1974). The seabed issues that will receive priority treatment at the Conference include defining the areas of the seabed to be under the exclusive national jurisdiction of coastal states, defining and establishing an international regime, and proposing appropriate international machinery for controlling and managing the exploitation of the resources located within the international regime.

WHAT ARE THE ALTERNATIVES?

A number of private groups as well as many of the governments to be represented at the 1974 Conference have proposed several alternative policies. For the shelf, two basic positions are either (1) to retain the 1958 definition and clarify its interpretation, or (2) to draft a new definition fixing the outer limit of national jurisdiction at some specific water depth or distance from shore. And for the deep seabed, the basic positions are either (1) to permit open exploration and exploitation so long as these activities do not interfere with other freedoms of the high seas, or (2) to establish an international regime and an international authority to manage and control development of resources in this area.

ASSESSMENT OF ALTERNATIVES

In the United States, variations of these alternatives are promoted as a means for achieving several important national ocean policy objectives, including providing for national security, insuring access to and the development of subsea energy and mineral resources, protecting the marine environment and adjacent coastal zones, and protecting the rights of a variety of present users.

The National Petroleum Council (NPC) has made the most detailed argument in support of retaining the 1958 definition. In its March, 1969, report on *Petroleum Resources Under the Ocean Floor*, NPC contends that the 1958 definition already provides for exclusive national jurisdiction "over the natural resources of the sea bottom . . . out to the edge of the submerged continent, irrespective of depth of water or distance from shore."[13] NPC goes on to argue that:

> it is the duty of the U.S. Government to assert these rights and to maintain them in full. Acceptance of any lesser result would be the giving away of rights already confirmed to this Nation by the Convention on the Continental Shelf and a giving away of potential resources essential to the future welfare and security of the country.[14]

As for the deep seabed, NPC proposes leaving the development of these resources open, "provided there is no unjustifiable interference with other freedoms of the high seas including navigation, fishing, and research."[15] Companion bills in the House and Senate (S. 2801 and H.R. 13076) formally adopt this view for hard mineral resources but attempt to provide a means for protecting the investment of U.S. nationals who might engage in mining these resources. Both bills would establish a national licensing system and an international registry clearing house as means for avoiding national and international claim-jumping.

In contrast to the NPC proposals, the draft treaty or working papers introduced by the Administration into the General Assembly of the United Nations would: (1) fix the outer limit of national jurisdiction at 200 meters, (2) have the adjacent coastal nation act as trustee for the international community in the area between 200 meters and the outer edge of the continental margin, and (3) establish an international authority to manage and control the exploration and exploitation of deep ocean resources.

These two basic alternatives differ most fundamentally on the issues of: to what extent coastal nations will exercise exclusive jurisdiction over adjacent submarine areas, and the desirability of having an international organization exercise jurisdiction over some portion of the seabed. Clearly the proposal exemplified by the NPC report is based on the assumption that our national policy should be to maximize the role of governments and avoid establishing an international organization. It is not at all clear that this policy alternative is or can be made attractive to a majority of governments.

From one point of view, dealing with a known, whether it be the U.S. government or the government of some other coastal nation, has obvious appeal. For the U.S., maximizing the extent of exclusive national jurisdiction would seem to maximize security of investment, national security, and environmental protection as well as provide the greatest possible insurance that seabed energy and other mineral resources will be developed and made available. On the other hand, if a new international organization were to be established, potential developers would be dealing with an unknown and the U.S. could be less confident of achieving its fundamental ocean policy goals.

It should be recalled that the Administration's proposal was in part a response to the issues raised by Ambassador Pardo in 1967. He and several of his developing-nations colleagues have argued that the benefits derived from the exploitation of resources located outside national jurisdiction should be used to benefit the entire international community, and they would use the benefits derived from the exploitation of these resources to promote the economic development of the developing nations. This position is particularly appealing to those countries which are landlocked.

While the governments of the developing nations are by no means single-minded, it seems unlikely that any seabed proposal not providing tangible benefits for their development will receive their support. The Administration proposal seems to accept this as a fact of international life and apparently seeks an accommodation which would satisfy this interest while giving coastal states an important role out to the 400-meter isobath.

Of course, it is not at all clear that developers would find governments, particularly those of new, non-western, frequently politically unstable, developing countries, any easier to work with than an international organization. Indeed, relations among international oil companies and oil-producing countries have been undergoing important changes—as, for example, with Libya, Ecuador, and Venezuela as well as with the Organization of Oil Producing and Exporting Countries (OPEC). The international oil companies, with their interest groups and associations, are beginning to show signs of recognizing that extended national jurisdiction may not be in the industry's best interest.

The cost of pressing for an NPC-like interpretation could be high, particularly if no new rule were adopted at the 1974 LOS Conference. To force the issue on these terms might well be to choose between an international regime and a disorganized system of unilateral actions: that is, not gaining agreement on the clear meaning of the provisions of the 1958 Convention *or* agreement on new, less ambiguous rules would likely result in a chaotic system within which individual governments assumed a right to act unilaterally. The most fundamental need from everyone's point of view is some kind of coordinated international system. (In his 1973 Energy Message, President Nixon announced that the Department of the Interior will begin in 1974 to lease tracts beyond the 200-meter isobath. However, as indicated in his 1973 Ocean Policy Message, these leases would be subject to any international regime which might be agreed upon.)

As we have indicated, two additional considerations affect choosing from among available policy options: a growing concern for the quality of the global environment and the inter-relatedness of a constellation of ocean policy issues of which mineral resources is only one.

Both the Nixon Administration's draft seabed convention and the Declaration issued following the Stockholm Conference on the Human Environment reflect a growing worldwide environmental concern. This is particularly true for the marine environment. The Administration's draft convention includes the requirement that all activities within the area under an international authority "shall be conducted with strict and adequate safeguards for the protection of human life and safety and of the marine environment."[16]

At Stockholm the view was that since most of the world's oceans are the common heritage of mankind, marine pollution is an international problem. Consequently, the Conference devoted much attention to the oceans, and urged several specific programs, including extensive monitoring by intergovernmental international organizations. And the Declaration issued by the Conference, since supported in the 27th General Assembly, calls for establishing a single international organization to lead and coordinate international environmental activities. More recently, concern for the marine environment led to an ocean-dumping agreement which singled out heavy-grade oils to be included on a dumping blacklist. In November, 1972, representatives of 91 governments, including all the major maritime powers, signed this agreement.

In short, the resolution of jurisdictional problems associated with marine resources will have to take into account this widespread concern for the quality of the global environment. And the pressures for having international organizations involved in monitoring and oversight functions are in effect supportive of those to establish an international seabed authority.

A final consideration is that the resolution of the mineral resources issue is closely related to achieving agreements on territorial sea, contiguous zones, transit rights, and living resources issues. The width of territorial seas that may be claimed, the effects of those claims on freedom of transit, and the special dependence of some countries on living resources in extended ocean areas adjacent to their coasts are currently problem areas also. Agreement on a seabed minerals policy is highly unlikely unless interests in these areas also are accommodated.

We have not discussed the ocean space proposal which would confront the inter-relatedness of a variety of surface, water column, living resources, and mineral resource problems by claiming extended national jurisdiction to include the entire area. At the present time, extending the coastal state's sovereign rights to 200 miles or even to a more modest 40 miles, as proposed by some governments, seems unlikely to be acceptable to most governments. This kind of solution would adversely affect the interests of a variety of users of ocean space. For example, large areas of the ocean would or could be denied to military vessels, the use of international maritime routes and passages could be affected, and fishermen could be denied their traditional fishing grounds.

Desirable Changes   While it would be desirable to gain agreement on the Administration's proposal, it seems unlikely that this proposal will now satisfy most governments. An attempt should be made to fix the outer limit of national jurisdiction and establish an international authority to manage and control the development of seabed resources beyond this fixed limit. Other ocean space interests should be taken into account, including fixing an outer limit for territorial sea and contiguous zone claims and providing for the recognition of the special interest of some coastal states in living resources in extended adjacent ocean areas.

1. U.S., Department of Transportation, Coast Guard, *Answers to Questions and Policy Issues Related to Overview Hearings on the Outer Continental Shelf Lands Act, Held by the Senate Committee on Interior and Insular Affairs, Pursuant to S. Res. 45, March, 1972*, pp. 19–26.

2. *Oil and Gas Journal*, 70 (December 4, 1972), p. 40.

3. These standards are established by the Water Quality Control Plan for California.

4. Convention on the Continental Shelf, Article 1. Parties to the Convention are listed in U.S., Department of State, *Treaties in Force on January 1, 1972* (Washington: Government Printing Office, 1972), pp. 332–33.

5. Convention on the Continental Shelf, Article 2.

6. *International Legal Materials* (1969), pp. 340–433.

7. *Ibid.*, pp. 364–65.

8. Convention on the Continental Shelf, Article 2.7.

9. Cited by National Petroleum Council, *Petroleum Resources under the Ocean Floor; Supplemental Report* (Washington: NPC, 1971), pp. 9–10.

10. U.S., Congress, Senate, Committee on Interior and Insular Affairs, *Outer Continental Shelf*, Report of the Special Subcommittee on the Outer Continental Shelf, 91st Cong., 2d Sess., December 21, 1970.

11. Wolfgang Friedmann, Oliver J. Lissitzyn, and Richard C. Pugh, *International Law, Cases and Materials, 1972 Supplement* (St. Paul: West Publishing Co., 1972), p. 92.

12. *Ibid.*

13. National Petroleum Council, *Petroleum Resources under the Ocean Floor* (Washington: NPC, 1969), p. 70.

14. *Ibid.*

15. *Ibid.*, p. 76.

16. Draft United Nations Convention on the International Seabed Areas, Article 9, August 3, 1970.

Part Four

A Comparison and Recommendations

XI. OCS in Perspective

THE CENTRAL energy supply question for the next 15 years is what portion of total United States energy demand will be met by domestic oil and gas. For a number of reasons, it is likely that the OCS will become increasingly important as a domestic source of these resources. Some of the broad social impacts associated with OCS development have been discussed in previous chapters, particularly Chapters VI through X. These impacts have been singled out because of their significance to major policy issues analyzed in this study. There are, of course, other impacts, and one of the purposes of the first part of this chapter is to identify and categorize additional impacts of OCS development in order to indicate their range and complexity.

Although this study has focused exclusively on the OCS, policy makers choosing among alternative petroleum sources have to make comparisons. For example, they have to compare the costs and benefits of alternatives for increasing domestic production and increasing imports if these domestic sources are not developed. In the second part of this chapter, three alternatives—the OCS, Alaska (the North Slope via TAPS*), and imports—will be compared. Since the latter two sources have not been assessed in this study, data on their broad social consequences were obtained from secondary sources, including the analyses of alternatives published by the Department of the Interior in a number of environmental impact statements.

OCS IMPACTS

As mentioned in Chapter II, the impacts of OCS development were initially identified by employing a matrix constructed of social and technology factors axes. Impacts which were identified can be divided into five categories: Economics, Environment, National Security, Multiple Use, and Government Management.

A number of variables contribute to the kind and magnitude of the impacts of OCS technologies. These variables include the following:

1. When will development take place?
2. Where will development be located, for example, geographical region, water depth, and distance from shore?

---

*TAPS is the trans-Alaska pipeline system for transporting oil by pipeline from the North Slope to Valdez and from there to the West Coast by tanker.

3. What will the rate of development be?

4. What specific technologies will be employed, for example, surface actuated subsurface safety valves, subsea completions, and will best available technologies be used?

5. What economic, administrative, and regulatory policies will be used, for example, the role of USGS, price of gas, and will changes be made in those policies?

The following impacts can be anticipated:

ECONOMICS

1. *National Income.* Each million barrels per day of domestic production can reduce the balance of payments deficit by approximately 1.5 billion dollars per year, depending on the price of foreign oil. Spent domestically, these dollars can have a substantial multiplier effect. On the other hand, foreign outlays can result in second round reinvestment in U.S. industries. (Chapter XI)*

2. *Federal Income.* Based on a price of $3.45 per barrel, each one million barrels per day of production will contribute a royalty of 210 million dollars annually to the federal treasury. (Recent and anticipated increases in the price of crude will substantially increase this revenue.) (Chapter IX)

3. *Regional Economics.* One of the most important regional economic benefits of offshore oil development can be the reduction of spending for foreign oil. (Chapter XI)

4. *Industry Income.* Offshore petroleum has apparently been generating a return of 4 to 7 percent. The return on individual leases apparently has been as high as 10 percent. Although industry now reports a deficit in OCS operations, substantial profits should accrue over the 10- to 20-year payout time. (Chapter III)

5. *Regional Employment.* Effects on employment are dependent upon the level of regional unemployment, manpower needs, and the availability of trained personnel. The most significant long-term effects may be from refineries or from the multiplier effect of payrolls. (Chapter XI)

6. *Capital Requirements.* The anticipated increase in the pace of leasing and movement to deeper water and more hazardous environments would increase industry's need for capital, possibly from outside sources or increased profits. (Chapters III, IV, and IX)

7. *Liability.* The unlimited liability of lessees has become a risk which tends to restrict widespread participation in OCS development to major oil companies. (Chapter IX)

*Reference should be made to chapters for source and a more extensive discussion.

8. *Role of Majors.* Owing to capital needs, liability, and technological complexity, the major oil companies will continue to dominate OCS development. (Chapter IV)

9. *Joint Ventures.* Combinations of major oil companies, gas companies, and independents may increase the variety of participants in OCS lease sales. (Chapter IV)

ENVIRONMENT

10. *Oil Spills.* Despite improved technology and possibly a lower accident rate, the anticipated expansion of OCS development will likely result in more accidents. Hazardous environments may contribute to this risk. (Chapter VI and Appendix B)

11. *Susceptible Species.* Certain species, such as birds, barnacles, and marine flowering plants will be adversely affected by oil spills. Most marine species seem relatively unaffected by crude oil; however, with more widespread OCS development, more species may be affected.

12. *Sensitive Environments.* Certain habitats and biological communities are likely to be more adversely affected than are others. Shallow water, Arctic, and tropical communities may be most adversely affected. (Chapter VII)

13. *Chronic Pollution.* As yet the long-term and possibly synergistic effects of chronic pollution on the marine environment cannot be predicted. Discharges do result in a decline in some species in the immediate vicinity of the platforms. (Chapter VII)

14. *Marsh and Nearshore Effects.* Dredging and channelization can adversely affect shallow water habitats such as marshes that are nursery grounds for important species. (Chapter VII)

NATIONAL SECURITY

15. *National Security.* Offshore oil and gas provide a domestic supply that is considered by many to be more secure than imports or TAPS. This supply could decrease reliance on foreign countries. (Chapter XI)

MULTIPLE USE

16. *Land Use.* On land, OCS development requires coastal staging areas for logistic support, pipelines, and processing facilities. (Chapter IX)

    a. *Staging Areas.* Harbors will be needed as staging areas for construction and production operations.

    b. *Pipeline Access.* Pipeline access and processing facilities will require coastal space.

c. *Refineries*. It would be economically attractive to locate refineries where offshore oil and a sales market coincide. Although refineries occupy several hundred acres, appearance and odor can increase their area of impact.

17. *Marine Traffic*. Increasing numbers of surface and subsurface fixed structures may interfere with marine traffic. (Chapter XI)

18. *Commercial Fisheries*. Development may interfere with commercial fishing operations. However, a decrease in total annual catch is not likely. (Chapter XI)

19. *Sports Fishing*. Although structures concentrate certain sports fish, an increase in the quantity of sports fish in a wide area has not been convincingly documented. (Chapter VII)

20. *Esthetics*. Development may result in unsightly structures on land and in the water. In a number of locations, however, development will be out of sight of land. (Chapter IX)

21. *Recreation*. Development may adversely affect tourism and recreational use of certain areas. Oil spills, such as the Santa Barbara spill, have adversely affected tourism over the short term. (Chapter XI)

GOVERNMENT MANAGEMENT

22. *Jurisdiction*. Development of OCS resources accentuates a number of jurisdictional disputes. (Chapter X)

a. *International*. Unilateral development of OCS areas beyond the 200-meter isobath may impede the settlement of ocean seabed jurisdictional issues and result in an unstable investment environment.

b. *State-Federal*. A number of states have jurisdictional claims beyond 3 miles which are likely to result in continuing conflict. Elements of these jurisdictional issues include, for example, who sets standards, enforces regulations, and receives bonuses and/or royalties.

c. *Local Government*. Local government policies can impede or hasten development on adjacent federal lands. This is especially true in obtaining zoning changes or construction permits.

23. *Planning*. Increased development will require improved cooperation and coordination in planning by government agencies.

24. *Resource Conservation*. Government policies, prices, and technology can affect the extent of gas flaring and venting. With increase in depth and distance from shore, only the larger oil and gas fields can be developed at anticipated price levels. (Chapter IX)

25. *Public Confidence*. Perceptions of government-industry conflicts

of interest, lack of clear agency responsibilities within government, and inadequate agency cooperation generate a reduced level of public confidence and acceptance of leasing initiatives. (Chapter IV)

26. *Public Participation.* Public participation in the administration of OCS operations has been greatly enhanced by the 102 statement process. It is likely that this public participation will continue. (Chapter IV)

27. *Expansion of Management Resources.* Increases in OCS development will call for increased budget and personnel in a variety of government agencies, particularly USGS, in order to acquire additional information and to perform adequate regulatory functions. (Chapter IX)

COMPARISON OF OCS WITH TAPS AND IMPORTS

OCS development takes place within a larger energy supply context and, as previously indicated, policy-makers must compare OCS oil and gas operations to other energy alternatives. The range of energy needs and sources of supply were discussed in Chapter I. On the basis of that discussion, it appears that although a number of energy sources may be utilized in the future, oil and gas will be called upon to provide the bulk of the nation's near-term energy needs. In the following sections, these sources of supply are discussed and the impacts likely to flow from their development compared.

PETROLEUM SOURCES

There are only four domestic areas from which it might be possible to increase domestic oil and gas production to satisfy anticipated 1985 demand levels.[1] These include: (1) onshore production in the lower 48 states, (2) offshore production in state waters, (3) Alaskan North Slope production, and (4) production on the OCS. Any demand which cannot be satisfied by the combination of these four sources will have to be satisfied with imports of oil and gas.

Prospects for major increases in onshore oil and gas production in the lower 48 states are viewed as doubtful in 1985 unless there are major increases in price.[2] Assuming maximum feasible domestic production in 1985, approximately 60 percent of domestic oil will be produced onshore.

Onshore gas production will be between 9.6 and 17.1 trillion cubic feet per year.[3] A substantial portion of the oil produced onshore will be as a result of secondary and tertiary recovery processes being used in fields that are already producing.

Petroleum is already being produced in state waters off Alaska, California, Louisiana, and Texas. Several other state offshore areas are promising;

however, the acreage still available is less than 10 percent of total offshore acreage to the 200-meter (656 feet) water depth.[4] Therefore, it is unlikely that significantly larger quantities of petroleum will be produced on state offshore leases by 1985.

Maximum offshore oil production for 1985 is projected to be about 20 percent of domestic production, or 2 to 2.6 million barrels per day.[5] This rate of production assumes development of both the Atlantic and Pacific OCS.[6] Offshore natural gas production is expected to be between 3.6 and 9.1 trillion cubic feet per year, most of which will probably come from the gas-rich Gulf Coast OCS. This will amount to about 30 percent of domestic gas production.[7]

If the trans-Alaska pipeline system (TAPS) is constructed, the Alaskan North Slope could also contribute up to 20 percent of domestic oil production in 1985.[8] In the event TAPS is not built, another delivery system through Canada is likely to be developed.[9] The trans-Canada pipeline will not be evaluated here, but it should be noted that it is attractive because it avoids most marine impacts.

As for natural gas, if a pipeline from the North Slope is built, Alaska can provide between 1.7 and 4.4 trillion cubic feet of natural gas per year.[10] The two principal alternatives which have been mentioned are trans-Canada and trans-Alaska. The latter would require liquification and trans-shipment by tanker.

Given the most conservative demand estimates and the most optimistic estimates of domestic supply, foreign petroleum imports will still be required. Indications are that resources available for imports will be adequate to meet whatever demand is required through 1985. However, this does not insure that these resources will be available to the U.S. at either economic or social costs the country is willing to pay.

METHOD OF COMPARISON

In the following sections, the impacts of these three alternatives—OCS, TAPS, and imports—will be considered and compared. These impacts have been separated into four areas: (1) Economic, (2) Environmental, (3) National Security, and (4) Multiple Use.

To structure this comparison, the impacts to be compared are those to be anticipated if each of the three sources supplied 2 million barrels of oil per day. This comparison is an abstraction in two respects. First, the level of oil imports will continue to be set to satisfy the difference between domestic supply and demand; thus imports will actually be at a level well above 2 million barrels of oil per day. Our comparison, therefore, does not include the full magnitude of impacts from imported oil, but only for a 2 million barrel/day increment which could alternatively be provided from either the OCS or from Alaska via TAPS. Second, this comparison does not consider gas supply alternatives. Since the OCS has extensive gas resources and production, and North Slope and imported gas can only be provided at somewhat higher prices, this omission will tend to present the OCS less favorably than is the actual situation.

ECONOMIC IMPACTS

The summary comparison presented here highlights the major points in the following categories: consumer costs, balance of trade, government revenues, and regional economic impacts.

Consumer Costs

Since imports are currently cheaper than domestic oil, import restrictions force consumers to pay more for oil. These higher costs hit hardest at lower economic groups since they spend a proportionately larger share of their income on energy. As an indication of the magnitude of this impact, a price increase of 25 cents per barrel of crude, if passed on to the consumer, would result in price increases from one-half to one cent per gallon for gas and other fuels.[11]

However, the price differential between foreign and domestic oil is not as large as it once was, and the difference has declined rapidly over the past few years. Although many analysts expect foreign oil to continue to be cheaper than domestic, recent actions by OPEC countries clearly indicate that there is no guarantee that this will continue to be so. In fact, reports as recent as March, 1973, indicate that some imports are coming in at higher prices than domestic.[12] A recent analysis in *Oil and Gas Journal* showed that the 1972 landed price of four typical foreign crudes ranged from $1.90 per barrel to $2.85 per barrel and averaged $2.50 per barrel.[13] This analysis also showed that since 1969, the price of these four crude oils had increased an average of 38 percent. The economic effects on consumers of these changed relationships, between domestic and imported crude, are unclear. The ultimate price of petroleum products is influenced by such a complex set of variables that, by itself, the source of supply is likely to have only a minimal effect.[14]

Balance of Trade

One of the most significant impacts of importing oil is on the balance of trade. Using NPC's estimated (weighted average) price of $4.14 (in 1970 constant dollars) for each barrel of imported oil, importing 2 million barrels of oil per day would cost $3.02 billion per year.[15] This excludes second round effects.

Other concerns include the subsequent use of these large dollar outflows being experienced and the difficulty in obtaining domestic refinery sites. With imports, there is a strong tendency to locate refineries outside the U.S. and import refined products. Exporting refining capacity not only intensifies balance-of-trade problems, but also raises serious environmental and national security issues, both of which are discussed below.

Government Revenues

Federal revenues derived from OCS development consist primarily of lease bonuses and royalties, although rentals, minimum royalties, and shut-in payments contribute a small fraction of the total income. Royalty payments have been one-sixth of the production value. As noted earlier, at a price of $3.45 per barrel, each one million barrels per day production will contribute $210 million annually to the federal treasury.

Lease revenue depends on the number, size, and location of lease sales during the year. For example, in 1972 Gulf of Mexico lease sales, the average bonus bid was $2,770 per acre. (This average bid per acre during 1972 was a substantial increase over previous years, as shown in the section on economics in Chapter III.) Using this average and projecting two lease sales of 75 tracts (5,760 acres each) per year, the annual bonus revenue would be $2.38 billion. This amount could either increase or decrease substantially depending on a number of factors such as crude prices and water depths which might affect the economics of any given lease sale.

Another way to estimate federal revenues is on a per unit of production basis. As shown in the section on economics in Chapter III, bonuses have averaged $.27 per barrel of reserves added. (This figure has probably increased because of substantially increasing per acre bids during the past several lease sales.) Combining this with a royalty of $.57 per barrel, total revenue would be $.84 per barrel produced. Thus, each one million barrels per day of production adds $307 million in federal revenues. Of course, this calculation doesn't correspond with the actual money flows since the bonuses are received at the time of the lease sale and not on a unit of production basis.

The state of Alaska, for example, received $900 million in bonuses for the North Slope and is expected to receive royalty and tax revenue totaling $300 million per year when production reaches 2 million barrels per day.[16]

Federal revenues which will accrue from the new import system will depend on the license fee. This fee is adjustable by the President, and may be changed as policy requires.

Regional Economic Impacts

OCS: It has been estimated that 67,000 persons in south Louisiana depend directly on the offshore oil industry for employment.[17] This includes both state and federal operations. If OCS operations are increased or begun in a new area, the impact will depend on the existing economic base and level of industrial development. For the East Coast, the incremental economic impact, while beneficial, would probably not be very significant because of the existing substantial industrial base.

An assessment of the economic impact of oil and gas development in the offshore areas of Canada's East Coast concluded that there would be no major regional impact on employment.[18] However, this study considered only jobs directly related to oil exploration, construction, and production activities, and did not include employment in the secondary or service sectors of the economy which are affected by how industrial employees spend their wages. In addition, the study pointed out that reducing the region's dependence on imports could attract industrial investment totally unrelated to the oil and gas industry.

The Georges Bank study, conducted by M.I.T.'s Offshore Oil Task Group, concluded that the value of an offshore oil find to a region depends largely on whether the federal government or the region receives lease and royalty payments.[19] The value of a gas find depends on who receives lease and royalty payments and whether or not gas prices are deregulated.[20]

TAPS: The impact of TAPS on the Alaskan economy can be summarized by the following points:

(1) It will have a major impact on employment—20,000 to 30,000 workers over a three-year period—heavily concentrated in specific job sectors and regions. However, it is expected that there will be little effect on the unemployment rate owing to a high rate of influx of workers with skill levels higher than those currently employed in the region.

(2) It will create a significant temporary growth in state personal income. However, it is also probable that it will increase prices and the cost of living in Alaska.

(3) After TAPS is constructed, the Alaskan economy may require a significant downward adjustment.

(4) Revenues paid directly to the state government could have a substantial impact, but this depends directly upon the policies and actions of the state.[21]

In addition, TAPS will require the construction of 33 tankers in U.S. shipyards. (The Merchant Marine Act of 1920, known as the Jones Act, requires that cargoes shipped between ports in the United States be carried in American ships.) This will generate substantial employment and income.[22] About $150 million will be spent upgrading U.S. shipyards for this construction and $1.1 billion will be spent for the ships themselves. The Maritime Administration estimates that this construction will generate 73,480 man-years of labor in shipyards and supporting industries and that fleet maintenance will generate 770 man-years of employment annually.[23]

Imports: The single most important factor in determining how a region's available income for other goods and services is affected by imports is the amount the region must pay for foreign oil.[24] Presumably reducing imports would make more income available for purchasing other goods and services within the region.

Summary of Economic Impacts

In comparing the overall economic trade-offs between OCS and foreign oil, it is instructive to subtract from the domestic price, say $3.45 per barrel, the $.84 per barrel that has been paid directly to the federal government. Comparing the remaining $2.61 per barrel with the price of foreign oil at $2.50 per barrel shows that, aside from balance of trade impacts, there is little difference in real economic costs to the U.S. economy between the two. (As mentioned earlier in this chapter, recent and anticipated changes in the price of foreign or domestic oil may alter these differences.)

When the Council of Economic Advisors made a comparison of TAPS and imports for Interior, they found an economic advantage for TAPS. Their analysis was based on a resource cost of $1.10 to $1.30 per barrel as compared to $2.80 per barrel for imports.[25]

Table 13. Sources and Location of Potential Spills and Discharges

Sources	Location
	TAPS
Drilling and production	North Slope Alaskan tundra
On-land pipelines	Alaskan tundra and forest
Tanker loading	Valdez Harbor, Prince William Sound
Tanker shipment	West Coast of North America
Tanker unloading	Washington & California inland waters
	OCS
Drilling and production	Ocean & coastal water adjacent to U.S.
Pipelines	Ocean, coasts, bays, and marshes
	IMPORTS
Drilling, production and loading	Worldwide
Pipelines to U.S.	Canada and Mexico
Tanker shipment	Ocean & coastal areas
Tanker unloading	Inland water of West, Gulf & East Coasts

When other economic advantages of domestic oil are considered, such as balance of trade and regional economic effects, at current prices, foreign oil shows no economic advantage and probably an economic disadvantage when compared with OCS or TAPS oil.

ENVIRONMENTAL IMPACTS

The impact of oil spills and discharges depends largely on what is spilled, where, in what amounts, during what season. In this section, sources and probable areas of exposure for the OCS, TAPS, and imports are identified. Estimates are also made of how much oil is likely to be spilled for each option and the likely biological effects.

Spill Sources and Rates

Potential oil spill sources and locations are listed in Table 13. The quantities of oil likely to be spilled in the ocean worldwide and adjacent to the U.S. are summarized in Table 14. These data are drawn from a more detailed discussion presented in Appendix B. Figures 41, 42, and 43 map possible oil spill sources and coastlines within 50 to 100 miles of a possible spill location.[26]

OCS: An eight-year average of major oil spills from 1964–1971 indicates that approximately 0.014 percent of oil produced offshore will be spilled into the ocean from a variety of accidents. (See Appendix B.) At a rate of 2 million barrels per day, OCS production would result in an average daily loss of 280 barrels of oil. Discharge from both minor spills and waste water treatment has been 0.0035 percent or 70 barrels per day. (See Appendix B.) Most losses result from activities conducted in coastal waters; however, some discharges occur where processing takes place onshore and in bays or estuaries as a result of pipeline failures.

OCS production is anticipated in a number of continental shelf locations

Table 14. Quantities of Potential Oil Spills and Discharges

Source	Major accidents	Minor and moderate spills	Ballast or waste water treatment	Total
OCS	280	52	18	350
TAPS	68–384	6	26–540	100–930
Imports, U.S. waters	68	3	0	71
Worldwide waters	384	6	540	930

Note: This table is based on barrels/day for 2,000,000 barrels/day produced and transported. See Appendix B.

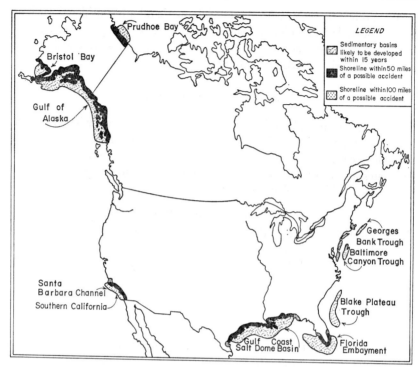

**Fig. 41. OCS Areas Likely To Be Developed and Coastlines
Possibly Affected in Event of an Oil Spill**

where potential petroleum-bearing sediment accumulations are found. As
indicated in Figure 41, this includes areas on the Atlantic Coast adjacent to
New England, New Jersey, North Carolina, and Florida. All of these locations are 30 or more miles offshore. Areas in the Gulf of Mexico also remain
to be developed as do offshore areas along southern California and in the
Gulf of Alaska. It is also possible that certain nearshore areas north of the
Aleutian Islands and in Prudhoe Bay could be developed by 1985.

TAPS: The discussion of the TAPS alternative assumes that the pipeline
will extend from Prudhoe Bay, across the Brooks and Alaskan ranges, then
to Valdez on Prince William Sound (Figure 42). Alternative land pipeline
routes, such as the trans-Canada pipeline, offer an entirely different blend
of possible consequences and specifically eliminate most marine impacts.[27]

Because of the extremely hazardous environment, the possibility of pipeline leaks or ruptures is probably greater with TAPS than for most pipelines in North America. Potential problems include earthquakes, slope

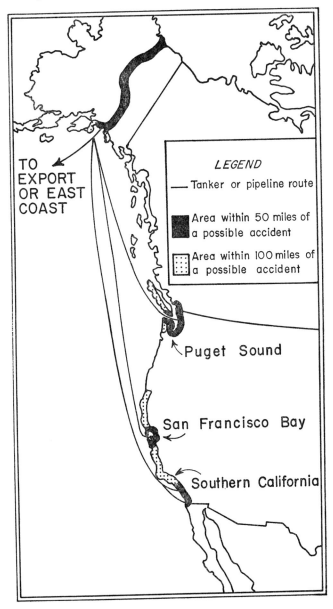

Fig. 42. Areas Possibly Affected in Event of an Oil Spill from TAPS

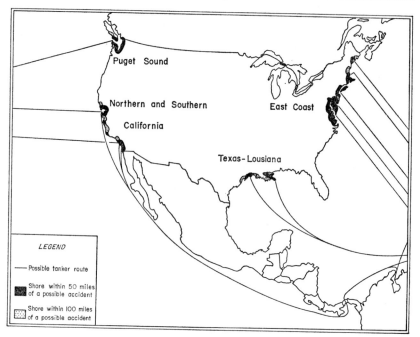

Fig. 43. Areas Possibly Affected in Event of an Oil Spill from Tanker Imports

failures, permafrost instability, stream bed erosion, and equipment failure. Some twenty-five major streams will be exposed since the pipeline will cross over them. Interior estimates that the maximum spill size at any location would be 65,000 barrels.

Discharges into Valdez Harbor from shore facilities or from several types of tanker losses could result in marine impacts. Daily discharges from ballast handling may range from as high as 540 barrels to as low as 26 barrels. The high estimate is based on using only load-on-top (LOT) operations; the low estimate is based on treating water discharged at Valdez to 20 parts per million of oil.[28] Discharges during transfer operations are expected to be between 1 and 6 barrels per day distributed over five harbors—Valdez, Seattle, San Francisco, Los Angeles, and San Diego.[29]

Marine casualties resulting from collisions, groundings, or storm damage could result in spills as large as 1.8 million barrels, the volume of the largest TAPS tankers.[30] Most of the tankers are to be much smaller than this, however. Three accident analysis models included in the TAPS environmental impact statement indicated an average of about one major tanker accident each year. Worldwide tanker accident data indicate that an average of 384 barrels might be spilled for each 2 million barrels transported. However, an analysis of casualties in U.S. waters indicates that only about 68 barrels per day would be spilled.

Overall, TAPS may be expected to release an average of 100 to 930 barrels of oil per day into the marine environment. (See Appendix B.)

Imports: Spill projections for imports are similar to those for the tanker system of TAPS. It is expected that two-thirds of the imports will be landed in Gulf Coast harbors and one-third in the New York area.[31] (See Figure 43.) Ballast will be discharged into foreign waters where the oil is to be loaded and would represent a significant contribution to world ocean pollution. The absolute quantities discharged would depend, of course, upon the treatment facilities or oil loading methods employed.

Combining transfer operation losses—6 barrels per day—and an average accident rate for tankers based upon models outlined in Appendix B, the loss of oil adjacent to U.S. waters would average about 71 barrels per day. As with TAPS, about three-quarters of the oil losses occur in coastal waters. Total marine pollution is also increased from spills from offshore production in other countries.

Prior to delivery to marketing centers, both TAPS and OCS pipelines transport only crude oil. Imports, however, involve shipments of crude and a variety of refinery products, including gasoline, kerosene, and residual fuel oil. During 1972, residual fuel oil accounted for 37 percent and crude oil 47 percent of maritime imports.[32] Although the more volatile petroleum products are less than 16 percent of current imports, their proportion is expected to increase in the future, owing primarily to local resistance to refinery construction in the U.S. and cost advantages which industry obtains by locating its refineries outside the U.S.

Biological Consequences

As indicated in Chapter VII, the biological consequences of these patterns of spills and discharges are difficult to predict. It should be emphasized that a number of variables affect the amount of oil lost and that little is known about the effects of these losses, especially in areas such as the Alaskan tundra and Prince William Sound.

Biotic Regions

As noted earlier in Chapter VII, biological impacts differ in various biotic provinces. In colder climates, the rate of biodegradation in oil dissipation is uncertain at this time; even in warm climates, there is evidence that certain fractions of hydrocarbons accumulate, either on the ocean surface or in bottom sediments.[33] In Pacific Coast areas north of Santa Barbara, the biota has not been exposed to chronic natural pollution and most north Pacific areas are relatively unpolluted. Recent studies imply that organisms in unpolluted locations would suffer more than, for example, organisms exposed to Union Oil's blowout in the Santa Barbara Channel.[34]

Only a limited amount of the information required for an accurate assessment of the oil spill impacts on certain biotic provinces is available. (Some oil pollution problems in specific geographic localities are summarized in Appendix D.) Environmental impact statements for OCS development in the Gulf of Mexico and for TAPS have cataloged possible consequences for some species and some of this information is summarized in Table 15. It is clear that a more comprehensive approach including the assessment of impacts on all U.S. coastal living resources is desirable.

Refined Products: Perhaps the greatest contrast between the OCS, TAPS, and imports is that 53 percent of marine transported petroleum imports are residual fuel oil and other refined products. Widespread destruction of aquatic life has been documented in spills involving fuel oil spills of a variety of types. Organism recovery has been slow, requiring as much as two or three years following the spill.[35] To the extent that domestic sources are refined and then trans-shipped by coastal barge or tanker, the difference in alternatives is minimized.

On-land Effects: Biological effects of crude oil on land are well documented. A variety of findings were reviewed by Interior and these point to the almost complete destruction of herbaceous and grassy plants which come in contact with crude oil.[36] In addition, these effects persist for three or more years. Clean-up of oil contaminated areas is usually impossible without destroying plant life. Studies by Alyeska (this is the acronym used to identify the corporate entity which will operate TAPS)

> . . . show that tundra species are killed where parts of the tundra plants are coated with Prudhoe Bay crude oil. On experimental plots, growth of above ground tundra plants was reduced 90 percent where sprayed with crude oil at a rate of 12 liters per square meter (approximately 400 barrels per acre). At rates as low as about 170 barrels per acre, mosses and lichens were killed.[37]

In the absence of leak and rupture experience, it is highly speculative to estimate the land impacts of TAPS. As for OCS and imports, they have only indirect impact on land until brought ashore.

Restricted Waters: Dissipation of oil in water is facilitated by a number of factors, including waves and currents. These processes are more effective in open waters than in bays and estuaries. Many of these restricted waters have valuable wildlife resources, compounding the detrimental effects of oil

**Table 15. Some Biological Resources Possibly Affected
Should a Major Spill Occur**

Location	Biological Group	OCS	Impact[a] TAPS	Imports[b]
Alaska	Vegetation (On land)	0	3	0
	Fish (Freshwater)	0	3	0
	Mammals (On land)	0	2	0
North	Vegetation (Marine)	2	2	0
Pacific	Invertebrates (Marine)	2	2	0
Coast	Fish (Marine)	3	2	0
(Alaska)	Birds (Marine)	3	3	0
	Mammals (Marine)	2	2	0
Pacific	Vegetation	2	2	2
Coast	Invertebrates	2	2	3
(Calif.)	Fish	1	1	1
	Birds	3	3	3
	Mammals	2	2	2
Gulf of	Vegetation	2	0	2
Mexico	Invertebrates	2	0	3
	Fish	1	0	1
	Birds	2	0	2
Florida	Vegetation	3	0	3
	Invertebrates	3	0	3
	Fish	1	0	1
	Birds	3	0	3
	Mammals	2	0	2
Atlantic	Vegetation	2	0	2
Coast	Invertebrates	2	0	3
	Fish	1	0	1
	Birds	3	0	3

[a] 0 = no effect; 1 = unlikely to be affected; 2 = possibly affected; 3 = likely to be affected.
[b] Takes into account imports of significant amounts of refined products.

spilled there. It is difficult to predict where a spill will spread, although certain meteorological data are useful. Dominant onshore winds along the Pacific Coast usually drive oil into harbors, as they did in the Santa Barbara spill. But along the Gulf and Atlantic Coast, this tendency is diminished. For example, the probability of a Georges Bank oil spill reaching shore has been calculated to be 5 percent or less.[38]

Since most tanker accidents occur in restricted waters, TAPS and imports generally pose greater hazards than does the OCS. Because the lighter, more toxic fractions of oil do not have time to evaporate, oil spilled close to shore can result in a greater loss of shoreline species. In addition, tanker spills usually occur in a single, large spill within a short time period, while the duration of a serious well blowout can be much longer.

Summary of Environmental Impacts

On a per barrel delivered basis, OCS production is likely to spill more oil adjacent to the U.S. than will imports. But many of these spills will likely occur well away from shore, especially on the Atlantic OCS. In addition, crude oil is less toxic than refined products. Both imports and TAPS are likely to result in accidents in congested bays and shipping lanes near the coast. And ballast treatment will be a major source of pollution for both. TAPS discharges will occur principally in Prince William Sound and discharges from imports at foreign terminals. However, there are indications that U.S. waters are not isolated from discharges taking place thousands of miles away. TAPS also involves significant onshore hazards. For all these reasons, OCS oil production is likely to result in less biological damage than will either TAPS or imports.

NATIONAL SECURITY IMPACTS

The national security issue involves military and economic risks due to supply interruptions and the effects of the large balance-of-trade deficit mentioned earlier. The Cabinet Task Force concluded, and apparently others generally agree, that "the risks to security from interruptions of oil supply do not, in the main, concern any danger to the functioning of the nation's armed forces."[39] Their conclusion was based on their finding that military needs during an emergency represent a very small fraction of total domestic consumption.

The primary security concern is the fear that exporting countries might withhold or significantly raise prices on oil exports to the U.S. Of course, the potential impact of such interruptions could be reduced by proper planning and control of import sources.

Both the source and the form of imports affect their reliability. Although recent actions raise questions of just how dependable South American crude supplies might be, it is generally assumed that western hemisphere sources are more dependable than eastern hemisphere sources. And interruption of crude supplies are less disruptive than are interruptions of refined products.

In projecting dependence upon eastern hemisphere sources, most studies assume western hemisphere oil will be imported to the extent to which it is available and that the deficit will be made up from eastern hemisphere sources. A series of complex factors will affect the future availability of energy supplies from any particular country.

Interior has estimated the potential contribution from western hemisphere sources in 1985;[40] thus the resulting percentage of dependence on eastern hemisphere petroleum sources can be determined. If the distribution of sources of imported oil is the same for the 2 million barrels/day increment considered here as for the remainder of imports, dependence on eastern hemisphere sources will be between 14 and 37 percent.

In conclusion, it is not possible to make precise, definitive statements about the exact national security risks that are involved with imports, much less state what levels are acceptable or unacceptable. However, both OCS and TAPS can significantly reduce our dependence on imports.

MULTIPLE USE IMPACTS

OCS development requires coastal staging areas for OCS support, for pipelines to come ashore, and often for facilities to process produced fluids. Sites have been difficult to obtain in coastal regions adjacent to the California OCS and similar problems may occur on the Atlantic Coast.

Land Use

For TAPS, both coastal and inland areas will be used as indicated in Figure 42. The proposed right-of-way for the pipeline is 150 feet wide,* 985 miles long, and will occupy 67 square miles of land. In addition to this, access roads, construction camps, and landing strips will occupy another 150 square miles.[41]

Coastal areas will also be used for TAPS. A tanker terminal will be needed at Valdez, and additional terminal facilities may also be needed in the southern ports, such as Puget Sound, San Francisco, and Los Angeles. No estimates have been made of the coastal land area needed for these facilities.

Foreign imports will also require receiving terminal and off-loading facilities. Small tankers which can now be accommodated could be used for these imports, but the magnitude of imports anticipated for 1985 indicates a need for deep-water port facilities capable of handling tankers in excess of 250,000 tons. These require water depths of more than 65 feet and only Puget Sound is naturally deep enough to accommodate them. Additional deep-water ports will be needed, particularly to serve the East and Gulf coasts. A number of locations for superports have been proposed off the coasts of Maine, New Jersey, Delaware, Louisiana, Texas, and California.[42] Local opposition to some of these sites has developed and state laws prohibiting or severely restricting such ports have been passed in Maine,[43] New Jersey,[44] and Delaware.[45]

* A federal district court found that this width violated the Minerals Leasing Act of 1920. The Supreme Court upheld this decision, on April 2, 1973. Congress is currently considering bills authorizing the proposed right-of-way.

Refineries will be needed regardless of the source of crude oil; hence, no first order advantage would accrue to either the OCS, TAPS, or imports in considering refinery siting. A second order effect might be the impacts of trans-shipping refined products if refineries are located well away from demand. An extreme of this effect would occur if refineries were located overseas and refined products imported. There are, however, balance of trade, national security, and environmental objections to that alternative.

Coastal Water Use

The coastal waters of the United States are all potentially available for a variety of uses and each of the three alternatives can conflict with other users. In the past, OCS development has involved the use of fixed multiple-well platforms, as well as various mobile rigs and support vessels. Interior has estimated that each 1,600 barrels per day of production will require construction of one new platform on the OCS.[46] This seems to be a high estimate and a more reasonable number for the future would be one for each 3,600 barrels per day (300 b/d per well with 12 wells per platform); and, in fact, with the anticipated discovery of large offshore fields, single platforms may well produce as much as 5,000–10,000 barrels per day. To produce 2 million barrels per day in 1985 on the OCS, 200 to 1,500 new platforms might be required.

The presence of these fixed structures will inconvenience commercial fishing,[47] although sports fishing catches will probably increase as a result of the artificial reef effect of the platforms.[48] The effect on commercial fishing has been identified as a problem in the Gulf of Mexico,[49] and provisions were made to reduce conflicts in advance of the 1972 Eastern Louisiana sales.[50] Estimates of the seriousness of this impact vary, however, and no quantitative data showing the effect have appeared.[51] There is some concern that this conflict will be more severe if the Atlantic OCS is developed. However, a recent study of OCS development on Georges Bank indicated that impacts on annual cod and mackerel catches would be negligible.

If extensive use of subsea wellheads and subsea production systems is included in OCS development, the number of platforms can be decreased below these estimates. This would improve the appearance of field development and reduce the possibility of conflicts with marine traffic. However, the possibility of conflicts with fishing would remain high unless some anti-fouling technique—such as placing fiberglass tents over subsea equipment—is used.

OCS development also carries with it the possibility of a major accident involving oil spills. These have been discussed in the previous section on oil pollution, but spills also have impacts on other users of coastal waters. Oil on the water prevents fishing boats from going out and fouls fishing gear.[52]

In some spills, fish have been damaged,[53] although this is more likely when the spill is refined products rather than crude.

Two other alternative uses of coastal waters may also be impacted by OCS development. The first is marine transportation. The large number of fixed platforms on the Gulf coast OCS have created a navigation problem for large merchant ships. To solve this problem, platform-free shipping fairways have been established by the Corps of Engineers. Apparently this has proved to be a satisfactory solution, but recently the Intergovernmental Maritime Consultative Organization (IMCO) promulgated right-of-way standards wider than those in use off the Gulf Coast.[54] Apparently no changes will be made in the Gulf OCS as a result of these new standards, but future OCS development in new areas will be affected.

Recreation is another use potentially affected by OCS development. The Commission on Marine Science, Engineering, and Resources stated that "marine recreation . . . ranks at least a close second to the offshore oil and gas industry in economic importance."[55] Since OCS development is at least three miles from shore, major first order conflicts would not be expected. Two conflicts are possible, however, one from the on-land staging areas and processing facilities mentioned earlier and another from the possibility of an oil spill reaching the beach. Both of these concerns are relevant considerations for OCS development off the Atlantic Coast since three particularly attractive areas for petroleum are located adjacent to the Cape Cod National Seashore, the Assateague Island National Seashore, and the proposed Cumberland Islands National Seashore.

Multiple use conflicts generated by TAPS and imports are due primarily to increased tanker traffic in harbors and waterways. Tanker traffic necessary to deliver 2 million barrels per day of oil would be 9 percent of total U.S. maritime tonnage in 1968.[56] Because of the size of tankers involved, this volume increase would result in fewer than 9 percent of the port calls at U.S. harbors. Increased maritime traffic, and the economics of very large tankers likely will lead to the construction of superport facilities.

SUMMARY AND CONCLUSIONS

An overall comparison of the three alternative sources of oil and gas analyzed in this chapter is summarized in Table 16. As can be seen, the OCS is preferable to increasing imports, and the OCS offers some advantages over TAPS.

OCS v. IMPORTS

The OCS offers advantages over increased imports in each of the categories in which the two alternatives are compared except multiple use. Land uses

Table 16. A Summary Comparison of Impacts

Categories of Impacts	OCS v. Imports	OCS v. TAPS
Economic		
Consumer costs	—	o
Balance of trade	+	o
Government revenue	+	+
Regional	+	+
Overall	+	+
Environmental		
Spill source (worldwide)	+	+
Spill rate (worldwide)	+	+
Location	+	+
Biological consequences	+	+
Overall	+	+
National Security (Overall)	+	o
Multiple Use		
Land Use	o	+
Coastal Use	—	—
Overall	—	?
OVERALL	+	+

Note: Obviously many of the judgments made in this table are speculative; however, all entries are based on the quantitative and qualitative analyses made in this study.

+ indicates an advantage for the OCS; — indicates a disadvantage for the OCS; o indicates no discernable difference; ? indicates that no conclusion could be drawn.

Source: U.S., Department of the Interior, *Final Environmental Impact Statement: Proposed Trans-Alaska Pipeline*, Vol. 1: *Introduction and Summary* (Washington: Government Printing Office, 1972).

for both are about the same: both require refineries; the OCS requires additional onshore facilities; and imports require increased port facilities. But OCS development has a greater overall potential for interfering with other uses, particularly fishing and marine transportation. If subsea production systems are widely used, this potential conflict with other users can be reduced.

There are a number of economic advantages for the OCS, although it now appears that imports may offer some advantage in terms of consumer costs. This advantage is at best slight and subject to considerable uncertainty in the future.

Considering worldwide environmental impacts, the OCS is less of a threat to the environment than increased imports would be. In part, this is due to the harmful effects of refined products which have to be considered with imports. If only U.S. waters are considered, imports appear to have an advantage, but this fails to take into account differences in kind of petroleum spilled and the fact that spills outside can produce effects within U.S. waters.

OCS v. TAPS

Developing OCS resources offers some advantages over TAPS. In large part this is due to the greater complexity and exposure to a wider variety of potential risks associated with developing the North Slope and transporting the oil by pipeline to Valdez and by tanker to West Coast U.S. ports. There is no experience upon which to base an estimate of the risk involved with TAPS, but if anything, the risk is probably greater than in the lower 48 states. It has been pointed out that TAPS suffers from both adverse marine and terrestrial impacts. An inland route for North Slope oil, while confronting different economic, timing, and security problems, would supply oil to a different market region. This alternative route might also provide some additional incentive to develop OCS supplies convenient to West Coast markets.

At the outset of the study, it was assumed that OCS development would continue. The overall objective of the study was to find ways to insure that development was optimal in a broad social sense. On the basis of our comparison of alternatives in this chapter, we have concluded that continued OCS development is socially preferable to increased imports or TAPS. This is on the basis of current policies, practices, and technologies. If changes result in more optimal development, the advantages of developing the OCS should become even greater.

1. National Petroleum Council, Committee on U.S. Energy Outlook, *U.S. Energy Outlook; A Summary Report* (Washington: NPC, 1972), p. 72.

2. *Ibid.*, p. 4.

3. NPC, *U.S. Energy Outlook*, 1972, p. 133.

4. U.S., Department of the Interior, *Statement, Questions and Policy Issues Related to Oversight Hearings on the Administration of the Outer Continental Shelf Lands Act, Held by the Senate Committee on Interior and Insular Affairs, Pursuant to S. Res. 45, March 23, 1972*, p. 5-A-28.

5. NPC, *U.S. Energy Outlook, Summary*, 1972, p. 36.

6. *Ibid.*, p. 64.

7. NPC, *U.S. Energy Outlook* (1972), p. 133.

8. U.S., Department of the Interior, *Final Environmental Impact Statement: Proposed Trans-Alaska Pipeline*, Vol. 1, *Introduction and Summary* (Washington: Government Printing Office, 1972), p. 30.

9. Luther J. Carter, "Alaskan Oil: Court Ruling Revives Canada Pipeline Issue," *Science*, 179 (March 9, 1973), p. 977.

10. NPC, *U.S. Energy Outlook*, 1972, p. 133.

11. "General Crude Oil Price Increase Seen As More Join Kansas, Oklahoma Boosts," *Wall Street Journal*, March 21, 1973, p. 9.

12. White House Favoring 2-Tier Oil Tariffs Over Quota Actions To Boost Imports," *Wall Street Journal*, March 19, 1973, p. 4.

13. *Oil and Gas Journal*, 70 (March 20, 1972), pp. 15–17.

14. Massachusetts Institute of Technology, Offshore Oil Task Group, *The Georges Bank Petroleum Study:* Vol. 1, *Impact on New England Real Income of Hypothetical Regional Petroleum Developments* (Cambridge: MIT, Sea Grant Project Office, February 1, 1973), p. 132.

15. NPC, *U.S. Energy Outlook*, 1972, p. 307.

16. U.S., Department of the Interior, *Analysis of the Economic and Security Aspects of the Trans-Alaska Pipeline*, Vol. 1: *Summary* (Washington: Government Printing Office, 1971), p. 8; and Tom Brown, *Oil on Ice*, ed. by Richard Pollak (San Francisco and New York: Sierra Club, 1971), p. 29.

17. U.S., Department of the Interior, Bureau of Land Management, *Final Environmental Statement: Proposed [September] 1972 Outer Continental Shelf Oil and Gas General Lease Sale Offshore Eastern Louisiana*, p. 77.

18. *Offshore*, 32 (September, 1972), pp. 71–72.

19. MIT, *Georges Bank Study*, Vol. 1, p. 264.

20. *Ibid.*

21. Interior, *Economic Aspects of TAPS*, Vol. 1, pp. 7–8.

22. *Ibid.*, p. 9.

23. *Ibid.*, p. G–2.

24. *Ibid.*

25. Interior, *Economic Aspects of TAPS*, Vol. 2: *Supporting Analyses*, p. K–3–4.

26. National Petroleum Council, Committee on Possible Future Petroleum Provinces of the U.S., *Future Petroleum Provinces of the United States; A Summary* (Washington: NPC, 1970), pp. 12–101; and Interior, *Trans-Alaska Pipeline Statement*, Vol. 1, p. 89.

27. Carter, "Alaskan Oil," p. 977.

28. Interior, *Trans-Alaska Pipeline Statement*, Vol. 4: *Evaluation of Environmental Impact*, p. 482.

29. *Ibid.*

30. Interior, *Trans-Alaska Pipeline Statement*, Vol. 1, p. 61.

31. Interior, *Trans-Alaska Pipeline Statement*, Vol. 5: *Alternatives to the Proposed Action*, p. 281.

32. *Oil and Gas Journal*, 71 (January 29, 1973), p. 106.

33. Ronald L. Kolpack, James S. Mattson, Harry B. Mark, Jr., and Ta-Ching Yu, "Hydrocarbon Content of Santa Barbara Channel Sediments," in *Biological and Oceanographical Survey of the Santa Barbara Channel Oil Spill, 1969–1970*, Vol. 2: *Physical, Chemical and Geological Studies*, comp. by Ronald L. Kolpack (Los Angeles: Allan Hancock Foundation, University of Southern California, 1971), p. 294; and *Man's Impact on the Global Environment*, Report of the Study of Critical Environmental Problems (SCEP), sponsored by Massachusetts Institute of Technology (Cambridge, Mass.: MIT Press, 1970), p. 140.

34. Robert Kanter, Dale Straughan, and William Jessee, "Effects of Exposure to Oil on *Mytilus Californianus* from Different Localities," in *Proceedings of the Joint Conference on Prevention and Control of Oil Spills*, June 15–17, 1971, Washington, D.C., Sponsored by American Petroleum Institute, Environmental Protection Agency, and U.S. Coast Guard (Washington: API, 1971), p. 485.

35. U.S., Department of the Interior, Bureau of Land Management, *Final Environmental Statement: Proposed [December] 1972 Outer Continental Shelf Oil and Gas General Lease Sale Offshore Louisiana*, p. 93.

36. Interior, *Trans-Alaska Pipeline Statement*, Vol. 4, p. 111.

37. *Ibid.*

38. MIT, *Georges Bank Study*, Vol. II, p. 99.

39. U.S., Cabinet Task Force on Oil Import Control, *The Oil Import Question* (Washington: Government Printing Office, February, 1970), p. 30.

40. BLM, *Final Environmental Statement: [September] 1972 OCS General Eastern Louisiana*, p. 137.

41. Interior, *Trans-Alaska Pipeline Statement*, Vol. 4, p. 257.

42. U.S., Congress, Senate, Committee on Interior and Insular Affairs, *Deep Water Port Policy Issues, Hearing*, before the Committee, 92d. Cong., 2d sess., on Current Federal Programs and Plans for the Formulation of a National Policy for Deep Water Port Development in the United States, April 25, 1972, p. 31.

43. Phil Berardeli, "East Coast States Ask Leasing Ban," *Offshore*, 31 (December 1971), p. 80.

44. "25 States Passed Laws in 1972 Dealing with a Wide Range of Environmental Problems," *New York Times*, November 4, 1972.

45. U.S., Executive Office of the President, Council on Environmental Quality, *Environmental Quality, Third Annual Report* (Washington: Government Printing Office, 1972), p. 186.

46. BLM, *Final Environmental Statement: [September] 1972 OCS General Eastern Louisiana*, p. 52.

47. BLM, *Final Environmental Statement: [December] 1972 OCS General Louisiana*, p. 231.

48. "Oil Platforms Called Boon to Fish in Gulf of Mexico," *Wall Street Journal*, December 7, 1971, p. 29.

49. U.S., Congress, Senate, Committee on Interior and Insular Affairs, *Outer Continental Shelf Policy Issues, Hearings*, before the Committee Pursuant to S. Res. 45, a National Fuels and Energy Policy Study, 92d. Cong., 2d sess., on Oversight on Outer Continental Shelf Lands Act, March 23, 24, and April 11, 18, 1972, Pt. 2, p. 1045.

50. BLM, *Final Environmental Statement: [September] 1972 OCS General Eastern Louisiana*, p. 52.

51. BLM, *Final Environmental Statement: [December] 1972 OCS General Louisiana*, p. 476.

52. Robert Easton, *Black Tide: The Santa Barbara Oil Spill and Its Consequences* (New York: Delacorte Press, 1972), p. 58.

53. Robert L. Dow, *Statement of Robert L. Dow, Maine Department of Sea and Shore Fisheries, Given at the Environmental Improvement Commission Public Hearing, Searsport, Maine, March 1971, Concerning Site Location Proposal of Maine Clean Fuels, Inc.*, p. 5.

54. IMCO Resolution A–161 (ES IV), *Recommendation on Establishing Traffic Separation Schemes and Areas to Be Avoided by Ships of Certain Classes*, Fourth Extraordinary Session, adopted 27 November 1968.

55. Commission on Marine Science, Engineering and Resources, *Panel Reports of the Commission on Marine Science, Engineering and Resources*, Vol. 3: *Marine Resources and Legal-Political Arrangements for Their Development* (Washington: Government Printing Office, 1969), p. VII–236.

56. U.S., Department of the Army, Corps of Engineers, *Waterborne Commerce of the United States, Calendar Year, 1968, Part 5: Summary* (Washington: Government Printing Office, 1968), p. 5.

XII. A Plan for OCS Development

BASED ON the assumption that OCS oil and gas resources will continue to be developed, this technology assessment was undertaken to determine how their development could be carried out in an optimal way. At appropriate places throughout the study, we have made proposals aimed at promoting changes for optimizing development of OCS oil and gas. These proposals are the bases for the specific recommendations to be made in this chapter. Taken together, these recommendations represent a plan for an OCS management system for achieving this objective.

OCS OPERATIONS

This chapter is divided into three parts: a summary of our conclusions regarding OCS operations, a summary of the weaknesses we have identified in the present management system, and our recommendations. The recommendations address four groups of issues: jurisdictional, general policy and management, management of the technologies, and needs for specific technologies.

CONCLUSIONS

The conclusions drawn from the study concerning OCS operations are as follows:

1. OCS oil and gas operations are not technology driven. Development of technology in this area has been evolutionary and incremental. This pattern will likely continue and significantly different technological options are not likely to become available short of major initiatives by either industry or government. This situation reflects the general adequacy of existing OCS technologies. And it leads to the conclusion that physical technologies likely to be used in the late 1980's will be similar to those now in use. (Subsea production systems are considered existing technologies.)

2. Until recently, economics has been the governing criterion in the development of OCS technologies. Government regulation of these technologies demanded capabilities that were well within state-of-the-art. The dominant concerns of government were adequate and efficient production and maximum revenue.

3. Safety (viewed broadly) and environmental issues only recently became major concerns in the development of OCS technologies. They continue to pose a serious challenge to the system for managing the OCS even though technologies responsive to these new concerns are being developed. A major problem is the inertia of a system which developed without having to respond to safety and environmental criteria.

4. In the past, participation in the management of OCS oil and gas operations was limited to the Department of the Interior and the petroleum industry. They shared a common commitment to the goal of maximum efficient recovery of the resources. This relatively closed management system was initially unable to sense and respond quickly to a changing social climate. Interest groups and federal agencies that represent concerns such as environmental conservation are now participating in the management system primarily through the impact statement process required by NEPA. These new participants are demanding changes from past patterns of operation.

5. But even the new demands being made on OCS technologies are well within state-of-the-art. The necessary modifications in the physical technologies required by a changing social climate can be met. Although the application of stringent environmental and safety criteria pose problems, the industry either has or can develop the required physical technologies and procedures.

OPTIMAL MANAGEMENT SYSTEM REQUIREMENTS

We found in our assessment that optimal development of OCS oil and gas requires that primary attention be devoted not to physical technologies but rather to the OCS management system. Existing inducements and sanctions internal to the petroleum industry are not adequate to insure sensitivity and rapid response by all operators to social concerns. In practice, those operators who attempt to meet the highest and usually most expensive standards put themselves at a competitive disadvantage with operators using less demanding standards. Government must, therefore, take responsibility for building the necessary inducements and sanctions into the OCS management system. With regard to the technologies, government must assure that the best available technologies are used and, where necessary, that new and/or improved alternatives are developed. Decisions on what constitutes "best available" are matters of judgment. Establishing unchanging substantive performance standards is not and will not be the best approach.

In formulating the recommendations in this chapter, the procedural approach employed in the Federal Water Pollution Control Act (FWPCA)

Amendments of 1972 is used. Since the effects of change are not known, the objective is to develop a management system which will carry out OCS oil and gas operations with minimum change. This means that technological and economic feasibility must be balanced against concerns such as the environment and alternative uses. Qualitative judgments are required on both technologies and impacts, and the management system must make choices where the knowledge base for assessing changes is either limited or a matter of controversy.

A major objective is a system capable of accommodating both conflicting interpretations of information and management goals. The management of OCS oil and gas operations through the 1980's will continue to be an overtly political, conflict-resolving process. It must be capable, at every level, of resolving issues when the facts are unclear. Further, it must be able to deal with issues which, over time, will change in their substance: that is, while environmental concerns are now of great importance, other substantive issues may be considered more important in the future, particularly if responses to current environmental concerns are effective.

The recommendations which follow assume that for conflicting interests to be successfully accommodated, policy-making and administration must be both open and formalized; to be adequate, lead-times will have to be substantial. Furthermore, it is assumed that the burden of proof for insuring minimum change in impact areas should be the responsibility of those who conduct OCS operations. On the other hand, the proposed management system also assumes that opponents should not be able to block development by applying unreasonable standards. For instance, development should not necessarily wait until complete knowledge of impacts is known; rather the management system should be responsive to all known and expected impacts.

In formulating a management system for the optimal development of OCS oil and gas, our view has been that a wholesale overhaul is not possible in the context of our political system. Although taken *in toto*, the recommendations represent a major modification of things as they are, they can be adopted individually, and each can result in an incremental improvement in the system.

The recommendations also reflect an effort to deal with issues in ways which will generate minimum controversy. Therefore, they mirror a view of political reality which says that modifications should take place at the lowest possible levels in the political system. Where possible, the recommendations require changes at the agency level or through inter-agency agreements. Formal presidential and congressional action have only been recommended as a last resort.

The proposed management plan addresses the following areas where changes of a general kind are needed.

1. Effective future management of the OCS depends upon conscious long-range planning. The present pattern of *ad hoc*, incremental policy-making is inconsistent with the lead-times necessary to carry out costly and complex OCS oil and gas operations. Stability and certainty are important to industry's ability to carry out operations economically, and long-range planning is needed to provide those conditions.

2. Planning is equally necessary to assure that environmental, safety, multiple use, and other significant criteria are adequately considered. Only the early identification of issues through planning will permit orderly accommodation of conflicting interests.

3. Adequate planning incorporating a diverse range of concerns will only be possible with broadened participation. Participation must include consumer and environmental interest groups as well as industry and government agencies. Active involvement should include not only those at policy-making levels, but should be extended downward to lower levels of the management system as well. To be meaningful, such participation requires general access to both information and decision-making.

4. For government to be capable of effective management, it must have greater expertise. At present, government's lack of information and expertise constrains its ability to decide in individual cases as well as to plan effectively. Additionally, government is at times unable to provide adequate information to justify its actions. In part this is because some information used in making management decisions is treated as proprietary and is not publicly disclosed.

5. Effective management also requires improved coordination and centralization of responsibility. The present system of divided and fuzzy responsibility makes balanced integrated management impossible. And, in many cases, it precludes the possibility of identifying the organizations responsible for mismanagement.

6. The agencies responsible for the day-to-day management of the OCS must have the authority, resources, and personnel necessary to require that optimum equipment and procedures are used. This includes the ability to require replacement of equipment judged inadequate and the development of adequate new equipment where necessary.

7. Effective management requires early efforts at reducing ambiguities and eliminating gaps associated with jurisdictional issues. These range

from fixing national-international and state-federal boundaries to clarifying agency responsibilities and the applicability of statutes.

8. Finally, no issue is more important to the management question than knowing what portion of the nation's energy demand the OCS is expected to supply. Only when those expectations are defined, can the pace of development be established.

RECOMMENDATIONS FOR MANAGING OCS

The following recommendations respond to those enumerated general needs as well as to specific issues identified in Chapters VI through X. Some of the recommendations call for a continuation of current practice and others, particularly several dealing with the management of technologies, are presently being implemented by the USGS. Their inclusion here results from the desire to provide an overall management plan for the OCS. At the end of each recommendation, the chapter dealing with the specific issues to which the recommendation is addressed is cited in parentheses.

JURISDICTION

Effective management of the OCS would be facilitated by the establishing of clear-cut jurisdictional boundaries. This includes fixing the outer limits of national jurisdiction and state-federal boundaries as well as specifying more precisely agency and organization responsibilities.

RECOMMENDATIONS

1. *National Boundaries.* The outer limit of national jurisdiction should be established as soon as possible along with an international authority to manage and control the development of seabed resources beyond this fixed limit. It is neither in the nation's interest to leave this boundary uncertain nor the area beyond open to unregulated development. Optimal development of oil and gas resources requires stability. Given the present international context, stability is most likely to be achieved by fixing national seabed boundaries and establishing an international regime. While it would be desirable to gain agreement on the existing Administration proposal, it appears unlikely that this proposal will be acceptable to either most governments or major domestic interests. (Chapter X)

2. *Federal-State Agreements.* Continuing efforts should be undertaken to establish interim agreements allowing oil and gas development in those areas where OCS development is scheduled and where the states claim jurisdiction beyond the three miles provided in the Submerged Lands

Act. A definitive boundary established by federal-state agreement would be desirable, but this appears unlikely since most federal-state conflicts are resolved in the courts. Interim agreements are a way to avoid allowing jurisdictional disputes to result in delays inconsistent with optimal OCS development. (Chapter X)

3. *Agency Jurisdiction.* The Congress should act to clarify ambiguities concerning the six-mile zone between the outer limit of the territorial sea and Florida and Texas. The major uncertainty here is the authority of federal agencies such as the Coast Guard to enforce certain regulations in these areas. Such clarification would apparently be non-controversial at present, and would preclude the likelihood of jurisdictional conflicts that might result from future oil and gas operations in those areas. (Chapter X)

4. *Energy Coordinator.* A top official of the executive branch, either a departmental secretary or a White House officer, should be a designated energy coordinator for the federal government. The coordinating role should be designated on the basis of organizational responsibility to assure long-term stability and continuity. (Chapter IX)

GENERAL POLICY AND MANAGEMENT

Resolution of these jurisdictional issues would contribute to the smooth operations of the management system. A major instrument in the proposed management system is expanded use of the 102 environmental impact statement process. The impact statement is an attractive vehicle since it provides access to both information and decision-making for a wide range of interests. It offers the potential for both formal and open decision-making for the OCS. This is in contrast to the closed, informal system that has previously operated.

The impact statements also offer the possibility of providing a mechanism for comprehensive planning on the OCS. Integrating energy, land use, and environmental planning in these statements is basic to the proposed management system. Effective development of the OCS requires a definition of the role these resources are expected to play in meeting the nation's energy needs. Demands made by federal courts which have reviewed lease sale impact statements have already moved government in the direction of a more orderly and formal energy policy. Existing legislation has also focused attention on land-use planning in coastal areas. Integrating planning for these two areas with the already existing environmental focus of the 102 statements is both possible and necessary.

RECOMMENDATIONS

5. *Impact Statement Hierarchy.* The OCS management process should include preparation of a hierarchy of impact statements that starts with a general programmatic statement. The objective of this series of impact statements is to provide a mechanism for continuous and flexible planning and assessment of all impacts of oil and gas operations on the OCS. (Chapter VIII)

6. *Lead Agency.* The Department of the Interior should be assigned lead agency responsibility for all 102 statements prepared for the OCS. Preparation of these statements should be coordinated with all agencies having responsibilities on the OCS. The rationale for assigning the lead agency role to Interior is in part linked to later recommendations which concentrate additional OCS administrative responsibilities in that Department. (Chapter VIII)

7. *Coastal Planning.* The Department of Commerce should be designated as having special responsibilities for providing the coastal-zone planning component in OCS impact statements. The objective is to use the statements as a mechanism for integrating energy, land use, and environmental planning. Existing legislation assigns responsibility to Commerce for land use planning in the coastal zone. Under the proposed management plan, Interior and Commerce would have primary responsibility for these three planning elements. (Chapter IX)

8. *Promotion-Regulation.* Promotion and regulation functions should remain divided within Interior, between the Bureau of Land Management (BLM) and the United States Geological Survey (USGS). The planning process inevitably requires coordination and interaction between these two components as do subsequent management actions. This need for coordination stems from the practical inability to separate fully promotion from regulation. Nonetheless, assigning separate responsibilities provides a continuous checking mechanism. In the following detailed recommendations for the management system, activities are specifically assigned to each of these two units as well as to other agencies. (Chapter IX)

9. *Ten Year Schedule.* BLM should formulate a ten-year development schedule for OCS oil and gas resources. A long lead-time is essential for an effective planning process. (Chapters VIII and IX)

10. *Programmatic Statement.* USGS should lead, with the close cooperation of Commerce, in preparing programmatic impact statements for each of the regions included in the ten-year development schedule.

These programmatic statements should be general development plans including energy, land use, and environmental concerns. The purpose should be to define the role and relationship of oil and gas operations to the overall uses of the area. To facilitate this, USGS should be provided with resources necessary to collect and analyze the data needed for this planning. The impact statements should also include an assessment of the capability of involved agencies to meet their obligations under the plan. Programmatic statements would provide early access to information and policy-making for all interested parties and therefore be the first step in the process of accommodation. (Chapters VIII and IX)

11. *Define Lease Areas.* Using the programmatic statements as a base, BLM should in consultation with USGS select areas (not tracts) defined by coordinates for inclusion on its five-year lease schedule. Specific designation of the areas to be leased is necessary to facilitate detailed data collection. (Chapter IX)

12. *Data Collection.* Based on the inclusion of areas on the five-year lease schedule, USGS should initiate its own data-collection program for each area to the extent required to prepare a lease sale impact statement. Collection procedures should assure that the data is public and available for inclusion in the statement. The data collection should be broad and include, among other things, geological and geophysical information as well as information on environmental and land use impacts. (Chapter VII)

13. *Hydrocarbon Studies.* The National Oceanic and Atmospheric Administration (NOAA) should initiate continuous hydrocarbon baseline and toxicity tests at the point that areas are included on the five-year lease schedule. This will provide a base for anticipating the impact of later operations. To assure maximum credibility, studies should be funded and carried out so as to preclude the appearance of bias. This is one rationale for having NOAA assume responsibility for these studies. (Chapter VII)

14. *Lease Impact Statement.* Based on the programmatic statement and nominations from industry, BLM, in cooperation with USGS, should prepare a lease sale draft impact statement to be available at least fifteen months prior to the sale and three months prior to the public hearing. Again preparation should involve a land use input from Commerce. This statement should be subsidiary to the programmatic statement and, while dealing with the same broad issues, concentrate on local impacts. It should not, however, repeat material such as energy-mix questions covered in the programmatic statement except where it is necessary to amend the plan described in the programmatic statement. This amending option is neces-

sary to insure a continuing and flexible planning process in response to changed values or new information. An assessment of the agency capabilities for managing oil and gas operations in the area should be included. (Chapter IX)

15. *Committee Review.* An *ad hoc* committee should be constituted by the Council on Environmental Quality (CEQ) to review draft impact statements for lease sales. The committee should represent a broad range of interests and expertise. The review and a report of the review should be open to the public. This review could provide additional assurance that the impact statements and actions being planned are both adequate and consistent with the regional plan. (Chapter VIII)

16. *Bonus Bid.* BLM should continue to administer the lease sale using present procedures including the bonus bid system. Selected experimentation with the staggered bonus system should be considered. The bonus bid system has the dual attractions of raising substantial revenue for government and being easily administered. (Chapter IX)

17. *USGS Management.* With limited exceptions, post-lease sale management of OCS oil and gas operations should be concentrated in USGS. The objective of this concentration of management is to eliminate gaps and overlaps and establish clear-cut responsibility. Such concentration will also assure that management decisions conform to the development plan laid out in the hierarchy of impact statements. Any impact statements triggered by post-lease sale activities should be the responsibility of USGS and be subsidiary to the lease sale statement. Where necessary, transfer of operational responsibility to USGS should be accomplished by inter-agency agreements. In summary, then, USGS should continue to administer all of its present post-lease activities plus the following: (Chapter IX)

   a. *OSHA.* By agreement between Labor and Interior, OCS responsibilities assigned to the Department of Labor by the Occupational Safety and Health Act (OSHA) should be administered by USGS. The standards themselves should be developed by Labor with the advice of USGS and the Department of Health, Education, and Welfare (HEW). Such an arrangement will increase the effective day-to-day administration of the OSHA standards since USGS is already equipped to inspect OCS facilities. Further, these safety and health concerns are intimately tied to equipment design and operational procedures that are already a USGS responsibility. As a final advantage, this approach relieves industry of an additional layer of inspectors.

b. *Environmental Administration.* USGS should be responsible for enforcing all environmental quality standards applicable to OCS oil and gas operations. Where necessary, agency responsibilities should be clearly defined in inter-agency agreements between Interior, Transportation, and EPA.

c. *Rights-of-Way.* By formal agreement between BLM and USGS, BLM should issue rights-of-way for common carrier pipelines only upon recommendation of the USGS. This will assure that coordination exists between common carrier lines and the gathering lines presently regulated by USGS. Such authority will allow USGS to insure that pipeline development conforms to the plans developed in the impact statements. Present responsibility for pipelines is fragmented, and some agencies are incapable of meeting their regulatory responsibilities.

d. *Pipelines.* By formal agreement between the Office of Pipeline Safety (OPS) and Interior, USGS should be designated as responsible for enforcing design and performance standards for offshore pipelines which are now under OPS jurisdiction. The standards, however, should be jointly formulated by OPS and USGS. USGS presently exercises such authority over gathering lines.

e. *Gas Reserves.* By formal agreement between the Federal Power Commission (FPC) and Interior, USGS should be required to provide estimates of recoverable gas reserves to be served by proposed new gas lines. Attached to the estimates should be an assessment of how the line will fit into the development plan established in the impact statements. Additionally, USGS should be available to FPC for consultation on all questions concerning lines. The purpose is to assist FPC in approving new pipelines so that they conform to the development plan established in the impact statements.

18. *OCS Orders: Coverage.* All design specifications and regulations for which USGS has administrative responsibility, including those resulting from inter-agency agreements, should be detailed in OCS orders for each USGS area. OCS orders should be a detailed composite of the regulations and criteria under which oil and gas operations are to be carried out. Such a composite would inform both industry and the interested public of operational standards. (Chapter VI)

19. *OCS Orders: Preparation.* All OCS orders should be reviewed in advance by committees representing both industry and other interested parties selected by the Chief of the Conservation Division of USGS. At present, preparation of OCS orders involves industry participation.

For example, in the Gulf Coast area, proposed orders are reviewed by the Offshore Operators Committee. Broadening the range of reviewers should assure sensitivity to a wide set of social concerns at the immediate management level. Placing selection in the Conservation Division in Washington should provide access to the best informed people in organizations such as the national environmental interest groups. (Chapter VI)

In the preceding management recommendations, USGS has been assigned primary responsibility. Throughout, however, the management system requires cooperation and coordination with other agencies; and, in certain instances, recommendations are included for independent actions by other agencies. In addition to those already covered, several other responsibilities should be made explicit.

RECOMMENDATIONS

20. *Platform Location.* The present Corps of Engineers responsibilities concerning platforms should remain unchanged. The responsibility for maintaining unimpeded navigation requires management by a single agency. (Chapter IX)

21. *Certification of Drill Rigs.* In addition to its present responsibilities for safety, the Coast Guard should establish formal certification and inspection requirements for jack-up drilling rigs. (Chapter X)

22. *Apply FWPCA to OCS.* The FWPCA Amendments of 1972 should be amended specifically to apply discharge provisions to the OCS. Under this arrangement, EPA would establish the standards, but as recommended earlier, USGS would have enforcement responsibility. There is no apparent reason why the general principle of a separate agency to set environmental standards should not be applicable to the OCS. Such a separation provides an additional check and increased public credibility in this sensitive area. (Chapter X)

23. *Environmental Monitoring.* With the start of exploratory drilling operations in any OCS area, NOAA should assure continuous monitoring of commercially useful and sensitive marine species for sublethal effects and possible tainting. Findings of measurable changes would require immediate action by the management system. (Chapter VII)

24. *Environmental R&D.* A single federal agency, probably either EPA or NOAA, should assume responsibility for monitoring, coordinating, and filling gaps in environmental research. The purpose is to assure a balanced R&D program. (Chapter VII)

25. *Clean-up R&D.* EPA should assume responsibility for monitoring, coordinating, and filling gaps in R&D aimed at improving clean-up and containment technology. The objective is to assure a balanced R&D program. (Chapter VIII)

26. *Clean-up Cooperatives.* The Coast Guard, with the advice of EPA and USGS, should establish specific equipment and performance standards to be met by the clean-up cooperatives which industry has established in its effort to comply with the lease requirements. This would assure coordination with the government's operational capabilities and help eliminate both overlaps and gaps. (Chapter VIII)

MANAGEMENT OF TECHNOLOGIES

At the immediate management level, a number of actions should be taken to insure the use of optimal technologies.

RECOMMENDATIONS

27. *Standards.* USGS should establish equipment requirements in terms of the objectives to be achieved. While these requirements should include detailed performance standards for all pieces of equipment affecting safety and environment, design specifications should not be allowed to act as a deterrent to technological development. The presently used fines and orders for suspension of operations are generally adequate. Detailed standards will require equipment suppliers to establish quality-control procedures. (Chapter VI)

28. *Failure Reporting.* USGS should establish improved reporting and systematic analysis procedures for failures, malfunctions, and equipment defects, as well as issue appropriate notices and warnings. (Chapter VI)

29. *Accident Investigation.* Interior should establish a board similar in function to the National Transportation Safety Board to investigate major OCS accidents. The Board should make appropriate recommendations for changes or additions to procedures and equipment. These recommendations should be available to the public. (Chapter VI)

30. *Review Technology.* USGS should appoint an independent and representative committee of experts to review state-of-the-art in OCS technologies periodically and recommend desirable changes in equipment and performance standards. (Chapter VI)

31. *Government R&D.* USGS should undertake an expanded research, development, and testing program as necessary to insure optimal regula-

tion and rapid development of new equipment and procedures. So far as possible, this work should be contracted with organizations outside the R&D system of the petroleum industry. This will help to insure that USGS and OCS operators maintain continuing, effective communications with other technological communities. (Chapter VI)

32. *Personnel Standards.* USGS should develop uniform standards and certification requirements for personnel who perform inspection and test functions. (Chapter VI)

33. *Personnel Training.* USGS should develop a program to establish improved and standardized training and procedures for operating personnel. This program should utilize the expertise of organizations and individuals such as behavioral scientists who specialize in training. (Chapter VI)

34. *Industry R&D.* Industry should expand its R&D programs with the objective of developing technologies that are responsive to broader criteria such as those associated with safety and environmental concerns. (Chapter VI)

35. *Industry Cooperation.* USGS should actively promote greater industry cooperation in the development of safety, accident prevention, and environmental protection technologies. Industry should be assured that cooperation in these designated areas will not be subject to anti-trust action. This could be accomplished by having the Anti-Trust Division of the Department of Justice issue guidelines for cooperative efforts or by having the Division give opinions on specific proposals. (Chapter VI)

36. *Systems Approach.* Industry should undertake a self-conscious program aimed at increased use of the systems approach in designing its technologies. Specific efforts should focus on increased redundancy and fail-safe designs. (Chapter VI)

37. *Human-factors Criteria.* Industry should focus specific attention on the use of human-factors criteria in equipment design aimed at minimizing human-error accidents. (Chapter VI)

38. *Subsea Production Systems.* USGS should encourage early development and use of subsea production systems. Parallel to this, efforts should be made to formulate those specifications and regulations necessary to insure safe operation of subsea production systems. (Chapter VI)

SPECIFIC TECHNOLOGIES

A number of the preceding recommendations are aimed at creating a system for identifying specific weaknesses in physical technologies. Even if they were immediately adopted, a substantial period would elapse before component weaknesses could be identified and corrected. The objective of what follows is to designate those components which either government or industry has already identified as needing improvement. In most cases, efforts are presently under way to correct these component deficiencies. They are identified here to provide a focus for action on possible short-term improvements. In those instances where better technologies are available, but in only limited use, the goal is to accelerate their deployment. Replacement of inadequate but serviceable components is hindered by economic constraints. This is particularly so with already operating drilling and production equipment. A decision to continue using less than the best available equipment may in any individual case be sound, but such decisions should be consciously made and not be the result of inertia.

RECOMMENDATIONS

39. *Inadequate Components.* USGS should immediately compile a list similar to the following one, and each year publish a summary review of the progress achieved in correcting weaknesses. This review should continue until the identification system previously recommended is operational. The physical technologies with weaknesses fall into three categories: need to be developed, need to be improved, and need to be deployed. (Chapter VI)

Need To Be Developed

The components that need to be developed are:

a. Surface actuated, fail-safe valves that can be substituted for existing velocity-actuated downhole safety devices without pulling the production tubing. The objective is to provide more reliable protection against loss of control in producing wells.

b. Downhole instrumentation for measuring pressure at the bit face. Such a capability would give immediate warning of potential blowouts.

c. Event recorders designed to survive accidents, similar to the "black boxes" in airplanes. These would provide a record of equipment malfunctions.

d. A device for identifying which wells on a burning multi-well platform are out of control. Presently efforts to re-establish control over wells are slowed by the difficulty in identifying the wells that are out of control.

e. Multi-phase pumps and pipelines capable of efficiently and simultaneously moving oil and gas in the same pipeline. This could help to reduce the number of pipelines, alleviate flaring of presently uneconomic wellhead gas, and simplify a move to subsea production systems.

f. Automated drilling equipment. This would reduce accidents due to human error during drilling operations.

Need To Be Improved

The components that need improvement are:

a. Drill bits with a longer life. Any improvement will result in fewer trips in and out of the drill hole, a sometimes dangerous procedure.

b. Automated, through-the-pipe equipment capable of identifying weak points in pipelines. This would facilitate preventive maintenance.

c. Velocity-actuated downhole safety devices. Since many of these will remain in use, any improvements in performance reduce the chances of losing control of wells.

Need To Be Deployed

The components which need to be deployed by all operators are:

a. Sand probes used with velocity-actuated downhole safety devices. These indicate when excessive sand erosion has occurred, and at that point the safety devices can be serviced or replaced.

b. Drilling mud monitors capable of indicating small changes in mud volume. These provide one indication of potential blowouts and allow for early counter action.

c. Automated mass-flow monitoring equipment on pipelines. These can indicate major pipeline leaks and reduce the quantity of oil introduced into the water.

d. Remote and protected controls for blowout preventors (BOP's). These can allow re-establishing control over wells where personnel cannot approach the work area.

Table 17 indicates, in a summary fashion, the points at which recommendations have been made for changes in the existing OCS management system. These changes offer policy-makers two choices. Adopted individually they provide responses to specific issues identified during the study and, therefore, a means to incremental improvements. Collectively the recommendations address three recurring needs if the OCS is to be optimally developed: first, the need for much longer lead-times in preparing for the development; second, the need for integrated energy, land use, and environmental planning on the OCS; and third, a need for an open, formal decision-making system capable of accommodating conflicting interests. If these needs are to be adequately met, major modifications in management are required.

Table 17. A Plan for OCS Development

Present	Recommended	Changes Required to Implement Recommendations
Jurisdictional Matters Affecting OCS Management		
Outer boundary of national jurisdiction uncertain	1. Fix outer boundary of national jurisdiction 2. Establish an international seabed authority	International agreement
Jurisdictional disputes between the federal government and state governments	Definitive agreement on state-federal boundary If not possible negotiate interim agreement	Legislative and/or Executive action
Ambiguous federal authority over 6-mile zone between territorial sea and OCS	Congress should clarify jurisdiction in this area	Amend Submerged Lands Act and/or OCS Lands Act
Uncertain	Top official designated federal energy coordinator on basis of organizational position	Presidential directive
OCS Development Planning Responsibilities		
BLM prepares a 5-year tentative OCS leasing schedule in consultation with USGS	BLM formulate a 10-year OCS development schedule in consultation with USGS	Department action
BLM, as lead agency, is preparing a programmatic statement on the 5-year OCS leasing schedule	USGS, as lead agency, but with cooperation of Commerce, prepare a programmatic impact statement which will serve as a general development plan for each region included in the 10-year schedule which integrates energy, environmental, and land use components	
	BLM, in consultation with USGS, define by fixed coordinates areas (not tracts) included on 5-year lease schedule	Bureau action

Table 17. A Plan for OCS Development (Continued)

Present	Recommended	Changes Required to Implement Recommendations
	OCS Development Planning Responsibilities *(Cont.)*	
USGS participation in group seismic shoots to collect data for tract evaluation; data is proprietary	USGS collect data to extent required to make tract evaluations. Data to be publicly available in lease sale impact statements	Increase appropriations for data collection
	NOAA initiate continuous hydrocarbon background studies of areas on 5-year lease schedule	Agency action
USGS grants exploration permits	Continue present responsibility, making all management decisions consistent with general development plan	
BLM receives and reviews lease nominations; BLM-USGS selects tracts BLM publishes list	Continue present responsibility, making all management decisions consistent with general development plan	
BLM prepares draft lease sale impact statement with inputs from other federal agencies	Based on the programmatic statement and nominations from industry BLM, with USGS, prepare draft lease sale impact statement to be available 15 months prior to sale and 3 months prior to public hearing; statement to supplement or amend programmatic statement as necessary	Department action
	CEQ constitute committees to review draft impact statements, review and report to be made public	Presidential directive
Interior publishes hearing notice	Continue present responsibility, making all management decisions consistent with the general development plan	
BLM prepares final lease sale impact statement; BLM publishes notice of lease sale 30 days after it is filed with CEQ	Continue present responsibility, making all management decisions consistent with general development plan	

Present	Recommended	Changes Required to Implement Recommendations
OCS Development Planning Responsibilities *(Cont.)*		
BLM administers lease sale using the bonus bid–fixed royalty system	Continue present practice; consider selected experimentation with the staggered bonus–fixed royalty	Staggering bonus bidding requires legislative action
Post-Lease Sale Management: USGS General Policy and Management		
General:	USGS prepare any post-lease sale impact statements judged necessary for especially sensitive areas	Department action
	USGS enforce all environmental quality standards	Inter-agency agreement
	USGS enforce OSHA on OCS	Inter-agency agreement
Drilling and Development: USGS requires lessee to submit exploratory drilling plan	Continue present responsibility, making all management decisions consistent with the general development plan	
USGS requires field development plan	See recommended changes under Management of Technologies	
USGS requires "Application for Permit to Drill"	Continue present responsibility, consistent with general development plan	
USGS enforces regulations covering safety and equipment concerns not included in Labor, Coast Guard, or state and local government regulations	Continue present responsibility, consistent with general development plan	
Production: USGS requires monthly production report	Continue present responsibility, consistent with general development plan	
USGS requires monthly report of oil runs, gas sales, and royalties	Continue present responsibility, consistent with general development plan	
USGS requires reports and logs of well completions and recompletions	Continue present responsibility, consistent with general development plan	

Table 17. A Plan for OCS Development (Continued)

Present	Recommended	Changes Required to Implement Recommendations
Post-Lease Sale Management: USGS General Policy and Management (*Cont.*)		
USGS enforcement of safety and equipment regulations same as drilling and development phase	Continue present responsibility, consistent with general development plan	
Transportation: USGS authorizes rights-of-use for gathering lines	Continue present responsibility, consistent with general development plan	
Companies apply to FPC for approval of common carrier gas lines	USGS provide FPC estimates of recoverable gas reserves; USGS assess lines consistent with general development plan	Inter-agency agreement
BLM authorizes transmission lines rights-of-way	BLM grants rights-of-way only on recommendation of USGS	Departmental action
OPS responsible for common carrier design and performance standards	USGS enforce design and performance standards for offshore pipelines	Inter-agency agreement
Management of Technologies		
USGS establishes and enforces general standards; trend toward more detailed standards	USGS establish equipment requirements in terms of objectives to be achieved; enforce by appropriate inspections and sanctions	USGS action
USGS requires limited reporting of failures and malfunctions	USGS improve reporting and analysis procedures for failures, malfunctions, and equipment defects; issue appropriate notices and warnings	USGS action
USGS investigates OCS accidents	Interior establish board similar to National Transportation Safety Board to investigate OCS accidents	Department action
	USGS appoint independent representative committee of experts to review state-of-the-art technologies periodically and recommend desirable changes	USGS action

Present	Recommended	Changes Required to Implement Recommendations
	Management of Technologies (*Cont.*)	
	USGS undertake expanded R&D program	Increased appropriation
	USGS develop uniform standards and certification requirements for personnel who perform inspection and test functions	USGS action
	Industry develop program of improved and standardized training procedures for operating personnel	Industry action
	Industry expand its R&D programs	Industry action
	USGS promote greater cooperation within industry in development of safety, accident prevention, and environmental protection technologies	Interior and Justice action
	Industry increase use of systems design approach	Industry action
	Industry increase use of human factors design criteria	Industry action
	USGS encourage development and use of subsea production systems	USGS and industry action
	USGS immediately compile a list of weak technological components; publish annual summary of progress in correcting weaknesses	USGS action
	USGS detail all specifications and regulations in OCS orders for each area	USGS action
USGS and industry groups review OCS orders	USGS appoint broadly representative committee for each USGS area to participate in review of OCS orders	USGS action

Table 17. A Plan for OCS Development (Continued)

Present	Recommended	Changes Required to Implement Recommendations
Other Agencies' General Policy and Management		
Corps of Engineers authorizes placement of any permanent or floating structure in navigable waters	Continue present responsibility, making authorizations consistent with general development plan	
Coast Guard enforces regulations covering safety, equipment, vessel transportation, and accidents on the OCS; jack-up rigs are not certified since they are not defined as vessels	In addition to present responsibilities, Coast Guard establish formal certification and inspection requirements for jack-up drilling rigs	Coast Guard action
USGS establishes and enforces discharge standards; FWPCA not clearly applicable	EPA establish discharge standards for OCS; USGS enforce standards	Amend FWPCA
	With start of exploratory drilling, NOAA assure continuous monitoring of commercially useful and sensitive marine species	Agency action
	EPA or NOAA assume responsibility for monitoring, coordinating, and filling gaps in environmental research	Inter-agency agreement
National Response Team R&D committee coordinates cleanup, containment R&D	EPA assume responsibility for monitoring, coordinating, and filling gaps in R&D aimed at improving cleanup and containment technology	National Response Team agreement
	Coast Guard establish equipment and performance standards for cleanup cooperatives	Legislative action

Appendices

Appendix A. Environmental Pollution and Public Opinion

IN THE COURSE of this study, an effort was made to determine the American public's attitude toward offshore oil operations—particularly public reaction to oil spills from tankers and offshore oil and gas facilities. Such information was unavailable. However, two articles by Hazel Erskine appeared in *Public Opinion Quarterly* during 1972 which provide a concise review of opinion polls which have surveyed attitudes toward environmental pollution in general.* The first article, "The Polls: Pollution and its Costs," appeared in the spring, 1972, issue. A companion article, "The Polls: Pollution and Industry," was published in the summer, 1972, issue. It was possible, from the polls reported by Erskine, to derive some public opinion data on the oil industry. Opinion poll results reported by Erskine and discussed here are based on nationwide samples and represent national averages unless otherwise indicated.

I. HISTORICAL TREND IN OPINION

Change in the American public's awareness of and attitude toward environmental pollution has been dramatic. Erskine calls this upsurge "a miracle of public opinion."[1] For example, when polls on pollution first appeared in 1965, only about one in ten Americans considered the problem very serious, but in more recent years environmental problems have become a major public concern. It was found in a national Harris poll conducted in January, 1971, that control of air and water pollution was considered by the public to be second only to the state of the economy as a most pressing problem.[2] Further, U.S. citizens currently express more willingness than in the past to pay personally and to have government pay to control and reduce pollution. And they show more definite feelings about who is responsible for pollution.[3]

Nationally, air and water pollution are identified almost equally as matters of public concern, although concern over specific forms of pollution

* For other opinion poll analyses relating to environmental pollution, see: Rita James Simon, "Public Attitudes Toward Population and Pollution," *Public Opinion Quarterly*, 35 (Spring, 1971), pp. 93–99, and Alvin W. Murch, "Public Concern for Environmental Pollution," *Public Opinion Quarterly*, 35 (Spring, 1971), pp. 100–106. The Simon and Murch articles were not cited in this discussion because of their regional focus.

varies regionally.[4] The discussion which follows is limited primarily to public opinion on water pollution and, more specifically, on water pollution by oil where it could be singled out.

II. WHO'S RESPONSIBLE FOR POLLUTION?

Industrial wastes are considered by Americans to be the major air and water pollutants. In a poll taken by Opinion Research Corporation (ORC) in May, 1970, for example, people were asked to look through a wide-ranging list of possible causes of air pollution and pick out those they thought to be the most important. The same question was asked about water pollution, with a list of possible causes provided. Of the people polled, 64 percent indicated "factories and plants" as one of the most important causes of air pollution, and 69 percent indicated the same source as one of the most important causes of water pollution. Vehicle exhausts ranked second as a cause of air pollution in this poll, and sewage ranked second as a cause of water pollution.[5]

Other pollutants of concern include domestic and farm byproducts, pesticides, and fertilizers. Natural pollutants, such as pollen, dust, and mud washing into streams, are the only causes of pollution which have declined in public censure. Again, specific concern varies regionally. People are most bothered by: exhaust in big cities in the Northeast and West, industry in the Midwest, and dust in the South. Insecticides and fertilizers are considered greater dangers to water supplies in the West than in any other part of the country.[6]

"To blame for water pollution"

Industry	Percent*
Chemical	62
Oil	49
Electric power	27
Steel	25
Pulp and paper	19
Auto manufacturers	17
Rubber	15

* Percent of all respondents (respondents could indicate more than one industry).

ORC found in the 1970 poll that seven industries headed the list as being responsible in the public's view for all types of environmental degradation.[7] On water pollution ORC reported the results shown in the accompanying table.

ORC conducted a series of polls between 1965 and 1970 which can be classified by geographic area—East, Midwest, South, and West. During this time period, the West showed the sharpest increase in the opinion that the oil industry is one of the industries most responsible for water pollution. The 1970 poll, for example, showed a significant increase over the 1968 poll, an increase from 26 to 36 percent of people polled who believed that the oil industry was one of those most responsible for water pollution. In only the 1970 poll did

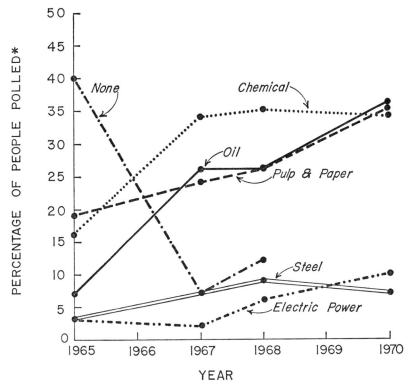

Fig. 44. Industries Considered Most Responsible for Water Pollution in the U.S. West

*Source: This information is based on public opinion polls conducted by Opinion Research Corp., in 1965, 1967, 1968, and 1970. Since the people polled were asked to choose from a list of industries "the ones you think are most responsible for water pollution in this part of the country," they had the option of choosing more than one industry.

the oil industry outrank both the chemical and pulp and paper industries as most responsible for water pollution. In her analysis of this finding and other recent opinion poll results, Erskine stated that "oil pollution leaps to first place regionally only for water pollution in the West, obviously because of the widely publicized oil slick disasters on the Pacific Coast."[8] She is referring to the two major oil spills which occurred in the Santa Barbara Channel during 1969. Change in public opinion concerning industry responsibility for water pollution in the West is illustrated in Figure 44.

III. POLLUTION CONTROL EFFORTS

Agent	Positive (%)*	Negative (%)*
Government		
Local	35	65
State	34	66
Federal	33	67
Local industry	32	68
Fellow citizens	18	82

*Respondents gave one response for each item.

A November, 1966, Harris poll[9] asked people to rate the job done by local, state, and federal government, by local industry, and by fellow citizens to control water pollution as excellent, pretty good, only fair, or poor. The responses are shown in the accompanying table. Americans' pessimism about pollution control efforts was also evidenced more recently in a May, 1970, ORC poll.[10] When asked how much effort companies in general are devoting to air and water pollution control, people responded as follows:

Very little	Fair amount	Great deal	No opinion
41%	41%	11%	7%

Corporate executives, when surveyed by ORC in May, 1965, expressed a different view of their own companies' efforts toward pollution control.[11] Most of the executives believed that their companies were putting forth a satisfactory effort in working with government officials on pollution problems, in developing pollution control techniques, and in working with other companies to control pollution. In this regard the only area in which most of them felt more attention was needed was informing the public of pollution control efforts.

As might be expected, recognition by the public of problems associated with pollution outshines consensus on solutions. A February, 1969, Gallup poll[12] indicated that, in comparison with previously cited poll results, solutions are harder to agree upon than placing blame for a problem. When people were asked what could be done to correct the water pollution problem, three responses dominated:

Stop industrial pollution	26%
Enforce present laws, pass new legislation	23%
Don't know	27%

Other responses were scattered through a wide range of possible solutions.

IV. IS THE PUBLIC WILLING TO PAY TO STOP POLLUTION?

Although Americans have shown little consensus on pollution problem-solving approaches, they have indicated their willingness to make some personal sacrifices to stop pollution. In a survey conducted by ORC[13] in

February, 1971, people were asked to suppose that a plant in their neighborhood, which employed many of their neighbors, was causing severe pollution and could not be fixed. Then they were asked if they would be in favor of closing down the plant to stop the pollution, or not. Their responses were:

	Put up with	Should not	Other,
Close down	pollution	have to choose*	No opinion
45%	22%	21%	12%

* Volunteered response.

It might be generalized from these results that if 45 percent of the people polled would be willing to shut down a local polluting plant in which they had some personal stake, and if the poll result is actually a representative opinion, there might be even less public reluctance to shut down a plant in which relatively few had personal involvement. For example, public support might easily be aroused for stronger federal legislation to control pollution from mine-mouth power plants or offshore oil wells if people thought they were causing severe environmental damage.

Willingness to spend government and personal funds to control pollution seems to be increasing. Harris polls showed an increase from 44 percent in 1967 to 59 percent in 1971 of people surveyed willing to pay $15 per year more in taxes to finance federal air pollution control programs.[14] Another Harris poll conducted in July, 1969, indicated 22 percent of people polled willing to accept a $200 per year increase in family expenses for real clean-up of the natural environment, and 55 percent willing to accept a $20 per year increase.[15]

Many of the poll results concerning the public's willingness to pay to stop pollution are difficult to interpret because of the scattered nature of the questions on this aspect of the pollution problem. This points to a need for greater consistency in the polling process aimed at determining public opinion on pollution. In the overview, however, there seems to be a well-established trend toward willingness to pay, but uncertainty as to how much the American citizen is willing to pay to stop pollution.[16]

1. Hazel Erskine, "The Polls: Pollution and its Costs," *Public Opinion Quarterly*, 36 (Spring, 1972), p. 120.

2. *Ibid.*, p. 125. This article reports the results of 36 opinion polls on environmental pollution. Many of these indicate a high-priority concern for pollution control. See, for example, polls by: Harris, April 3, 1967 (p. 126); Harris, July, 1969 (pp. 127–128); California Poll, August, 1969 (p. 129); Gallup Poll, October, 1969 (p. 130); California Poll, August, 1970 (p. 130); and Harris, August, 1971 (p. 131).

3. *Ibid.*, p. 120.

4. Hazel Erskine, "The Polls: Pollution and Industry," *Public Opinion Quarterly*, 36 (Summer, 1972), pp. 268–69. In a February 1969 Gallup poll, 2 out of 3 people polled listed air or water pollution as the most pressing environmental problem. Responses from these people were about equally divided between air pollution and water pollution.

5. *Ibid.,* pp. 265–66. Poll data are from Opinion Research Corporation, May, 1970.

6. *Ibid.*, p. 263.

7. *Ibid.*

8. *Ibid.*, p. 264. Poll data are from Opinion Research Corporation, 1965, 1967, 1968, and 1970 (pp. 272–73).

9. *Ibid.*, p. 277. Poll data are from Louis Harris and Associates, November 1966.

10. *Ibid.* Poll data are from Opinion Research Corporation, May 1970.

11. *Ibid.*, p. 276. Poll data are from Opinion Research Corporation, May 1965.

12. *Ibid.*, p. 269. Poll data are from a Gallup Poll, February 1969.

13. *Ibid.*, p. 280. Poll data are from Opinion Research Corporation, February 1971.

14. Erskine, "Pollution and Its Costs," p. 132. Poll data are from Louis Harris and Associates, July 24, 1967, April 23, 1970, and June 9–15, 1971.

15. *Ibid.*, p. 133. Poll data are from Louis Harris and Associates, July 10, 1969.

16. A comparison of the polls conducted in order to determine willingness to pay indicates the general trend toward willingness and the uncertainty as to how much Americans are willing to pay. See, for comparison, polls by: Harris, July 1970; ORC, January–February 1971 (2 questions); and Roper, October 1971 in Erskine, "Pollution and Its Costs," pp. 134–35.

Appendix B. Oil Pollution and Accidents

OUR OBJECTIVE in this appendix is to present a comprehensive analysis of oil pollution and accidents associated with oil and gas operations. Our analyses are presented in five major categories: OCS Oil Pollution in Perspective, Major Accidents in OCS Operations, Major Oil Spill Accidents, Chronic Oil Pollution, and Future Considerations and Comparisons. Three annexes provide difficult-to-obtain data: Workman Safety, Major Accidents by Company, and A Data Base for Offshore Accidents.

OCS OIL POLLUTION IN PERSPECTIVE

The annual average direct influx of all polluting oil into the waters of the world for 1969 and 1970 is estimated to be approximately 35 million barrels (5 million metric tons).

OIL POLLUTION IN THE WORLD'S WATERS

Of the total of all polluting oil in the world's waters, approximately 30 percent can be attributed to tankers and tank barges and 17 percent to all other vessels. Slightly less than 50 percent came from non-marine operations such as industrial and petrochemical plants, refineries, and the disposal of automobile crankcase oil.

Normal offshore oil and gas operations contributed only about 2 percent of the total. This figure is somewhat misleading, since it does not include abnormal discharges and accidents. Table 18 provides a detailed breakdown of worldwide oil discharge by volume and percent. It presents more comprehensive and recent data than earlier estimates by Max Blumer,[1] the National Academy of Sciences–National Research Council (NAS–NRC),[2] the Environmental Protection Agency (EPA),[3] and the Study of Critical Environmental Problems (SCEP).[4]

These previous estimates ranged from a low of 14.5 million barrels (SCEP) to a high of 70 million barrels (Blumer). The low estimate by SCEP was due primarily to an estimation of only 3.2 million barrels from rivers and sewage outfalls carrying industrial and automotive wastes. The high estimate by Blumer was based to a large extent on newspaper clippings and Blumer's assumptions. Although many sources were not included, Blumer's may be viewed as a valuable estimate. The most out-

**Table 18. Estimated Annual Direct and Indirect
Oil Pollution of the World's Waters, 1969–1970**

Source	Volume[a] (barrels)	Percent of Total Direct Pollution
Marine Operations	16,100,000	46.1
Tankers	9,710,000	27.7
LOT Tankers (ballast cleaning operations)[b]	1,860,000	5.3
Non-LOT Tankers (ballast cleaning operations)	4,910,000	14.0
Discharges (bilge, pumping, leaks, etc.)	700,000	2.0
Vessel casualties	1,750,000	5.0
Terminal operations	490,000	1.4
Tank Barges	490,000	1.4
Discharges (bilge, pumping, leaks, etc.)	140,000	0.4
Barge casualties	224,000	0.6
Terminal operations	126,000	0.4
All Other Vessels	5,950,000	17.0
Discharges (bilge pumping, leaks, etc.)	4,200,000	12.0
Vessel casualties	1,750,000	5.0
Non-Marine Operations	17,400,000	49.9
Refineries and petrochemical plants	2,100,000	6.0
Industrial machinery	5,250,000	15.0
Highway motor vehicles	10,100,000	28.9
Offshore Oil and Gas Operations	1,400,000	4.0
Normal Operations	700,000	2.0
Blowouts and Accidents	700,000	2.0
Total Direct Pollution	35,000,000	100.0
Natural Seepage[c]	«700,000	
Atmospheric Fallout	63,000,000[d] to 630,000,000	
Total Oil Pollution into World's Waters	98,000,000 to 665,000,000	

Sources: *Man's Impact on the Global Environment*, Report of the Study of Critical Environmental Problems (SCEP), Sponsored by Massachusetts Institute of Technology, (Cambridge, Mass.: MIT Press, 1970).

NAS-NRC, *Marine Environmental Quality* (Washington: National Academy of Sciences, 1971).

standing difference may be the figure of 19 million barrels of oil from tanker ballast cleaning operations. This compares with the seven million barrels shown in Table 18 from such cleaning operations.

The estimate of 700,000 barrels of oil lost from normal offshore operations is not discussed in detail in any of the studies, but all sources give the same figure. It was first reported in the SCEP study and was based on a survey by Exxon and the American Petroleum Institute (API). It included *only* normal operations; that is, accidents were *not* included. None of the sources gives an estimate of worldwide oil spills as a result of offshore blowouts and accidents. Some measure of the magnitude of such spills may be obtained by projecting the loss ratio of offshore U.S. production. This gives a figure close to the 700,000 barrels lost in normal operations and increases the contribution of all offshore operations to 4 percent of the total.

Two representative major U.S. spills and the associated spill volumes are the Union Oil blowout in the Santa Barbara Channel, variously estimated at 18,500 barrels to 780,000 barrels,[5] and the Shell blowout of 1970 in the Gulf of Mexico, estimated at 53,000 to 130,000 barrels.[6] The uncertainties involved in estimating worldwide spill volumes are obvious.

In foreign waters, a blowout in the Persian Gulf in 1971 spilled an estimated 200,000 barrels.[7] A year earlier, in 1970, a Saudi Arabian pipeline ruptured during a storm and spilled an estimated 100,000 barrels into Tarut Bay.[8] From the above examples, it appears that the 1.4 million barrels attributed to worldwide offshore operations may be considered a reasonable estimate.

During 1969–1970, approximately 9 billion barrels of petroleum was transported by tanker and barge each year. The amount lost to the world's waters was about 0.1 percent of the total. Of the total annual world production of 14 billion barrels, approximately 0.2 percent was lost.

DISTRIBUTION OF OIL POLLUTION

Because tanker transport operations, offshore production, and other sources of oil pollution are not geographically uniform, the base load of hydro-

---

U.S. Department of the Interior, *Final Environmental Impact Statement: Proposed Trans-Alaska Pipeline*, Vol. 3: *Environmental Setting Between Port Valdez, Alaska, and West Coast Ports* (Washington: Government Printing Office, 1972).

Technology Assessment Group, Science and Public Policy Program, University of Oklahoma.

[a] Divide by 7 to convert barrels to metric tons.

[b] LOT means load on top.

[c] « means very much less than.

[d] SCEP.

[e] NAS–NRC.

carbons or the concentrated accident sources tend to produce a non-uniform distribution of oil pollution in the oceans. As might be expected, the highest concentrations occur near ports and harbors, along tanker and cargo routes, and in semi-enclosed seas such as the Mediterranean, the Black Sea, the North Sea, the Persian Gulf, and the Gulf of Mexico. The total area of these bodies of water is just over 2 percent of the world's oceans, but about 25 percent of the total oil pollution from ship and land sources can be expected to occur in those waters. Future oil development in the Alaskan North Slope and the Canadian northern archipelago could produce serious contamination in the Arctic Ocean. On the high seas, winds and ocean currents concentrate oil pollution in the subarctic and equatorial convergence zones such as the Sargasso Sea.[9]

Natural Seeps: One useful way to study environmental pollutants is to compare naturally occurring and man-made pollutants. If the man-made component is small, there is little reason for concern. On the other hand, if the man-made source is large, adverse effects can be expected. Both SCEP[10] and NAS–NRC[11] have estimated worldwide seepage from geological formations to be considerably less than 700,000 barrels per year. This is less than 2 percent of the amount that man introduces directly into the world's waters.

One specific case is noteworthy. At Coal Oil Point, near Santa Barbara, California, the estimated annual seepage rate from natural seeps is 18,500 barrels according to the USGS. An independent study, quoted by the Division of Oil and Gas of the State of California, estimated the rate to be 50 to 70 barrels of oil per day.[12] On an annual basis, this amounts to between 18,200 and 25,600 barrels. Interestingly enough, the low estimate is about the same as the amount estimated by USGS to have been spilled from Union Oil's Platform A blowout in the Santa Barbara Channel.

Atmospheric Fallout of Airborne Hydrocarbons: The estimated emission of petroleum hydrocarbons to the air in 1970 was about 630 million barrels.[13] This is about 18 times the 35 million barrels lost directly to the world's waters. A fraction of the 630 million barrels exists as very small particles or is caught in rain. Much of it may settle out on the surface of the ocean.

NAS–NRC implies that all 630 million barrels may find their way to the oceans. SCEP assumes that 10 percent settles onto the ocean. This 63 million barrels is roughly twice the direct influx of oil into the world's waters and is expected to increase to 126 million barrels by 1980.

This effect is important for two reasons. First, oil is dispersed over wide ocean areas and could concentrate chlorinated hydrocarbons such as DDT and dieldrin which are highly soluble in oil films. The effect would be that

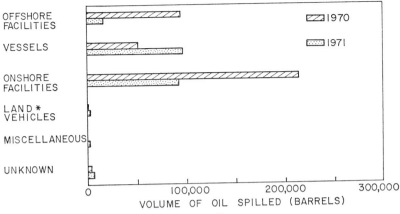

*Apparently does not include crankcase oil.

Fig. 45. Oil Pollution from Offshore Facilities in Perspective
Source: U.S., Department of Transportation, Coast Guard, "Polluting Incidents in and around U.S. Waters, 1970–1971" (unpublished data).

the small larval stages of fishes and plant and animal plankton, which spend part of the night hours quite near the surface, are likely to extract and concentrate still further the chlorinated hydrocarbons present in the surface layer.[14] The second reason is that thin oil films can alter the interchange between the atmosphere and the oceans and could possibly alter the climate. The mechanism is a reduction of turbulence, evaporation, and the radiation emission of the surface. It is still unknown whether the contribution by oil pollution is significant.[15]

OIL POLLUTION IN U.S. WATERS

Some perspective on oil pollution from OCS oil and gas operations can be gained by reviewing the 1970 and 1971 Coast Guard data of *Polluting Incidents in and Around U.S. Waters*.[16] As of this printing, 1972 oil spill data were not available. A comparison between oil pollution from offshore facilities and other polluting sources, such as vessels, onshore facilities, and land vehicles, is shown in the bar graphs in Figure 45 and in tabular form in Table 19. In 1970, offshore facilities contributed 25.6 percent of the total volume of oil spilled whereas in 1971 the contribution was only 7.5 percent.* For both years, the percentage contribution to the *number* of spills was unchanged (roughly 25 percent). The absolute number of spills, however,

* In 1972, the offshore facilities contributed 5,644 barrels, or 1.3 percent of the total volume spilled.

Table 19. Polluting Incidents in and Around U.S. Waters, 1970 and 1971

Source	Number of Spills	Percent of Total	Volume (Barrels)	Percent of Total
Offshore facilities				
1971	2,595	29.7	15,767	7.5
1970	882	23.8	93,019[a]	25.6
Vessels				
1971	2,134	24.4	92,911	44.1
1970	1,217	32.8	51,037	14.1
Onshore facilities				
1971	1,338	15.4	91,982	43.7
1970	710	19.1	215,200	59.3
Land vehicles[b]				
1971	77	0.9	2,410	1.2
1970	25	0.7	769	0.2
Miscellaneous				
1971	239	2.7	1,453	0.7
1970	23	0.6	5	0.0
Unknown				
1971	2,353	26.9	5,941	2.8
1970	854	23.0	3,137	2.9
Total				
1971	8,736	100.0	210,464	100.0
1970	3,711	100.0	363,167	100.0

Source: U.S., Department of Transportation, Coast Guard, "Polluting Incidents in and Around U.S. Waters, 1970–1971" (unpublished data).

[a] Most of the offshore facilities pollution for 1970 was from two blowouts, which spilled 83,500 barrels of oil.

[b] Apparently does not include crankcase oil.

changed because of a change in reporting small spills which took place during the last quarter of 1970. The large difference in the volume of oil spilled resulted from two offshore blowouts in the Gulf of Mexico, the Chevron and Shell platform production-blowouts, which spilled a combined 83,500 barrels.

The two other major categories, vessels and onshore facilities, showed large changes from 1970 to 1971, owing primarily to a few very large tanker spills and storage tank ruptures.

DISTRIBUTION

Most oil polluting incidents in and around the United States take place in areas of high population density and shipping activity. Table 20 shows that between 75 percent and 90 percent of the spill volume takes place in inland and coastal waters. As with Table 19, the Coast Guard figures do not include discarded crankcase oil from highway vehicles. It is reasonable to expect that the total oil introduced into inland and coastal waters is actually much higher than the data would indicate.

Table 21, which relates oil pollution to specific areas, shows the wide variation in both volume and incidents from year to year. For the Gulf Coast, where major OCS oil operations take place, the total volume resulting from polluting incidents was 12.1 percent in 1971 and 31.5 percent in 1970. For the Pacific Coast, where there are some OCS and state offshore oil operations, the contribution was 24.6 percent in 1971 and only 2.8 percent in 1970. Much of the 1970 total can be attributed to tanker spillage. The Atlantic Coast, where there were no offshore operations, contributed 19.3 percent in 1971 and 33.5 percent in 1970, again primarily from tanker operations. For the Great Lakes, the contribution was 28 percent for 1971 and 26.0 percent for 1970. This is primarily from waterborne transportation and industrial operations. It is interesting to note that in 1971 more than twice as much oil was discharged into the Great Lakes as into the waters off the Gulf coast.

Table 20. Polluting Incidents by Location, 1970 and 1971

Location	Number of Spills	Percent of Total	Volume (Barrels)	Percent of Total
Inland waters				
1971	631	7.2	33,568	16.0
1970	174	4.7	37,068	10.2
Coastal waters[a]				
1971	7,516	86.1	160,905	76.4
1970	2,784	75.1	227,544	62.7
Contiguous zone				
1971	396	4.5	15,504	7.4
1970	349	9.4	74,796	20.6
High seas				
1971	193	2.2	488	0.2
1970	404	10.9	23,759	6.5
Total				
1971	8,736	100.0	210,465	100.0
1970	3,711	100.0	363,166	100.0

Source: U.S., Department of Transportation, Coast Guard, "Polluting Incidents in and Around U.S. Waters, 1970–1971" (unpublished data).

a Includes the Great Lakes.

Table 21. Polluting Incidents by General Area, 1970 and 1971

General Area	Number of Spills	Percent of Total	Volume (Barrels)	Percent of Total
Atlantic Coast				
1971	2,145	24.6	40,565	19.3
1970	886	23.9	121,620	33.5
Gulf Coast[a]				
1971	3,974	45.5	25,482	12.1
1970	1,766	47.6	114,223	31.5
Pacific Coast				
1971	1,609	18.4	51,872	24.6
1970	717	19.3	10,227	2.8
Great Lakes				
1971	377	4.3	58,977	28.0
1970	216	5.8	97,463	26.8
Inland				
1971	631	7.2	33,568	16.0
1970	126	3.4	19,634	5.4
Total				
1971	8,736	100.0	210,465	100.0
1970	3,711	100.0	363,166	100.0

Source: U.S., Department of Transportation, Coast Guard, "Polluting Incidents in and Around U.S. Waters, 1970–1971" (unpublished data).

[a] West of Longitude 83° 15′.

A tabulation of the type of material which is spilled into and around U.S. waters shows that roughly one-third is light oil, one-third heavy oil, and one-third other types of oil. (See Table 22.) Light oil is defined by the Coast Guard as gasoline, light fuel oil, kerosene, and light crude oil. Heavy oil is defined to include diesel oil, heating oil, fuel oil, heavy crude, and asphalt. From the standpoint of lethality to marine organisms, gasoline and light oils have been found to be considerably more dangerous than heavy crudes.

MAJOR ACCIDENTS FROM OCS OIL AND GAS OPERATIONS

A major accident is one resulting in injury and property or environmental damage involving fixed structures. There were 43 of these in OCS oil and gas operations from 1953 through 1972. The causes and results of these accidents are listed in Table 23.

A historical correlation shows an overall increase in the frequency of major accidents corresponding to an increase in OCS oil and gas operations. This is demonstrated in Figures 46 and 47. (OCS oil/condensate and gas production[17] and the number of major accidents by causal factors are plotted for the time period 1953–1972 in these two figures.) Since the peak occurred in 1968, the number of accidents has decreased through 1972. It should be noted, however, that four major platform accidents— Union Oil in the Santa Barbara Channel (1969) and Chevron (1970), Shell (1970), and Amoco (1971) in the Gulf of Mexico—have all occurred since 1968.

The Gulf of Mexico accounts for some 99 percent of cumulative production and more than 90 percent of 1972 OCS oil and gas production. Because of this, most of what will be discussed in this section pertains to the Gulf of Mexico.

Table 22. Type of Material Discharged in and Around U.S. Waters, 1970 and 1971

Type of Material	Number of Spills	Percent of Total	Volume (Barrels)	Percent of Total
Light oil[a]				
1971	4,320	49.5	67,202	31.9
1970	770	20.8	64,282	43.4
Heavy oil[b]				
1971	1,603	18.4	69,861	33.2
1970	2,462	66.4	121,196	33.9
Lubricating oil				
1971	168	1.9	533	0.3
1970	38	1.0	241	0.1
Other oil				
1971	462	5.3	63,645	30.2
1970	65	1.8	78,182	21.5
Other[c]				
1971	1,238	14.1	7,103	3.4
1970	376	10.1	4,189	1.1
Unknown				
1971	945	10.8	2,121	1.0
1970	—	—	—	—
Total				
1971	8,736	100.0	210,465	100.0
1970	3,711	100.0	363,166	100.0

Source: U.S., Department of Transportation, Coast Guard, "Polluting Incidents in and Around U.S. Waters, 1970–1971" (unpublished data).

a Gasoline, light fuel oil, kerosene, light crude.

b Diesel oil, heating oil, heavy fuel oil, heavy crude, asphalt.

c Animal or vegetable oil, waste oil, sewage, refuse and garbage, dredge spill, other material (1971); hazardous materials and chemicals, other chemical waste, any gas or vapor, other waste (1970).

Table 23. Forty-three Major Accidents on the Outer Continental Shelf 1953–1972: Causal Factors and Results

Results	Causal Factor					Total
	Drilling	Production	Pipeline	Collision	Weather	
Number	19	15	4	2	3	43
Oil	0	3	4	1	3	11
Oil and gas	2	7	0	0	0	9
Gas	17	2	0	0	0	19
Other	0	3	0	1	0	3
Oil spills	2	10	4	1	3	20
Oil volume (barrels)	18,500–780,000	84,000–135,400	175,000	2,600	9,200–9,700	290,000–1,100,000
Deaths	23	33	0	0	0	56
Injuries	7–8	91–100	0	0	0	98–108
Fires	7	12	0	1	0	20
Major rig/ platform damage	4	9	0	2	0	15
Duration	2 hrs.–5.5 mos.	10 min.–4.5 mos.	1–13 days	1 day	1–3 days	10 min.–5.5 mos.

Sources: Data came primarily from USGS, Coast Guard, *Offshore*, and *Oil and Gas Journal*.

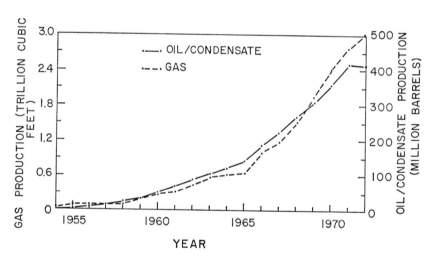

Fig. 46. Oil/Condensate and Gas Production on the Outer Continental Shelf, 1954–1972
Source: USGS.

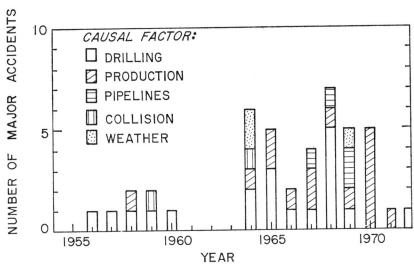

Fig. 47. Forty-Three Major Accidents by Causal Factors on the Outer Continental Shelf, 1954–1972

Sources: *Offshore; Oil and Gas Journal;* and U.S., Department of the Interior, Geological Survey, Conservation Division, "Incidents on the Outer Continental Shelf Resulting in Injury and Property or Environmental Damage (1953 to November 17, 1971)" (unpublished data).

DRILLING ACCIDENTS

The purpose of this section is to describe the past yearly rate of major drilling accidents and to estimate, for forecasting purposes, the probability of the occurrence of a future major accident. All of the 19 major drilling accidents listed resulted in blowouts. Seventeen resulted from high pressure gas only. Two of the drilling blowouts involved both oil and gas; one of these was the Santa Barbara blowout.

An examination of the drilling and blowout rate over the period 1953–1971 reveals that there were two time periods during which most blowouts occurred: 1956–1960 and 1964–1969. During these two periods, the percentage of new well starts resulting in drilling blowouts was a little less than 0.2 percent.[18]

There appears to have been no decrease in the percentage of blowouts over the years. If only blowouts from wells producing oil and gas are counted for the period 1964–1971, the percentage is 0.03 percent. If it is assumed that, in the future, blowouts persist at the rate for the period 1964–1971, then for every 10,000 new well starts, it can be expected that there will be 19 gas well blowouts and three oil and gas well blowouts.

Since BLM's tentative five-year schedule for the Gulf of Mexico[19] indicates that as many as 4,500 holes may be drilled, the figures reported above suggest that there will be nine gas well blowouts and one oil and gas well blowout over the five-year period. This pattern has already been borne out in part, since in 1972 there was one gas well blowout on the OCS and two in Louisiana state waters.

By using a Poisson probability model, a model commonly used to describe random events, the probability of at least one gas or oil and gas blowout can be calculated for any given year. As used here, the model assumes a drilling rate of 900 new well starts per year, the drilling rate for the past few years. The drilling rate also can be inferred from BLM's tentative five-year leasing schedule. On the basis of these figures, the probability of at least one serious gas or oil and gas blowout from drilling operations is 92 percent per year.

OCS drilling blowouts can also be compared with conditions on land. According to Rush Johnson & Associates, a Houston insurance firm, 106 blowouts occurred in drilling 273,000 wells in eight major oil-producing states from 1960 through 1970.[20] Thus the percentage of wells drilled resulting in blowouts is 0.039 percent. Most of the blowouts reported onshore are from high pressure gas wells rather than from wells producing oil and gas. The same is true offshore on the OCS. The blowout rate onshore is a factor of five smaller than on the OCS. This factor may represent a reasonable limit which can be achieved easily.

PRODUCTION ACCIDENTS

There were 15 major production accidents between 1953 and 1972. The period 1964–1971 was chosen as the period on which to base accident rate calculations since it was a period when oil and gas production increased sharply and for which spill data are available. This is also the period during which there were three major platform fires and blowouts in the Gulf of Mexico. The average accident rate for this period is 0.034 percent of wells completed.[21] An examination of these data shows that the production accident rate is not decreasing. Therefore, it may be assumed for forecasting purposes that there will be no change in the near future.

On the basis of the average production accident rate, it is expected that for a cumulative 6,000 completed wells, there will be two major production accidents per year. Again by using a Poisson probability model, the probability of one or more accidents per year is estimated to be 87 percent. The tentative BLM five-year schedule estimates as much as a 50 percent increase in the number of wells drilled.[22] At the end of this period, it is expected that the number of major production accidents will increase to three per year with a probability of 95 percent of one or more occurring per year. No major production blowout was recorded by USGS for 1972.

PIPELINES

There have been four major pipeline accidents that spilled a total of 175,000 barrels. The largest spill, which occurred in 1967, was about 161,000 barrels and was caused by an anchor which bent the pipe. The pipe, operated by Humble Pipeline Company, spilled oil for as long as 10 days. (Two other spills were about 7,000 barrels each. One was caused by an anchor, and the cause for the other was unreported.)

A fourth pipeline accident was due to a split in a marine riser. This accident occurred in 1969 on Union Oil's Platform A in the Santa Barbara Channel and spilled about 900 barrels.

MAJOR OIL SPILL ACCIDENTS

The total amount of oil that has been reported spilled in major OCS accidents is 290,000–1,100,000 barrels for the period 1964–1972. The major accidents causing spilled oil occurred during drilling, production, and pipelining as shown in Table 23.

OCS OIL OPERATIONS

Before 1964, the volume of oil spilled was not reported. The large range in estimated quantity of spilled oil can be attributed to the difficulty of estimating spills from uncontrolled blowouts. For example, for the Santa Barbara blowout (1969), estimates range from 18,500 barrels (USGS) to an upper limit of 780,000 barrels (by Foster, Charters, and Neusel).[23] Another example is the Shell blowout in the Gulf of Mexico (1970). Estimates range from a low of 53,000 barrels (USGS) to an upper limit of 130,000 barrels (EPA).[24]

The average amount of oil spilled during the 1964–1971 period was 140–530 barrels per million barrels of oil and condensate produced. The low estimate corresponds to USGS figures. There are large variations from year to year depending on the size of a spill in a particular year. A measure of this is the standard deviation which, measured from the USGS average, is 230 barrels of oil spilled per million barrels of oil and condensate produced. The 1971 rate of oil spilled from major oil spill accidents is about 200 times smaller than the 1970 rate. Furthermore, the 1971 rate is about 100 times smaller than the USGS average for 1964–1971. The average amount of 140 barrels of oil spilled per million barrels of oil and condensate produced will be used for forecasting purposes later in this report. For 1972, according to USGS, the major oil spill record was 450 barrels.

Table 24. Major Oil Spills from Tankers

Date	Name	Location	Cause	Material	Barrels	Total Spill (Barrels)
1956						
9- 6	Seagate	25 miles N. Grays Harbor, WA	Grounding	Fuel oil	100,000 est.[a]	100,000
1957						
3-	Tampico	Pacific Coast, Baja Calif., Mex.[b]	Grounding	Diesel	60,000	60,000
1960						
9- 1	P. W. Thirtle	Narraganset, Newport, RI	Grounding	Bunker C	<142,000 est.[a]	142,000
1962						
7-17	Argea Prima	Guayanilla Harbor, PR[b]	Grounding	Crude	28,000	
9-20	Martita	Los Angeles Harbor	Collision	Bunker C	4,300	32,300
1967						
5- 2	Evie	Alaska	Grounding	Jet fuel	6-10,000	
9- 6	R. C. Stoner	Wake Island[b]	Grounding	Mixed	143,000	153,000
1968						
2- 8	Pegasos	270 miles E. Cape Hatteras, NC	Hull failure	Bunker C	2,000 est.[a]	
3- 3	Ocean Eagle	San Juan, PR[b]	Grounding	Crude	83,400	
3- 7	General Calocotronis	Eleuthera Island, Bahamas[b]	Grounding	Crude	21,000–37,000	
11- 5	Kenai Peninsula	Delaware River, Fort Miffin, PA	Collision	Crude	800-1,000	
12-13	Wituvater	Cristobal, CZ	Hull failure	Bunker C Diesel	15,000	138,400

1969						
2–9	*Algal*	Buzzards Bay, Long Island Sound	Grounding	#6 F.O.	up to 4,000	
3–4	*Yukon*	Cook Inlet, AK 120 miles SE.	Grounding	Crude	1,000	
11–5	*Keo*	Nantucket, MA	Hull failure	#4 F.O.	210,000	215,000
1970						
2–4	*Arrow*	Chedabucto Bay, Nova Scotia[b]	Grounding	Bunker C	36,430	
2–13	*Delian Apollon*	Tampa Bay, FL	Grounding	Bunker C	476	
3–29		New London, Harbor	Rupture	#2 F.O.	400	
6–13		New Haven Harbor, CT	Rupture	#4 and #6	857	38,163
1971						
1–18	*Oregon Standard*	San Francisco, CA	Collision	Bunker	20,000	
1–22	*Esso, Gettysburg*	Connecticut	Grounding	Kerosene and #2 F.O.	18,583	
6–24		California	—	Crude	1,553	
8–27	*Manatee*	California	Human error	NFO	5,463	45,599
1954–1971						924,000
1964–1971						590,000

Note: Major spills represent less than 2 percent of total spills from tankers.

Sources: Dillingham Corporation, *Systems Study of Oil Spill Cleanup Procedures*, Vol. 1: *Analysis of Oil Spills and Control Materials* (La Jolla, Calif.: Dillingham Corporation, 1970). National Petroleum Council, *Environmental Conservation, The Oil and Gas Industries*, (Washington: 1972) Vol. 2, pp. 244 and 252; U.S., Department of the Interior, Geological Survey, Conservation Division, *Recorded Oil Spill Incidents Involving 1,000 or More Barrels Since 1957*, July 29, 1971, and *Supplement No. 1*, December 31, 1971.

a Estimates are based on the description given by Dillingham.

b These accidents did not occur adjacent to the 50 U.S. states.

WATERBORNE TRANSPORTATION

Oil Tanker Accidents: This section describes major oil spills from tankers and compares them to OCS operations. A list of major oil spills in and around U.S. coastal waters is given in Table 24. A major oil spill is defined as one of approximately 1,000 barrels or more. The total amount of oil spilled for the period 1964–1971 is 590,000 barrels. This period was chosen in order to compare tanker spills with spills from OCS operations. The size of an oil spill from a tanker is easier to estimate than an OCS spill because of the finite size of the tankers. The average amount of oil spilled was 34 barrels per million barrels of oil transported.[25] There are large variations from one year to another. A measure of this is the standard deviation which, measured from the average, is 35 barrels of oil spilled per million barrels of oil transported. The spill rates for 1970 and 1971 were 17 and 21 barrels respectively per million barrels transported.

Although the volume of oil spilled from tankers is roughly within a factor of two of the oil spilled from OCS operations, the rate of spillage is considerably less, a factor of 4 or more. This is due to the large volume of oil transported, which is approximately 2.2 billion barrels per year.[26]

Tank Barges: Tank barges, which are not self-propelled, are a major source of oil pollution. While they are not usually used for waterborne transportation on the open ocean, they are used extensively in coastal and inland waterway transport. Coast Guard data from 1970 and 1971 show that tank barges contributed 88 percent and 42 percent respectively of oil spillage from petroleum transporting ships.[27] (See Table 25.) The average spill rate for 1970–1971 is about 16 barrels of oil spilled per million barrels of oil transported. This is about one-half of the rate for tankers.

Table 25. Tankers and Tank Barge Oil Spills in U.S. Waters, 1970–1971

Spills	Number of Spills[a]		Volume (barrels)	
	1970	1971	1970	1971
Tankers	247	386	5,080	39,600
Tank barges	381	828	39,400	28,500
Total	628	1,214	44,480	68,100

Source: U.S., Department of Transportation, Coast Guard, "Polluting Incidents in and Around U.S. Waters, 1970–1971."

[a] Includes river, harbor, lake, and estuary traffic.

CHRONIC OIL POLLUTION

The purpose of this section is to estimate the contribution of minor and moderate oil spills to total oil pollution from OCS oil operations.

OCS OIL OPERATIONS

Minor and Moderate Oil Spills: The causes of polluting spills for 1970 and 1971 are shown in Table 26. However, this data combines state and federal waters and extends only out to 12 miles from the shoreline: that is, OCS operations beyond 12 miles are not included.

Line leaks and pipe ruptures or leaks combined produced 1,643 spills of 13,309 barrels in 1971. This was 61 percent of the spills and 85 percent of the volume of oil spilled from offshore facilities. This was in a year when the only spill from an offshore blowout was Amoco's (500 barrels).

A comparison of 1971 with 1970 is revealing. First, in a year of platform accidents, the total volume of oil spilled is mostly by blowouts. In 1970, for example, three platform accidents from fire and explosion contributed 90 percent of the oil spilled. In 1971, as discussed above, 85 percent of the oil spilled was from line leaks and pipe ruptures or leaks. Second, personnel error decreased from 58 spills of 3,426 barrels in 1970 to 69 spills of 40 barrels in 1971. (This decrease may be due to increased number of categories shown for 1971 and the result of regulatory and public pressure.)

The best estimate for the spill rate is obtained by dividing the total volume of oil spilled for 1971 by all state and federal offshore production.[28] The estimate thus obtained is 26 barrels of oil spilled per million barrels of oil/condensate produced.

BLM reported the following for the OCS in 1971: 1,272 spills and 3,511 barrels of oil spilled.[29] This amounts to a spill rate of 9 barrels per million barrels produced. This data is incomplete since the area covered does not include the operations which take place in state waters. Combining the Coast Guard data for the region within the 12 mile limit with this data for the OCS yields a total spill rate for offshore operations of less than 35 barrels spilled per million barrels produced.

Waste Water: Waste water is defined as the water from the oil formation which is produced from a reservoir along with the oil. It is separated by passing the produced oil and water through separation and treating facilities. Additional treating facilities separate the entrained oil from the water, but treatment is less than 100 percent efficient. Present OCS orders have established an average limit of 50 parts per million of oil in water prior to disposal into the Gulf of Mexico. On the basis of data presented

Table 26. Cause, Number, and Volume of Oil Spills from Offshore Facilities in U.S. Waters, 1970 and 1971

Cause of Spill[a]	1971[b] Number of Spills	1971[b] Volume (Barrels)	1970[b] Number of Spills	1970[b] Volume (Barrels)
Fire and explosion	—[e]	—	3	83,500
Line leak	1,267	9,062	—	—
Pipe rupture or leak	376	4,247	21	1,205
Valve failure	325	734	9	1,255
Other rupture or leak	99	359	—	—
Pump failure	173	277	14	84
Collision	1	167	—	—
Other equipment failure	57	149	—	—
Tank overflow	29	64	10	542
Hose rupture or leak	21	49	8	129
Other personnel error	69	40	58	3,426
Natural phenomena	14	19	3	0
Improper hose connection	15	18	—	—
Storage tank rupture	10	11	10	1,140
Intentional causes	6	6	—	—
Other casualty	5	3	—	—
Minor hull structural failure	1	3	3	216
Vessel tank rupture	2	2	—	—
Automatic shutdown device failure	—	—	1	395
Alarm failure	—	—	1	0
Unknown causes	125	557	20	220
Total	2,595	15,767	161[d]	92,113[d]

Source: U.S., Department of Transportation, Coast Guard, "Polluting Incidents In and Around U.S. Waters, 1970–1971."

[a] Reporting requirements differ between 1970 and 1971.

[b] —means not reported.

[e] The AMOCO fire spill of 500 barrels may be included in unknown causes.

[d] This excluded 721 minor spills which accounted for an additional 906 barrels.

by BLM for 1971, approximately 3,600 barrels of oil were introduced into the Gulf of Mexico from waste water.[30] On this basis, the spill rate is about 9 barrels per million barrels of oil/condensate produced.

TANKER OPERATIONS

Minor and Moderate Oil Spills: The purpose of this section is to investigate the contribution of minor and moderate oil spills to total oil pollution from tanker operations. The cause, number, and volume of oil spills from tanker operations have been tabulated for 1970 and 1971 as shown in Table 27. The causes are arranged in decreasing volume for 1971. The distinctive feature of this list is that the collision and grounding categories contributed to the bulk of the volume of spilled oil. For 1971, this contribution was 92 percent, and for 1970 it was 61 percent. The rest of the spilled oil came from a large number of small spills for a large variety of causes, as shown in Table 27. In 1971, there were 367 spills, excluding collision and grounding, resulting in an average spill of about 9 barrels. For 1970, the situation was similar, 231 spills resulting in an average spill of about 9 barrels. The increase in the number of spills for 1971 may be due to the change in re-

Table 27. Cause, Number, and Volume of Oil Spills from Tankers in U.S. Waters, 1970 and 1971

Cause of Spill	1971[a]		1970[a]	
	Number of Spills	Volume (Barrels)	Number of Spills	Volume (Barrels)
Collision	6	26,152	4	700
Grounding	13	10,239	12	2,382
Other equipment failure	37	666	1	—
Other rupture or leak	34	662	—	—
Hose rupture	16	459	15	118
Valve failure	17	306	18	30
Other personnel failure	58	271	87	494
Line leak	8	203	—	—
Tank overflow	18	127	13	93
Storage tank rupture or leak	19	84	—	—
Pipe rupture or leak	10	73	10	125
Intentional discharge	22	47	9	16
Tank rupture	8	37	18	901
Hull structural failure	8	22	4	50
Pump failure	5	26	9	70
Improper hose connection	5	15	—	—
Other casualty	2	6	—	—
Natural phenomenon	3	2	2	25
Capsizing/overturning	—	—	6	Unknown
Unknown	97	253	30	55
Total	386	39,650	239[b]	5,060[b]

Source: U.S., Department of Transportation, Coast Guard, "Polluting Incidents In And Around U.S. Waters, 1970–1971." Reporting procedures differ between 1970 and 1971.

a —means not reported.

b This excludes 8 minor spills which accounted for an additional 30 barrels.

porting procedures. With the exclusion of collisions and groundings, the volume for minor and moderate spills is 3,260 barrels for 1971 and 2,010 barrels for 1970. The volume of petroleum moved by tanker was approximately 2.25 billion barrels per year for 1970 and 1971. Therefore, for 1971, the spill rate was 1.4 barrels of oil spilled per million barrels of oil moved by tanker. The spill rate for 1970 was 0.9 barrels per million barrels moved.

Waste Water: Tank cleaning operations is the one other source of chronic oil pollution. According to the Coast Guard, load-on-top (LOT) tank cleaning operations discharge 270 barrels of oil per million barrels of oil transported worldwide by LOT tankers.[31] This is the preferred method of shipping from the point of view of minimizing oil discharge. Non-LOT tank cleaning operations discharge 2,160 barrels of oil per million barrels of oil transported by non-LOT tankers. This is eight times the discharge rate compared to LOT tankers. The present mix of tankers, which is 75 percent LOT, discharges 740 barrels of oil per million barrels of oil transported by tanker. The Intergovernmental Maritime Consultative Organization (IMCO) proposed in the 1959 amendments to the 1954 Convention that not more than 67 barrels of oil per million barrels (.0067 percent) of the total cargo capacity of a tanker be discharged.[32]

FUTURE CONSIDERATIONS AND COMPARISONS

In this section, the total oil pollution from OCS oil and gas operations will be compared to imports and the proposed tanker link of TAPS. Comparisons will be made for the U.S. and worldwide. Total oil pollution is broken down into the three categories discussed previously: major oil pollution accidents, minor and moderate spills, and waste water/ballast water pollution. The basis for this breakdown stems from the different environmental impact of each category. All spill or discharge rates are based on a production or transport rate of 2 million barrels per day.

OCS OPERATIONS

The quantity of potential oil spills and discharges into U.S. and worldwide waters from OCS operations are summarized from the preceding discussion. They are shown in Table 28 at a production rate of 2 million barrels of oil/condensate per day produced and pipelined to shore. This rate was chosen since it represents potential 1985 production and can be compared directly with TAPS (North Slope Alaska). The total of the averages ranges from a low of 350 barrels per day to a high of 1,130 barrels per day. This range is due to the uncertainty in major spills.

Table 28. Quantities of Potential Oil Spills and Discharges into U.S. and World Waters

Source	Major Accidents	Minor and Moderate Spills	Ballast or Waste Water Treatment	Total
OCS	280–1060[a]	52[b]	18[c]	350–1,130
TAPS	68[d]–384[e]	6[f]	26[g]–540[h]	100–416 (ballast treatment)
				614–930 (100% LOT)
Imports				
U.S. waters	68[d]	3[i]	0[j]	71
World's waters	384[e]	6[f]	540[h]	930[k]–2,100[l]

Note: Table is based on barrels per day for 2,000,000 barrels per day produced and transported.

[a] Based on 1964–1971 experience on the OCS, 280 is from USGS data.
[b] Based on 1971 Coast Guard spill data for offshore facilities in U.S. waters.
[c] Based on 1971 Gulf of Mexico OCS data.
[d] Based on 1964–1971 experience in and around U.S. waters.
[e] Based on 1969–1970 worldwide casualty analysis.
[f] Based on 1971 Coast Guard spill data for tankers (twice because moving between two ports).
[g] Ballast treatment facility with an effluent of 20 parts per million.
[h] 100% LOT tankers.
[i] Based on 1971 Coast Guard spill data for tankers.
[j] No ballast or waste water treatment is needed in U.S. ports.
[k] Excludes pollution from foreign offshore production.
[l] Includes pollution from foreign offshore production.

IMPORTS

In and Around U.S. Waters: The average quantity of oil spilled from major accidents and from minor and moderate spills is the same as discussed above under tankers. Since the disposal of ballast takes place on the high seas or in foreign ports, these disposals produce little contribution to oil pollution in and around U.S. waters. On this basis, the total quantity of oil spilled averages 71 barrels per day, as shown in Table 28.

World's Waters: The average quantity of oil spilled from major accidents, 384 barrels per day, is based on a worldwide analysis conducted for 1969 and 1970 by Porricelli, Keith, and Storch,[33] and the Coast Guard. This spill rate is higher than the spill rate for the U.S. because of the high shipping density and shallow waters in and around the English Channel.[34] However, since the world rate is of interest here, the 384 barrel per day quantity is the best estimate.

The minor and moderate average spill rate of 6 barrels per day is twice the 1971 spill rate as analyzed earlier for tankers operating in the U.S. The reason for taking twice the rate is that spill rates may occur both in foreign and U.S. ports. For ballast water, an estimated 540 barrels per day will be discharged assuming that the tankers use LOT ballast techniques. (It is doubtful that IMCO regulations or ballast treatment facilities will be used.) The total amount of oil pollution is an average of 930 barrels per day, as shown in Table 28.

This estimate of the contribution of tankers to oil pollution has ignored the fact that imports will come primarily from foreign offshore production, for example, Lake Maracaibo, Venezuela, and the Persian Gulf. World-wide normal offshore production contributes 600 barrels of oil pollution per two million barrels of oil produced. Major oil pollution accidents, such as blowouts, add approximately another 600 barrels per day. The total of about 1,200 barrels per day should be added to the 930 barrels per day to give a more accurate picture of the extent to which imported oil pollutes the world's waters. This amounts to roughly 2,100 barrels per day as the total discharge to the world's waters.

TANKER LINK OF TAPS

Since the tanker link of TAPS has not yet been built, there is no direct experience in estimating the oil pollution that system will cause. Nevertheless, U.S. and worldwide experience can be used to estimate potential oil spills and discharges from tankers shuttling back and forth from Valdez to West Coast ports.

The range of oil spilled from major accidents is from 68 to 384 barrels per day. The low estimate is from U.S. experience over the period 1964–1971 (as explained earlier under the discussion of tankers). The high estimate is based on a worldwide analysis for 1969–1970 (as discussed above under imports).

The minor and moderate spill rate of 6 barrels per day is twice the 1971 spill rate analyzed above for tankers. This is because the tankers will be operating uniquely between U.S. ports. The range for ballast or waste water treatment depends on the system adopted. Upper and lower limits are given here. The lower limit of 26 barrels per day represents a ballast treatment facility in Valdez with an effluent standard of 20 parts per million.[35] The upper limit of 540 barrels per day would correspond to the discharge from tankers using LOT techniques. The total amount of oil pollution averages 100–416 barrels per day for a system using ballast treatment and 614–930 barrels per day for tankers using LOT techniques, as shown in Table 28.

COMPARISON

Source	Barrels/Day
In and Around U.S. Waters	
Imports	71
TAPS (ballast treatment)	100–416
OCS (low estimate)	350
TAPS (100 percent LOT)	614–930
OCS (high estimate)	1,130
World's Waters	
TAPS (ballast treatment)	100–416
OCS (low estimate)	350
TAPS (100 percent LOT)	614–930
OCS (high estimate)	1,130
Imports (including foreign offshore production)	2,100

The three sources of future oil can be ranked according to the degree of pollution. From the least polluting to the most polluting, they are listed in the accompanying table. From this ranking, it is seen that, for in and around U.S. waters, imports are the least polluting; as for the world's waters, imports are the most polluting.

FUTURE DEVELOPMENTS

Worldwide offshore petroleum production was 3.2 billion barrels in 1971, which was 19 percent of worldwide production.[36] It is estimated that offshore production may be as high as 12.8 billion barrels by 1980.[37] If worldwide offshore oil pollution persists at the same rate, as of 1969–1970, then this source will contribute as much as 4 million barrels of oil to the world's waters. This estimate is slightly more than 10 percent of the 1969–1970 average of total oil pollution of 35 million barrels.

One area in which rapid improvement could be achieved is ballasting techniques. Table 18 shows that 4,910,000 barrels per year come from cleaning operations of non-LOT tankers whereas only 1,860,000 barrels per year come from LOT tankers. However, only 25 percent of the world fleet are non-LOT tankers. If these were to be converted to LOT tankers, their discharge rate would be reduced from 4,910,000 barrels per year to 617,000 barrels per year. The total oil discharged from ballasting would be correspondingly reduced from 6,770,000 barrels per day to about 2,500,000, or a reduction by 270 percent. According to the SCEP report, "in technological terms the appropriate remedial measure appears to be clearly indicated. The difficulty lies not in available technology but in the means of bringing about its use."[38]

Another technique which shows some promise as a means of reducing oil pollution from ballast operations is an oil-eating bacteria.[39]

By 1980, it has been estimated that world crude oil production will double from the 1970 level of about 14 billion barrels to 28 billion barrels.[40] Crude oil transported by tanker has also been estimated to increase from about 9 billion to 19 billion barrels.[41] If significant measures are not taken to limit direct losses of oil to the world's waters, then it is expected that, by 1980, oil pollution will reach 70 million barrels. This is twice the quantity of oil pollution for the years 1969–1970, as shown in Table 18.

Annex A. WORKER SAFETY

The purpose of this section is to provide an estimate of fatal and non-fatal injury rates for OCS oil and gas operations and, then, to compare those estimated rates with similar reported rates for the petroleum/natural gas industry as a whole and for the coal mining industry as a whole.

According to USGS, there were 56 fatalities and 83 injuries which were a result of "major incidents" which occurred in connection with OCS oil and gas operations between 1953–1971.[42] (The USGS defines a "major incident" as one resulting in injury and property or environmental damage.) Of these 56 fatalities, 48 are reported on an annual basis for the period between 1964–1971. These are shown in Table 29 under the heading "Major Incidents."

On the other hand, a Coast Guard tabulation of fatal and non-fatal injuries associated with fixed and mobile drilling rigs under federal registry reports that there were 71 deaths and 82 injuries during fiscal years 1966–1971.[43] It is possible that some of these deaths and injuries may have occurred in foreign waters, although it is likely that such foreign-water deaths and injuries would be quite small since there were only 13 mishaps reported in foreign waters out of a total of 363 reported mishaps. It is important to note that this tabulation does not include, for example, persons falling or knocked overboard, crushed or maimed by drilling equipment. A separate tabulation for these latter types of accidents has been obtained from the Coast Guard[44] and the Bureau of Land Management[45] for the period of time between 1967–1971, and are included in Table 29 under the heading "Routine Operations."

Thus, since USGS reports only major incidents in connection with OCS oil and gas operations, their data indicate fewer fatalities over a longer period of time than does Coast Guard data. Coast Guard data include vessels under federal registry, and using these data results in a picture of more fatalities over a shorter span of time. In any event, it is apparent that the total number of reported fatalities should be viewed as a minimum estimate since both surveys are incomplete.

For purposes of comparison, the overall fatality rates for the petroleum/natural gas industry[46] and the coal mining industry[47] are shown in Table

**Table 29. Estimated Fatal Accidents on the OCS,
Petroleum/Natural Gas, and Coal Mining Industries, 1964–1971**

Year	Major Incidents[a]	Routine Operations[b]	OCS Total	Petroleum/ Natural Gas Industry[c]	Coal Mining Industry[c]
1964	22	NA	22	109	242
1965	1	NA	1	78	259
1966	0	NA	0	103	233
1967	6	1	7	88	222
1968	0	6	6	102	311
1969	0	6	6	95	203
1970	19	0	19	134	260
1971	0	15[d]	15	115[e]	181
1964–1971	48	28	76	824	1911

NA: Not Available. [a] USGS. [b] CG. [c] BOM. [d] BLM. [e] Estimate.

29. OCS oil and gas operations account for about 10 percent of all fatal accidents reported for the petroleum/natural gas industry. (It should be noted that this does not include the distribution of natural gas.) The number of fatal OCS accidents is 4 percent of the figure for all fatal accidents reported for the coal mining industry.

Fatality rates are commonly compared on the basis of man-hours worked. Because there is no central source for obtaining these data for the OCS, the comparison was made on an energy-produced basis for the time period 1964–1971. On this basis, the fatal accident rate average is 3.2 fatalities per quadrillion BTU's. Energy-produced included crude oil, condensate, and natural gas.[48] As may be seen in Table 30, the years 1967–1971, which represent a better data base than 1964–1971, reflect *no* marked decline. The fatality rate for OCS operations is about 1.4 times the fatality rate for the whole petroleum/natural gas industry.[49]

Note that there is no significant downward trend in the fatality rate for this industry. It is unlikely that the fatality rate for OCS operations is more than twice the rate reported here. So roughly speaking, an upper estimate would represent a fatality rate twice that of the petroleum/natural gas industry as a whole.

On the other hand, the energy-averaged fatality rate for OCS operations is about 20 percent of that for the coal mining industry. Since the fatality rate for coal mining shows a decreasing trend, the fatality rate for coal mining is approaching the rate for OCS operations. For example, in 1970 and 1971, the fatality rate for OCS operations was 30 percent of that for coal mining.

Table 30. Estimated Fatal Accident Rate for OCS Operations Compared to Petroleum/Natural Gas and Coal Mining Industries, 1964–1971

Year	OCS	Petroleum/Natural Gas Industry	Coal Mining Industry
1964	16.5	2.8	18.5
1965	0.7	1.9	18.9
1966	0	2.4	16.4
1967	2.8	1.9	15.1
1968	1.9	2.1	21.4
1969	1.6	1.9	13.7
1970	4.2	2.5	16.4
1971	2.9	NA	10.6
1964–1971	3.2	2.2[a]	16.2

Note: This table is based on an energy-produced basis and on fatalities per quadrillion BTUs.

NA: Not Available. [a] 1964–1970.

Non-fatal injury rates are not discussed because of the lack of data for OCS operations. Comparison of the sparse data available was difficult in part because of inconsistent definitions of non-fatal injuries. (The collection and analysis of these data would be a worthwhile task for the Occupational Safety and Health Administration in order to identify problem areas.)

Since a number of fatal and non-fatal injuries occur when there are large production blowouts, oil spills, and gas blowouts, attempts to minimize these types of accidents should reduce the number of fatalities by roughly a factor of two. Non-fatal injuries should also be decreased.

Annex B. MAJOR ACCIDENTS BY COMPANY

The purpose of this section is to identify variability in performance records of the companies engaged in OCS petroleum operations with regard to major accidents. The frequency and seriousness of these accidents are correlated with oil/condensate production. Major accidents can be divided into three categories. The "most serious" accidents are defined as those in which spilled oil is greater than 1,000 barrels, loss of life is greater than one, or loss of property is greater than $5 million. The "very serious" accidents are defined as those in which spilled oil is in the range of 100 to 1,000 barrels, loss of life is limited to one person, property damage is greater than $1 million but less than $5 million, or the duration of an accident is one week or longer. The "serious" accidents are defined as those in which

Table 31. Major Accidents Classified by Degree, Location, and Company, 1953–1971

Operator	Major Accidents			OCS			State Waters			Cumulative State and Gulf	
	Most Serious	Very Serious	Serious	Total Accidents	Oil Spilled	Fatalities	Total Accidents	Oil Spilled	Fatalities	State OCS 1968 (%)[a]	OCS 1971 (%)[a]
Amoco	3	2	1	3	450	22	3	NA	0	1.2	0.9
Continental (CAGC)	3	2	3	8	3,000	13	0	0	0	4.9	7.2
Shell	2	0	3	5	53,000–130,000	7	0	0	0	16.5	17.1
Exxon	2	2	2	5	161,000	4	1	NA	0	18.2	11.9
Gulf	2	3	2	6	6,500	1	1	0	7–11	12.1	15.5
Union Oil	1	2	1	4	19,000–780,000	0	0	0	0	3.7	2.3
Chevron (SOCAL)	2	0	2	3	38,000	0	1	0	0	20.5	11.8
Chambers and Kennedy	1	0	0	1	100–1,400	9	0	0	0	NA	NA
Mobil	1	1	1	2	2,800	0	1	NA	0	2.9	2.0
Signal	1	0	0	1	5,100	0	0	0	0	NA	2.7
Tenneco	1	0	0	1	1,600	0	0	0	0	1.8	1.8
Texaco	0	0	1	1	0	0	0	0	0	1.2	15.7
Phillips	0	0	1	1	0	0	0	0	0	2.6	2.0
Sinclair	0	0	1	1	0	0	0	0	0	NA	NA
Gracey-Hellum,											
McDermott	1	0	0	0	0	0	1	0	3	NA	NA
ARCO	0	1	0	0	0	0	1	0	1	3.0	0.6
Union Producing	0	1	0	0	0	0	1	0	0	NA	NA
Total	20	15	18	42	290,000–1,100,000	56	10	NA	11–15	88.6	89.7

NA—Not Available. [a] Oil and condensate.

oil spilled is less than 100 barrels, there is no loss of life, or property damage is less than $1 million.

On the basis of these definitions, the companies are listed in decreasing order of "most serious" accidents. (See Table 31.) Two sources were used for making comparisons with production. The cumulative oil and condensate production for the OCS through 1968[50] was used along with Gulf of Mexico production for the OCS and state waters for 1971.[51]

Among the large producers on the OCS (those which have production exceeding 10 percent of the total OCS production), the companies with the best records are Gulf, in terms of the least oil spilled; and Chevron, with the least number of fatalities. The large producers with poorer records are Shell, Exxon, and Chevron, for oil spilled; and Shell, Exxon, and Gulf, for fatalities. No major producer escaped having a serious accident.

For the small producers (that is, those with production less than 10 percent of total OCS production), the companies which polluted the most are Union Oil, Signal, Continental (CAGC), Mobil, Tenneco, Amoco, and Chambers and Kennedy. The small producers which had the most casualties are Amoco, Continental (CAGC), and Chambers and Kennedy. The other companies had no fatalities associated with major accidents.

Annex C. A DATA BASE FOR OFFSHORE ACCIDENTS

A data base on major offshore accidents was compiled for this accident analysis. The areas included were the Gulf of Mexico OCS, the Pacific OCS, and state and foreign waters.

The completeness of the data base can be tested by comparison with three known public statements. At the time of Union Oil's Santa Barbara spill of January 28, 1969, the President's Panel on Oil Spills, 1969, Office of Science and Technology, reported that,

> . . . since 1954 approximately 8,000 offshore wells have been drilled. Twenty-five blowouts occurred of which 17 leaked gas only. Two resulted in serious oil pollution incidents and nine constituted serious blowouts that persisted for several days with fire (9 cases) or fire hazards and hazards to personnel (29 deaths).[52]

This statement is essentially correct, but applies only to the OCS. This can be seen from the following: the data base shows that the 25 blowouts are from:

18 drilling blowouts (2 oil and gas and 16 gas only)
 6 production blowouts (3 oil, 1 oil and gas, and 1 gas only)
 1 storm blowout (1 oil)

25 blowouts (8 oil or oil and gas, 17 gas only)

Of these, 17 leaked gas only, which is in agreement with the President's Panel. The two which resulted in "serious" oil pollution were Union Oil Company's blowout in the Santa Barbara Channel at 18,500–780,000 barrels and the Mobil Oil blowout in the Gulf of Mexico at 2,500–3,000 barrels. Two production blowouts at 500 barrels each were apparently not considered serious. There were 9 fires, 6 from drilling and 3 from production operation. The casualties to personnel are very nearly correct: 23 from drilling accidents and 7 from production, for a total of 30 deaths (instead of 29).

At the time of the Chevron Oil Company's platform fire in the Gulf of Mexico on February 10, 1970, *Offshore* wrote a summary of the safety record for federal waters in the Gulf of Mexico: "Out of 7,800 wells drilled in federal waters there since 1956, only 26 blowouts that can be considered as serious occurred. That includes this month's platform fire at Main Pass, which probably is the largest ever in the Gulf."[53]

The above confirms that 25 blowouts had been recorded prior to the Chevron fire. One additional blowout occurred outside the Gulf of Mexico, Union Oil's blowout in Santa Barbara. If this one is subtracted and Chevron's blowout is added, the total for the Gulf OCS is 25. The discrepancy of one accident may come from classification of one other accident as a blowout. *Offshore* quotes USGS as saying that only two wells had spilled much oil. One spill contained 2,400 barrels and the other flowed 50 barrels per day of condensate for two weeks. The first one would be the Mobil Oil storm blowout, and the second must be the Gulf Oil drilling blowout. This tabulation did not consider two production blowouts, both of which spilled 500 barrels, or the production blowout of CAGC in 1958, for no oil was reported spilled but evidently was spilled in large quantities.

Finally, as of April, 1972, according to the American Petroleum Institute, Western Oil and Gas Association, and the Mid-Continental Oil and Gas Association,

> of the over 14,000 wells that have been drilled in the U.S. federal and state waters, only 25 have created pollution hazards as a result of blowouts. Only three oil spill incidents have been large enough to attract widespread attention. Evidence indicates that even these three accidents resulted in no lasting harm to the environment.[54]

The data for the OCS as presented in Table 23 shows the following:

19 drilling blowouts (2 oil and gas, 17 gas only)
15 production blowouts (3 oil, 7 oil and gas, 2 gas only, 3 other)
 3 storm blowouts (3 oil)
_____
37 blowouts (15 oil or oil and gas; 19 gas only, 3 other)

Table 32. Major Blowouts Spilling Oil/Condensate on the OCS and in State Waters, 1953–1972

Blowout	Date	Place	Company	Volume of Oil Spilled (Barrels) or Duration of Spill
Drilling	1969	Santa Barbara Channel–OCS	Union Oil	18,500–780,000
Production	1970	Gulf of Mexico–OCS	Shell	53,000–130,000
Production	1970	Gulf of Mexico–OCS	Chevron	30,500
Storm	1969	Gulf of Mexico–OCS	Mobil	2,500–3,000
Production	1971	Gulf of Mexico–OCS	Amoco	400–500
Production	1964	Gulf of Mexico–OCS	Gulf	500
Production	1958	Gulf of Mexico–OCS	CAGC	1 month, 6 days
Drilling	1962	Cook Inlet	Amoco	14 months
Production	1961	Galveston Bay	Exxon	6 months
Production	1960	S. Louisiana	Union Producing	4 months
Drilling	1966	Gulf of Mexico–OCS	Texaco	2 days
Production	1966	Gulf of Mexico–OCS	Union Oil	15 minutes
Hurricane	1964	Gulf of Mexico–OCS	CAGC-1 Gulf-2 Shell-1 Sinclair-4 Tenneco-3	days

The total of 37 blowouts does not include at least 11 blowouts from Hurricane Hilda in 1964. These are not documented by USGS. Of the 37 blowouts, if only the ones that flowed oil are counted as creating a pollution hazard, there were 15 blowouts which created a pollution hazard. The remaining 10 must have occurred in state waters. A survey of *Offshore* and the *Oil and Gas Journal* has revealed that there were 8 recorded blowouts in state waters: 2 in Alaska, 4 in Louisiana, and 2 in Texas. Of these 8 blowouts, 3 blew oil or condensate, one in Alaska, one in Louisiana, and one in Texas. On the basis of this analysis, it appears that there are 2 blowouts involving oil in state waters which are not accounted for by the data base.

The statement that "only three oil spill incidents have been large enough to attract widespread attention," means that the oil spill has been in the amount of tens of thousands of barrels as shown in Table 32.

Finally, in late 1972, on the basis of recent data, there was one major blowout in the Gulf of Mexico OCS, and there were two blowouts in Louisiana waters. They all leaked gas primarily.

CONCLUSION

The record of blowouts on the OCS seems to be complete on the basis of this discussion. For state waters, there appear to be 2 blowouts which leaked oil that are unaccounted for. Documentation on other types of accidents listed in Table 23 depends almost completely on USGS records.

The principal sources for the data base of major accidents are the following:

U.S. Department of the Interior, Geological Survey, Conservation Division, "Incidents in the Outer Continental Shelf Resulting in Injury and Property or Environmental Damage (1953 to November 17, 1971)" (unpublished data).

U.S. Department of the Interior, Bureau of Land Management, *Final Environmental Statement: Proposed [December] 1972 Outer Continental Shelf Oil and Gas General Lease Sale Offshore Louisiana.*

U.S. Department of the Interior, *Statement, Questions and Policy Issues Related to Oversight Hearings on the Administration of the Outer Continental Shelf Lands Act Held by the Senate Committee on Interior and Insular Affairs, Pursuant to S. Res. 45, March 23, 1972.*

Offshore.

Oil and Gas Journal.

Since this analysis was made, USGS published a compilation of accidents on February 20, 1973, "Accidents Connected with Federal Oil and Gas Operations On the Outer Continental Shelf through 1972." Five tables cover various aspects of accidents: Table A, "Blowouts"; Table B, "Explosions and Fires"; Table C, "Pipeline Breaks or Leaks"; Table D, "Significant Pollution Incidents"; Table E, "Major Accidents Connected with Federal Oil and Gas Operations on the Outer Continental Shelf."

Differences between USGS data and the data base used for the accident analysis in this appendix are:

(1) accidents in state and foreign waters were *not* included in USGS data;

(2) 13 "major accidents" on the OCS which were tabulated by USGS in its tabulation, "Major Accidents Connected with Federal Oil and Gas Operations on the Outer Continental Shelf," are not included in the data

base used here. This may have resulted from a change in the definition of what constitutes a "major accident." The data used in this appendix include two accidents *not* tabulated in that table.[55]

(3) USGS included a number of smaller accidents in its Tables A through D which are not included in the analysis in this appendix.

1. Max Blumer, "Scientific Aspects of the Oil Spill Problem," *Environmental Affairs*, 1 (April, 1971), pp. 54–55.

2. National Academy of Sciences (NAS)–National Research Council (NRC), Ocean Science Committee, *Marine Environmental Quality: Suggested Research Programs for Understanding Man's Effect on the Oceans* (Washington: National Academy of Sciences, 1971), pp. 6–8. These data add deliberate dumping to SCEP's data.

3. Marvin Zeldin, "Oil Pollution," *Audubon*, 73 (May, 1971), p. 100. This is a secondary source of Environmental Protection Agency (EPA) data. According to Kurt Jackobson, Chief, Oil Spills Pollution Control Program of EPA, there is a chronic release of waste oil. This amounts to 50 percent of 1.76 billion gallons per year of production. Expressed in terms of tons, this is about 3 million tons. This figure is in agreement with the estimate quoted in the *Audubon* article. These are SCEP data, but the amount of industrial and automotive wastes is increased.

4. *Man's Impact on the Global Environment,* Report of the Study of Critical Environmental Problems (SCEP), sponsored by the Massachusetts Institute of Technology (Cambridge, Mass.: MIT Press, 1970) p. 267.

5. USGS estimate: 10,000 barrels initially, 8,500 barrels from subsequent leakage, for a total of 18,500 barrels. U.S., Department of the Interior, Bureau of Land Management, *Final Environmental Statement: Proposed[December] 1972 Outer Continental Shelf Oil and Gas General Lease Sale Offshore Louisiana*, p. 95.

President's Panel estimate: 24,000 to 71,000 barrels. U.S., Executive Office of the President, Office of Science and Technology, *The Oil Spill Problem*, First Report of the President's Panel on Oil Spills (Washington: Government Printing Office, 1969) p. 4.

Allen estimate: 79,300 barrels. Robert Easton, *Black Tide: The Santa Barbara Oil Spill and Its Consequences*, Delcorte Press, New York, 1972, p. 251.

Coast Guard estimate: 100,000 barrels or more. U.S., Coast Guard, Law Enforcement Division, cited in Dillingham Corporation, *Systems Study of Oil Spill Cleanup Procedures*, Vol. 1: *Analysis of Oil Spills and Control Material* (La Jolla, California: Dillingham Corporation, February 1970), p. A–28.

Foster, Charters, Neusel estimate: 78,000 to 780,000 barrels. M. Foster, A. C. Charters, and M. Neusel, "The Santa Barbara Oil Spill and Distribution of Pollutant Crude Oil," *Environmental Pollution*, 2, 1971, p. 99.

EPA estimate: at least 77,000 barrels. Environmental Protection Agency, Statement, p. 1334 in U.S., Congress, Senate, Committee on Interior and Insular Affairs, *Outer Continental Shelf Policy Issues, Hearings*, before the Committee Pursuant to S. Res. 45, a National Fuels and Energy Policy Study, 92d Cong., 2d sess., March 23, 24, and April 11, 18, 1972.

6. USGS estimate: 53,000 barrels. BLM, *Final Environmental Statement: [December] 1972 OCS General Louisiana*, pp. 112, 134.

EPA estimate: 130,000 barrels. Senate Interior Committee, *OCS Policy Issues*, p. 1333.

7. U.S., Department of the Interior, *Statement, Questions and Policy Issues Related to Oversight Hearings on the Administration of the Outer Continental Shelf Lands Act Held by the Senate Committee on Interior and Insular Affairs, Pursuant to S. Res. 45, March 23, 1972*, pp. 98–102.

8. Easton, *Black Tide*, p. 297.

9. Roger Revelle, Edward Wenk, Bostwick H. Ketchum, and Edward R. Corino, "Ocean Pollution by Petroleum Hydrocarbons," in *Man's Impact on Terrestrial and Oceanic Ecosystems*, ed. by William H. Matthews, Frederick E. Smith, and Edward D. Goldberg (Cambridge, Mass.: MIT Press, 1971), p. 305.

10. *Ibid.*, p. 303.

11. NAS-NRC, *Marine Environmental Quality*, p. 8.

12. California, Resources Agency, Division of Oil and Gas, *California Offshore Oil and Gas Seeps*, by Elbert R. Wilkinson (Sacramento: California Resources Agency, 1972), p. 5.

13. SCEP Report, p. 140; NAS-NRC, *Marine Environmental Quality*, p. 8.

14. SCEP Report, p. 142.

15. *Inadvertent Climate Modification*, Report of the Study of Man's Impact on Climate (SMIC), sponsored by the Massachusetts Institute of Technology (Cambridge, Mass.: MIT Press, 1970), p. 165.

16. U.S., Department of Transportation, Coast Guard. "Polluting Incidents in and around U.S. Waters, Calendar Year 1971" (unpublished data); and "Polluting Spills in U.S. Waters—1970" (unpublished data).

17. The data for production for 1954–1971 were obtained from: U.S., Department of the Interior, *Statement, Questions and Policy Issues Related to Oversight Hearings on the Administration of the Outer Continental Shelf Lands Act, Held by the Senate Committee on Interior and Insular Affairs Pursuant to S. Res. 45, March 23, 1972*, Table 55, p. 65. 1972 data were obtained from Russell G. Wayland, USGS.

18. The data for new well starts for 1954–1971 were obtained from: *Ibid.*, Table 16, p. 26.

19. U.S., Department of the Interior, Bureau of Land Management, *Final Environmental Statement: Proposed [December] 1972 Outer Continental Shelf Oil and Gas General Lease Sale Offshore Louisiana*, p. 7.

20. National Petroleum Council, *Environmental Conservation: The Oil and Gas Industries; A Report* (Washington: NPC, 1972), Vol. 2, p. 146.

21. Interior, *Question and Policy Issues*, Table 10, p. 20.

22. BLM, *Final Environmental Statement: [December] 1972 OCS General Louisiana*, p. 7.

23. See reference 5.

24. See reference 6.

25. The volume of petroleum transported by tanker is approximately equal to the volume of combined coastal waterborne trade and import/export trade. Over the period 1964–1971, the volume moved was approximately 2.2 billion barrels per year. These data were taken from the following sources: U.S., Department of the Army, Corps of Engineers, *Waterborne Commerce of the United States, Calendar Year 1968* (Washington: Government Printing Office, 1970); American Petroleum Institute, "National Summaries," *Petroleum Facts and Figures, 1971* (Washington: API, 1971), pp. 258–259; National Petroleum Council, Committee on U.S. Energy Outlook, *U.S. Energy Outlook: An Initial Appraisal, 1971–1985, an Interim Report* (Washington:

NPC, 1971), Vol. 2, p. 57; U.S., Department of the Interior, *Final Environmental Impact Statement: Proposed Trans-Alaska Pipeline*, Vol. 3: *Environmental Setting Between Port Valdez, Alaska and West Coast Ports* (Washington: Government Printing Office, 1972), Table 64, p. 433.

26. *Ibid.*

27. Coast Guard, "Polluting Incidents, 1970–1971."

28. State offshore and OCS production aggregated 616 million barrels of oil/condensate for 1971. Interior, *Questions and Policy Issues*, Table 53, p. 63.

29. BLM, *Final Environmental Statement: [December] 1972 OCS General Louisiana*, p. 131.

30. *Ibid.*, p. 133.

31. Interior, *Trans-Alaska Pipeline Statement*, Vol. 3, p. 443.

32. *Ibid.*, Vol. 4: *Evaluation of Environmental Impact*, p. 468.

33. *Ibid.*, Vol. 3, pp. 427–41.

34. *Ibid.*, Vol. 4, p. 475.

35. *Ibid.*, p. 467.

36. *Offshore*, 31 (June 20, 1971), p. 37.

37. *Ibid.*

38. SCEP Report, p. 266.

39. "Oil Eaters," *Time*, May 21, 1972, p. 60.

40. SCEP Report, p. 266.

41. *Ibid.*

42. U.S., Department of the Interior, Geological Survey, Conservation Division, "Incidents in the Outer Continental Shelf Resulting in Injury and Property or Environmental Damage (1953 to November 17, 1971)" (unpublished data sheet).

43. Senate Interior Committee, *OCS Policy Issues*, Pt. 3, p. 1358.

44. Private communication: P. C. Lauridsen, LCDR, U.S. Coast Guard, Chief, Information and Analysis Staff, by direction of the Commandant.

45. BLM, *Final Environmental Statement: [December] 1972 OCS General Louisiana*, p. 368.

46. U.S., Department of the Interior, Bureau of Mines, *Minerals Yearbook 1968*, Vols. 1 and 2: *Metals, Minerals, and Fuels* (Washington: Government Printing Office, 1969), Table 11, p. 138; U.S., Department of Commerce, *Statistical Abstracts 1972* (Washington: Government Printing Office, 1972), p. 653.

47. Bureau of Mines, *Minerals Yearbook*, Vols. 1 and 2, Table 9, p. 137; Charles Culhane, "Mine Safety Report/Administration Congress Move to Tougher Regulations to Reduce Deaths, Injuries," *National Journal*, 5 (February 24, 1973), p. 277.

48. Interior, *Questions and Policy Issues*, Table 55, p. 117.

49. Bureau of Mines, *Minerals Yearbook* Vols. 1 and 2, Table 1, p. 810 (All oil demand 1964–1968); NPC, *U.S. Energy Outlook: Initial Appraisal*, Vol. 2, p. 16 (This data is for 1970. To convert to BTU's multiply oil in barrels by 5.8×10^6.); Senate Interior Committee, *OCS Policy Issues*, Pt. 3, p. 1358 (For gas, convert to BTU's, multiply a standard cubic foot by 1,032.); Bureau of Mines, *Minerals Yearbook*, Vols. 1 and 2, p. 301 (bituminous coal and lignite production), Table 1, p. 380 (anthrocite production); Commerce, *Statistical Abstracts*, p. 656 (To convert to BTU's multiply coal in tons by 26×10^6).

50. U.S., Department of the Interior, Bureau of Mines, *Offshore Petroleum Studies: Composition of the Offshore U.S. Petroleum Industry and Estimated Costs of Producing Petroleum in the Gulf of Mexico*, by L. K. Weaver, H. F. Pierce, and C. J. Jirick, Information Circular 8557 (Washington: Government Printing Office, 1972).

51. Clean Gulf Associates Oil Spill Contingency Agreement. Exhibit B, June, 1972.

52. U.S., Executive Office of the President, Office of Science and Technology, *Offshore Mineral Resources: A Challenge and an Opportunity*, Second Report of the President's Panel on Oil Spills (Washington: Government Printing Office, 1969), p. 3

53. *Offshore*, 30 (March, 1970), p. 27.

54. *OCS Policy Issues, Hearings*, Pt. 2, p. 898.

55. These two accidents are: A freighter collision with an unmanned CAGC production platform [*Offshore*, 20 (January 1960), p. 18; 20 (August 25, 1960), p. 20]; and 4 Sinclair and 4 Tenneco blowouts during Hurricane Hilda (1964) [*Offshore*, 25 (June 21, 1965), p. 42; 24 (November 1964), p. 15; 30 (May 1970), p. 33].

Appendix C. Offshore Petroleum Reserves, Resources and Production

IN THE COURSE of our study, we found that reserves, resources, and production data are generally inconsistent and of either questionable or low accuracy. This is primarily because of a lack of (1) consistent definitions and terms, and (2) detailed geological and geophysical knowledge. In this appendix we will attempt to use consistent definitions and terms to identify where petroleum has been and is expected to be found and provide selected production data. Data on reserves, resources, and production will be presented for the world, the U.S., and specific areas of the U.S.

DEFINITIONS

Considerable effort has been made to classify minerals according to the degree of certainty of their discovery. Two terms are used to categorize certainty: *reserves* and *resources*. For petroleum, reserves refer to petroleum economically recoverable in identified geologic deposits; resources is a more inclusive term, including reserves, deposits which have been discovered but which currently cannot be economically recovered, and deposits which have not yet been discovered. In short, resources are what would be found if it were possible to find every existing oil and gas deposit.

The relationship of petroleum liquids reserves and resources on the U.S. continental shelf to a water depth of 200 meters (656 feet) is graphically illustrated in Figure 48. (Although the definitions used here are in terms of petroleum liquids and the continental shelf, the same terms are applicable to all mineral resources and geographical areas.)

In Figure 48, the large square represents continental shelf petroleum liquids resources. (Petroleum liquids include crude oil and the natural gas liquids (NGL) produced with the oil.)

USGS estimates that mineral resources on the continental shelf include 775 billion barrels of petroleum liquids.[1] Using currently available exploration technologies, five-eighths of this resource are considered to be *ultimately discoverable*.[2] The remaining three-eighths are *undiscoverable*, primarily because of the size and location of deposits and the limitations of currently available exploration technologies.

As indicated in Figure 48, approximately 43 percent of ultimately discoverable petroleum liquids resources on the U.S. continental shelf are

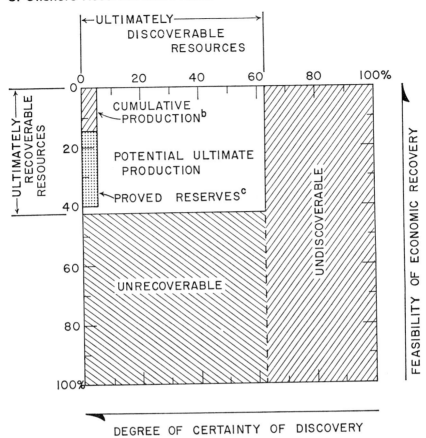

Fig. 48. Schematic Diagram of Reserves and Resources of Petroleum Liquids on the U.S. Continental Shelf[a]
[a]Drawn approximately to scale. [b]As of January 1, 1973. [c]As of March, 1973.

expected to be *recoverable*. The remaining 57 percent are expected to be *unrecoverable* and left in the ground: that is, even though 57 percent, or 276 billion barrels, is expected to be discovered, they probably will not be recoverable.

Two other terms used in Figure 48 are *cumulative production* and *proved reserves*. Cumulative production is used to identify the total amount of petroleum liquids which have been produced; proved reserves are those which have been discovered but not yet produced. Together cumulative production (5.5 billion barrels)[3] and proved reserves (10.1 billion barrels)[4] constitute only about 8 percent of the *potential ultimate production* of petroleum liquids—potential ultimate production is the amount ultimately recoverable from the amount ultimately discoverable.

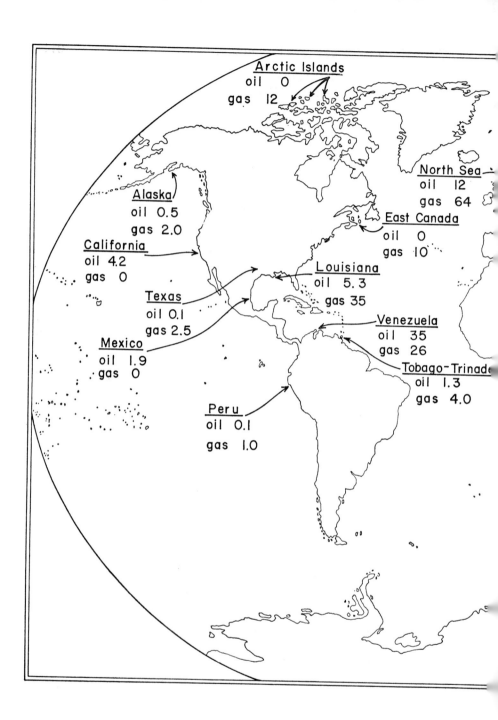

Arctic Islands
oil 0
gas 12

Alaska
oil 0.5
gas 2.0

California
oil 4.2
gas 0

Texas
oil 0.1
gas 2.5

Mexico
oil 1.9
gas 0

Peru
oil 0.1
gas 1.0

Louisiana
oil 5.3
gas 35

North Sea
oil 12
gas 64

East Canada
oil 0
gas 10

Venezuela
oil 35
gas 26

Tobago-Trinade
oil 1.3
gas 4.0

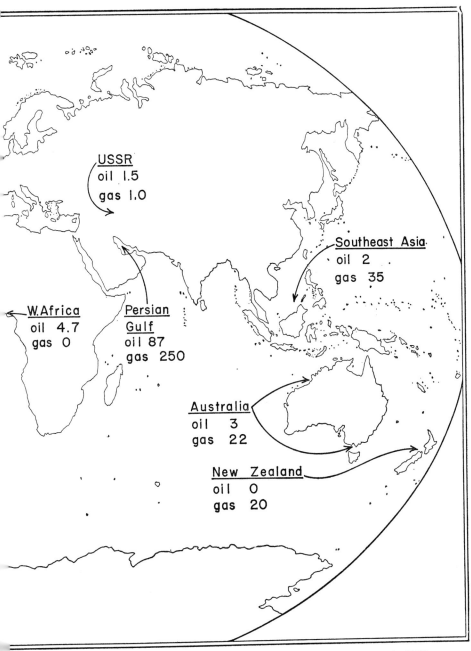

Fig. 49. Worldwide Offshore Oil and Gas Reserves as of March, 1973 [a]

[a]Oil in billion barrels; gas in trillion cubic feet; includes state waters and OCS.

A final term sometimes used as a measure of production is *potential production*, which is potential ultimate production minus cumulative production. In other words, potential production is the portion of potential ultimate production which has not already been produced.

WORLDWIDE RESERVES, RESOURCES, AND PRODUCTION

Figure 49 indicates where petroleum is found and produced around the world. As of January 1, 1973, worldwide cumulative production offshore was 37 billion barrels.[5] Proved reserves offshore were 158 billion barrels of oil and 488 trillion cubic feet of gas. These account for about one-fourth of total worldwide proved reserves.[6] In terms of areas, proved reserves in the Persian Gulf are larger than in any other area of the world, exceeding those of the U.S. by almost a factor of ten.

Lewis G. Weeks, former chief geologist for Exxon and a past president of the American Association of Petroleum Geologists, estimates potential ultimate production of petroleum liquids and gas offshore to a water depth of 1,000 feet to be the equivalent of 1,550 billion barrels of oil.[7] (See Table 33.) Since his estimates are based on geological data, these amounts change when the data change. For example, in 1965, he estimated that 700 billion barrels of petroleum liquids would be recovered by primary recovery methods; in 1971, his estimate was up to 790 billion barrels.[8]

As for production, approximately 9.1 million barrels per day were produced offshore in 1972.[9] This was about 18 percent of total worldwide production.[10] (See Figure 50.) Only three offshore areas produce more than 500,000 barrels per day—Venezuela (2.4 million), the U.S. (1.8 million), and the Persian Gulf (3 million).[11] However, the North Sea is expected to become a major offshore source of petroleum. In 1971, North Sea produc-

Table 33. World Potential Ultimate Production of Petroleum Liquids and Gas

Source	Offshore (to 1,000-foot water depth)	Onshore	Total
Petroleum liquids by primary recovery	790	1,500	2,290
Petroleum liquids by secondary recovery	360	1,000	1,360
Petroleum gas	400	800	1,200
Total	1,550	3,300	4,850

Note: Table is based on billions of barrels of oil equivalent.
Source: Lewis G. Weeks, *Oil and Gas Journal*, (December 13, 1971), Table 2, p. 93.

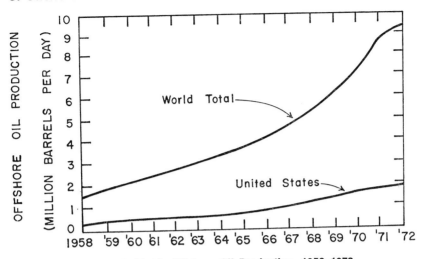

Fig. 50. Worldwide Offshore Oil Production, 1958–1972

Source: *International Petroleum Encyclopedia* (Tulsa, Okla.: Petroleum Publishing Co., 1972), p. 256; *Oil and Gas Journal*, 71 (April 30, 1973), p. 126.

tion was 61,000 barrels per day.[12] By 1985, it is estimated that the daily rate will be 3.7–4.9 million barrels.[13] In comparison, U.S. daily production from the OCS in 1972 was about 1.1 million barrels (excluding state offshore), and it is expected that 1985 production will be at a 2-to-4 million barrel per day rate.[14]

It is anticipated that worldwide offshore production will continue to increase, and by 1980 account for 25–42 percent of total worldwide production. This would require a daily production rate of 25–35 million barrels as compared to the 9.1 million barrels produced daily in 1972.[15]

U.S. RESERVES, RESOURCES, AND PRODUCTION

OCS and Continental Slope: Only limited resource data have been available to inform persons responsible for making development policies for the OCS. In testimony before the Senate Interior Committee in 1972, Hollis Dole, a former Assistant Secretary of Interior, indicated that less than 3 percent of the U.S. OCS has been adequately mapped to permit assessment of its total energy resource potential.[16] Most of the mapping that has been done has been limited to offshore California, Louisiana, and Texas.

Despite this lack of data, however, resource estimates have been published covering the entire OCS. One of the most comprehensive of these

Table 34. Resource Estimates for the U.S.

Resource	OCS to 200 meters (656 feet)	Continental Slope 200 to 2,500 meters (8,250 feet)
Petroleum liquids (Billion barrels)	710	690
Natural gas (Trillion cubic feet)	1,640	1,590

is based on a 1968 study which USGS conducted for the Public Land Law Review Commission.[17] (USGS actually prepared two estimates although only one is discussed here. The second estimate was based on a system of favorability ratings and, although it differs in detail, it agrees in magnitude with the estimate described in this section.)

USGS based its resource estimate on an extrapolation of the results of drilling to a depth of 20,000 feet. Beginning with an assumption that petroleum will occur with equal frequency in all sedimentary rocks, a total resource estimate is calculated by multiplying an estimate of the total volume of sedimentary rock by the amount of petroleum which has been found in each cubic unit of sedimentary rock in the past. Based on USGS's model and the assumption that experience on the continental slope will be the same as on the OCS, total resource estimates for the U.S. are shown in Table 34.

A Comparison of Potential Production Onshore and Federal Offshore: Total potential onshore production in the U.S. (lower 48 plus Alaska) is estimated by USGS to be approximately 305 billion barrels of petroleum liquids and 1,424 trillion cubic feet of natural gas.[18] (See Figure 51.) Potential offshore production for the same area, excluding state offshore, is 368 billion barrels and 1,598 trillion cubic feet. (State offshore represents less than 10 percent of the potential production of the continental shelf.) As may be determined from Figure 51, when only the lower 48 states are considered, potential production onshore and from federal offshore—the OCS and continental slope—are approximately equal. For Alaska, federal offshore potential is expected to be more than twice as much as onshore.

Cumulative production onshore in the lower 48 states to January 1, 1973, was 107 billion barrels of petroleum liquids and 417 trillion cubic feet of gas.[19] As can be seen in Figure 51, this means that potential onshore production is roughly 2½ to 3 times the amount already produced. Also, it is likely that most of the prime onshore fields have been found and exploited. The reverse seems true for prime fields offshore.

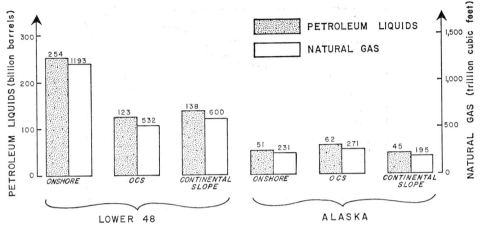

Fig. 51. Potential Production of Petroleum Liquids and Natural Gas from Onshore, OCS, and Continental Slope (as of January 1, 1973)
Sources: USGS; *Oil and Gas Journal.*

Proved Reserves: Estimates for proved reserves come mainly from industry with the American Petroleum Institute reporting on crude oil and natural gas and the American Gas Association on natural gas. A first step toward an independent evaluation of gas supply was conducted recently by FPC in cooperation with USGS, the U.S. Naval Petroleum and Shale Reserves Office, OMB, the Census Bureau, and the regulatory and conservation agencies of the major gas-producing states. FPC's report was based on geological and engineering estimates made by government specialists using raw geological, geophysical, and engineering data supplied by industry. FPC's results show that the proved reserves are nearly 10 percent below the estimate of the American Gas Association. A similar appraisal of oil reserves has been proposed.[20]

Production: Annual petroleum production from 1953 through 1972 from the OCS, offshore (federal and state), and total U.S. is shown in Figures 52 and 53.[21] As can be seen, in 1972, the OCS accounted for about 12 percent of total U.S. production. Offshore production accounted for approximately 18 percent of all petroleum liquids and almost 17 percent of all natural gas.

U.S. REGIONAL PRODUCTION AND DEVELOPMENT

A number of specific regions of the U.S. OCS are now under development or may be developed by 1985. These have been identified in BLM's tenta-

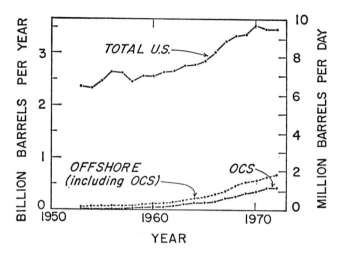

Fig. 52. Oil/Condensate Production—OCS, Offshore, and Total U.S., 1953–1972
Sources: Department of the Interior; *Oil and Gas Journal*, 71 (January 29, 1973), p. 100; and 71 (April 30, 1973), p. 126.

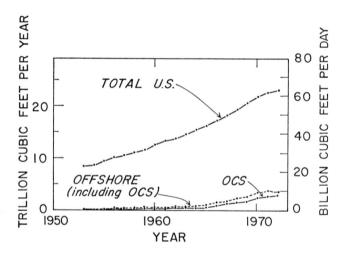

Fig. 53. Natural Gas Production—OCS, Offshore, and Total U.S., 1953–1972
Sources: Department of the Interior; *Oil and Gas Journal*, 71 (January 29, 1973), p. 101; *Offshore*, 33 (June 20, 1973), p. 81.

Table 35. OCS and State Offshore Production of Oil/Condensate and Natural Gas by Coastal Region for 1971

Coastal Region	Oil/Condensate[a]		Natural Gas[b]	
	OCS	State Waters	OCS	State Waters
Louisiana	386	58	2,640	579
Texas	1	2	127	281
California	31	72	16	45
Alaska	0	66	0	84
Total	418	198	2,783	989

Source: Department of Interior.
[a] Million barrels. [b] Trillion cubic feet.

tive five-year lease schedule as well as by the President in his 1973 Energy Message. In this section, present and anticipated distribution of production from these regions will be discussed.

The distribution of 1971 offshore production is given in Table 35 for the coastal regions of the U.S.[22] Present production is confined almost exclusively to the Gulf Coast. Future development is likely to change this picture. The potential ultimate production of petroleum liquids and natural gas from the OCS and the continental slope is shown in Figure 54.[23] Although significant potential exists in the Gulf of Mexico, the other regions have comparable potential, and leasing in the next 15 years will be structured in an attempt to develop these other coastal regions.

The potential impact on production of offshore lease sales between now and 1985 is shown in Figures 55 and 56. The length of time necessary to develop a new region can also be seen in Figure 56. Although it is presently anticipated that the Atlantic OCS will be leased before 1976, it is not expected to deliver much oil before 1985. Anticipated gas production emphasizes the gas-rich Gulf coast, with little gas contributed by the Atlantic or Pacific regions.

The geographic locations of the present or anticipated resources in OCS regions are shown in Figure 57.

Gulf of Mexico: According to BLM, the potential production on the Gulf of Mexico OCS is 3.2 billion barrels of oil and 24 trillion cubic feet of gas. The tentative five-year lease schedule estimates an additional potential production of 2.5 to 5.0 billion barrels of oil and 20 to 40 trillion cubic feet of gas.[24]

According to the President's 1973 Energy Message, expanded OCS lease sales to begin in 1974 will include areas beyond the 200-meter isobath. These will be the first lease offerings on the Gulf continental slope. It is indicated that deep water tracts will extend out to 600 meters (1,980 feet).[25]

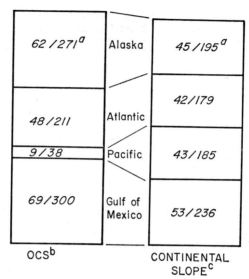

OCS[b]		CONTINENTAL SLOPE[c]
62/271[a]	Alaska	45/195[a]
48/211	Atlantic	42/179
9/38	Pacific	43/185
69/300	Gulf of Mexico	53/236

Fig. 54. Potential Ultimate Production of Petroleum Liquids and Natural Gas from the OCS and Continental Slope

Source: USGS.

[a]Petroleum liquids (billion barrels) / natural gas (trillion cubic feet).
[b]From state waters to 200 meters (656 feet).
[c]From 200 to 2,500 meters (8,250 feet).

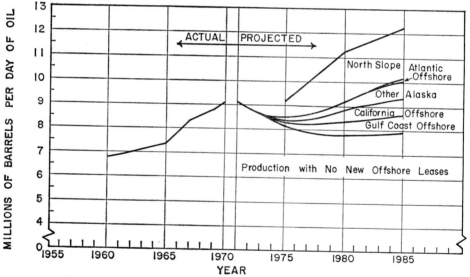

Fig. 55. Effect of New Offshore Leases and North Slope on Oil Production

Source: National Petroleum Council, Committee on U.S. Energy Outlook, *U. S. Energy Outlook*: A Summary Report (Washington: NPC, 1972) p. 125.

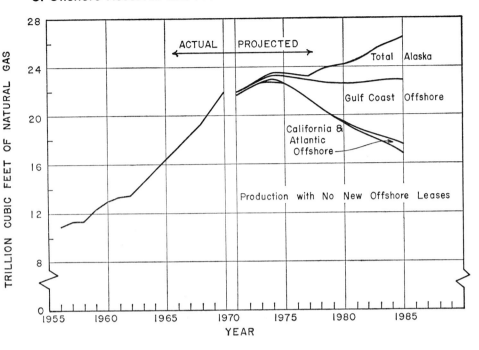

Fig. 56. Effect of New Offshore Leases and Alaskan Production on Gas Production
Source: NPC, *U. S. Energy Outlook*, 1972, p. 126.

Pacific: Exploration and drilling on the OCS in the Santa Barbara Channel have already identified resources which have not yet been developed. Most notable is the Santa Ynez field with proved reserves of one to three billion barrels in 1,000 feet of water.[26] The field is some five miles offshore, and Exxon will use five large platforms in developing the field.[27] Production may be as much as 200,000 barrels per day.

No new leasing is expected in the Santa Barbara Channel, but leasing on the OCS beyond the Channel Islands of California may be expected.[28]

Atlantic: There is much talk about where oil and gas can be found on offshore Atlantic. A recent paper by John C. Maher of USGS deals with this problem.[29] In his opinion, the most promising areas in U.S.-controlled waters are the Bahama platform (Florida embayment), the seaward extension of the Cape Fear arch, the long basement ridge at the edge of the continental shelf off New England, and the Southeast Georgia embayment. The outer shelf in Canadian waters off Nova Scotia and Newfoundland offers equally good possibilities.

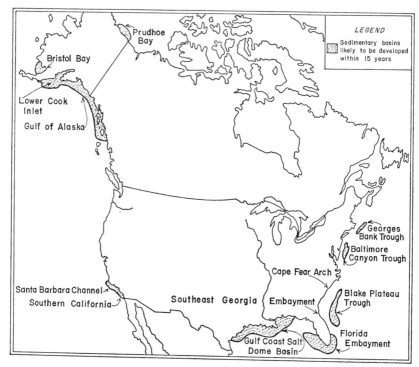

Fig. 57. OCS Areas Likely To Be Developed within 15 Years

Two areas of interest are the Baltimore Canyon trough and the Georges Bank trough, which lie in water depths of less than 500 feet and are both accessible with present technology. The Baltimore Canyon trough lies about 40 miles offshore, and the northernmost part of the trough is about 60 miles from New York City. The Georges Bank trough is about 215 miles long and 25 to 30 miles wide in places, and lies about 70 miles off Cape Cod. According to the American Association of Petroleum Geologists, potential production of hydrocarbons on the continental shelf north of Florida may be 5.5 billion barrels of oil, 37 trillion cubic feet of gas, and 1.1 billion barrels of NGL. Estimates for the continental slope are 4.5 billion barrels of oil, 30 trillion cubic feet of gas, and 0.9 billion barrels of NGL.[30]

Alaska: The Cook Inlet subprovince has proved reserves of 2.6 billion barrels of oil and 5 trillion cubic feet of gas. In addition, there is potential production of 7.9 billion barrels of oil and 14.6 trillion cubic feet of gas.[31]

The Cook Inlet subprovince is in state waters, but extends to the OCS. Apparently, the lower Cook Inlet is a probable sale site.

The Bristol Bay Basin lies 80 percent offshore. It is conjectured that potential production of from 1 to 5 billion barrels of oil (or its gas equivalent) is reasonable.[32] Sales are under serious consideration.[33]

Resource estimates for the Gulf of Alaska include 40 billion barrels of oil, 120 trillion cubic feet of natural gas, and 2.2 billion barrels of NGL.[34] The Middleton Island–Icy Bay area is estimated to have resources of 1 billion barrels of oil, 80 million barrels of NGL, and 3 trillion cubic feet of natural gas. Based on USGS finding and recovery criteria, the potential production of the Gulf of Alaska could be 10 billion barrels of oil, 60 trillion cubic feet of natural gas, and 1.1 billion barrels of NGL.

It should be noted that there is some question whether the Prudhoe Bay field (offshore North Slope) will be developed by 1985 because of the extreme environmental conditions.[35]

1. U.S., Department of the Interior, Geological Survey, *Energy Resources of the United States*, by P. K. Theobald, S. P. Schweinfurth, and D. C. Duncan, Circular 650 (Washington: Government Printing Office, 1972), p. 15. Approximately 93 percent of petroleum liquids resources is crude oil and seven percent is natural gas liquids.

2. *Ibid.*, p. 21.

3. As of January 1, 1973, *Ibid.*, p. 15 and *Oil and Gas Journal*, 71 (April 30, 1973), p. 126.

4. As of March, 1973, *Offshore*, 33 (April, 1973), p. 60.

5. *International Petroleum Encyclopedia* (Tulsa, Okla.: Petroleum Publishing Co., 1972), p. 262; *Oil and Gas Journal*, 71 (April 30, 1973), p. 126.

6. *Offshore*, 33 (April, 1973), p. 60.

7. Lewis G. Weeks, "Marine Geology and Petroleum Resources," *8th World Petroleum Congress* (Moscow, 1971); "World Offshore Science in Rapid Change," *Oil and Gas Journal*, 69 (December 13, 1971), p. 91.

8. Lewis G. Weeks, "Industry Must Look to the Continental Shelves . . . ," *Oil and Gas Journal*, 63 (June 21, 1965) p. 127; "World Offshore Petroleum Resources," *Bulletin of the American Association of Petroleum Geologists*, 49 (October, 1965), p. 1680.

9. *Oil and Gas Journal*, 71 (April 30, 1973), p. 126.

10. *Offshore*, 32 (June 20, 1972), p. 81.

11. *Oil and Gas Journal*, 71 (April 30, 1973), p. 126.

12. *Offshore*, 32 (June 20, 1972), p. 82.

13. *Offshore*, 33 (April, 1973), p. 113.

14. For 2 million barrels per day estimate, see National Petroleum Council, Committee on U.S. Energy Outlook, *U.S. Energy Outlook; A Report* (Washington: National Petroleum Council, December, 1972), p. 122; for 4 million barrels per day estimate, see U.S., President, "Message on Energy," *Congressional Record*, 119 (April 18, 1973), p. S7693.

15. *Offshore*, 32 (June 20, 1972), p. 81.

16. U.S., Congress, Senate, Committee on Interior and Insular Affairs, *Outer Con-*

tinental Shelf Policy Issues, Hearings, before the Committee on Interior and Insular
Affairs, Senate, Pursuant to S. Res. 45, a National Fuels and Energy Policy Study,
92d Cong., 2d sess., on Oversight on Outer Continental Shelf Lands Act, March 23,
24 and April 11, 12, 1972, Pt. 1, p. 5.

17. *Ibid.*, Pt. 1, p. 192; U.S. Congress, Public Land Law Review Commission, *Study
of Outer Continental Shelf Lands of the United States* (6 vols.; Springfield, Va.:
Clearinghouse for Federal Scientific and Technical Information, November, 1969),
Vol. 4, Table 5, p. 5–A–27. Estimates of resources and potential production of petro-
leum liquids and natural gas have been given in the following sources: National
Petroleum Council, *Future Petroleum Provinces of the United States; A Summary*
(Washington: NPC, July, 1970); American Association of Petroleum Geologists,
Committee on Future Petroleum Provinces of the U.S., *Future Peteroleum Provinces
of the United States; Their Geology and Potential*, Memoir 15 (2 vols.; Tulsa, Okla.:
American Association of Petroleum Geologists, 1971); and Potential Gas Committee,
Potential Supply of Natural Gas in the United States (as of December 31, 1970)
(Golden, Colo.: Potential Gas Agency, Mineral Resources Institute, Colorado School
of Mines Foundation, Inc., 1971). The overall totals are substantially smaller than the
USGS estimates. The difference in estimates is accounted for mostly by the fact that
certain land and water areas were excluded from the NPC, AAPG, and PGC esti-
mates. These studies are most useful for detailed discussions of particular areas.

18. USGS, *Energy Resources*, Tables 14–18, pp. 14-18; 1971 and 1972 production
from *Oil and Gas Journal*, 71 (January 29, 1973), p. 101.

20. "FPC's Gas-Reserve Total Smaller than AGA's," *Oil and Gas Journal*, 71 (May
21, 1973), p. 62.

21. Senate Interior Committee *OCS Policy Issues*, Pt. 1, Tables 53–55, pp. 115–17;
OCS 1972 data from Russell G. Wayland, USGS; total 1972 U.S. oil/condensate and
natural gas production from *Oil and Gas Journal*, 71 January 29, 1973), pp. 100–101;
1972 offshore oil/condensate production from *Oil and Gas Journal*, 71 (April 30,
1973), p. 126.

22. Senate Interior Committee, *OCS Policy Issues*, Pt. 1, Tables 53–55, pp. 115-17.

23. *Ibid.*, Pt. 1, Table 5, p. 192.

24. U.S., Department of the Interior, Bureau of Land Management, *Final Environmental Statement: Proposed [December] 1972 Outer Continental Shelf Oil and Gas
General Lease Sale Offshore Louisiana*, p. 7.

25. "Gulf Sale Beyond 200 Meters Likely in 1974," *Oil and Gas Journal*, 71 (April
30, 1973), p. 87.

26. U.S., Congress, Senate Committee on Interior and Insular Affairs, *The President's Energy Message, Hearing*, before the Committee on Interior and Insular Affairs, Senate, pursuant to S. Res. 45, 92d Cong., 1st sess., June 15, 1971, pp. 95–96.

27. "Humble Unwraps Big Find in Channel," *Oil and Gas Journal*, 67 (July 14,
1969); Howard M. Wilson, "Pace Is Slow, But Rigs Are Busy Again in the Channel,"
Oil and Gas Journal, 68 (October 5, 1970), p. 61; "Humble Oil's Big Plans for Deep-
water Giant in Channel," *Oil and Gas Journal*, 68 (December 7, 1970), p. 30.

28. President, "Message on Energy," p. S7693.

29. U.S., Department of the Interior, Geological Survey, *Geological Framework and
Petroleum Potential of the Atlantic Coastal Plain and Continental Shelf*, by John C.
Maher, Professional Paper 659 (Washington: Government Printing Office, 1971). See
especially pp. 64–65.

30. AAPG, *Future Petroleum Provinces*, p. 1307.

31. *Ibid.*, pp. 109 and 119.

32. *Ibid.*, p. 108.

33. "U.S. To Lease 15 Million Acres of Offshore," *Oil and Gas Journal*, 71 (May 21, 1973), p. 80.

34. "Alaskan Gulf Potential: 40 Billion Barrels," *Oil and Gas Journal*, 70 (January 17, 1972), p. 62.

35. NPC, *U.S. Energy Outlook*, 1972, p. 97.

Appendix D. Research on the Biological Effects of Oil Pollution

In this appendix, research on the biological effects of oil pollution is summarized to supplement the analysis presented in Chapters VII and XI. In the first section, problems presented by oil pollution in geographically distinct areas are identified as are specific research needs for each offshore area where petroleum development may take place on the U.S. OCS. The second section consists of an annotated bibliography of recent oil pollution investigations. A listing of oil spills that have resulted in documented bird kills is presented in the third section; and the final section surveys recent spending on oil pollution research.

CERTAIN OIL POLLUTION PROBLEMS BY GEOGRAPHIC LOCALITY

As indicated in Chapters VII and XI, the biological effects of oil pollution can be expected to differ regionally. These differences are primarily due to the physical and biological characteristics of the marine environment, which contrast greatly among certain North American coastal waters. In recognition of these distinctive areas, shallow water biotic provinces have been established which reflect the different species composition of these areas.[1] The larger categories of these provinces are shown in Figure 58. Although precise boundaries are open to some dispute, owing to the overlapping nature of species distributions, these relatively distinct categories are recognized by most marine biogeographers.

Along the West Coast, the cold water Arctic and cool-temperate Aleutian provinces include most of Alaska and Canada. The temperate Oregonian province extends from Canada to Point Conception in California, where a warm-temperate fauna continues to almost the tip of Baja California. Most of the coast of the Gulf of Mexico consists of a warm-temperate Gulf fauna, except for the tip of Florida which has many tropical species. The Virginian Province along the Atlantic Coast resembles the Gulf of Mexico up to Cape Cod; beginning at that point, the American Atlantic cold-temperate fauna continues northward to Nova Scotia. Our purpose here is to describe certain problems which relate to the assessment of environmental risk of oil pollution from petroleum development in these relatively distinctive areas.

326

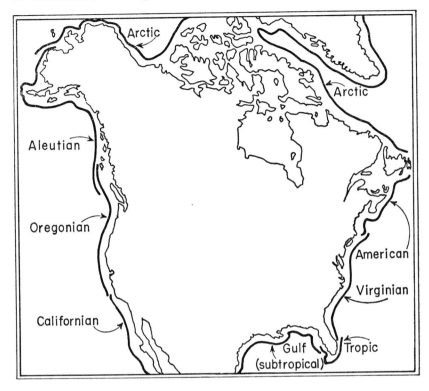

Fig. 58. Shallow Water Biotic Provinces

ARCTIC

Areas offshore the North Slope have negligible tides, few biodegraders, ice barriers, and a biota that has not been regularly exposed to petroleum.[2] In addition, it has been suggested that widespread spills may absorb significant quantities of sunlight which may result in climatic changes, as relatively small annual changes may markedly affect the heat budget of the atmosphere.[3] The lack of mixing in the Arctic may hinder the already low degradation rate. Kinney, *et al.*, suggest that spill problems and biodegradation mechanisms should be investigated in terms of the physical stability of oil in the ice pack and in the comparatively poorly mixed surface water.[4] The effects may be further aggravated by the shallow waters characteristic of the Beaufort and Chukchi seas.[5] Although little information is available on the possibility of "upsetting" the biological interactions which may be important in the maintenance of Arctic life, the most obvious pollution damage can be incurred by the millions of birds which migrate along the Beaufort Sea Coast and depend on ice-free water for feeding.

The characteristics of Prudhoe Bay crude oil spilled in the Chukchi Sea has been tested by Glaeser.[6] He found that oil slicks did not spread thin and that their movement was primarily a function of the wind and currents. In summer temperatures when surface waters reach 0° Celsius (C) the volatile fractions evaporate, and the specific gravity changes from 0.91 to 0.96 in 12 days (with loss of "gasoline and lighter fractions"). Biodegradation of crude oil may not be a significant factor in oil removal as no fungi or bacteria native to the area were found that could utilize oil at even summer temperatures.

The marine life of the shallow Arctic seas consists of a unique biota. Communities of organisms living on the undersurfaces of ice, for example, are not found elsewhere. The phytoplankton consists of algae with unusually high cholorophyll levels, and the zooplankton contain unique and abundant species of protozoans, crustaceans, and numerous other invertebrates. Fish, birds, and whales and other mammals also frequent the shallow Arctic seas. In summary, the effects of future pollution incidents on this area is not at all understood.

ALEUTIAN

Kinney, *et al.*, state that spills from platform and pipeline accidents were responsible for the addition of 2,000 to 10,000 barrels of oil per year in Cook Inlet.[7] Combined with onshore processing and shipping activities, 9,500 to 17,500 barrels of crude oil are added annually to the Inlet. The visual half-life of surface crude oil is only one day, and 1,000 barrels of crude oil which leaked from a broken pipeline completely disappeared from the surface in 3–4 days. Removal of Cook Inlet crude is a function of both biodegradation and the relatively unique turbulence and turbidity of the waters. Experiments with crude oil incubated in the laboratory suggest that at 10° C, degradation of crude oil is almost complete after two months, and after one year only 5 percent of the original quantity remained. It should be noted, however, that summer temperature in Cook Inlet water is usually 5° C (41° Fahrenheit). At this temperature, biodegradation rates may be reduced by a factor of 7. Degradation rates below 5° C are not known, and the prevailing temperature during winter is between −1.8° and 0.0°C.

The dramatic temperature-related decrease in biodegradation is most likely due to three factors: (1) the decrease in metabolic activity of bacteria and other species in response to lower temperature; (2) lower standing crop of bacteria; and (3) the increased viscosity of oil, which tends to form thicker films and clump, thus making it less amenable to bacterial attack.[8] These three are multiplicative, so that degradation in colder environments is extremely slow. But despite the many small spills and low rate of biodegradation, oil does not seem to be accumulating in Cook Inlet.

Other features of oil pollution also seem minimal as Kinney, *et al.*, report that accumulation of microbiologically fractionated compounds appeared to be negligible.[9] The build-up of toxic metals from crude oil also appears minimal as such annual additions were calculated at three orders of magnitude below ambient levels. These conditions of pollution mobility may be unique within Alaska and point to intense mixing associated with Cook Inlet.

The natural wildlife resources of Alaska are a significant economic and esthetic asset to major portions of the human population. This area is a major breeding and migratory area for birds, and has valuable and unique fishery and mammal resources. At this time information on the actual impact of Alaskan oil activities is not known. However, it is reasonable to speculate that at certain times of the year birds would be adversely affected by an oil spill. Currently, research is being conducted on these and other facets, such as the toxic effects of oil on salmon eggs and larvae.

OREGONIAN (NORTHERN CALIFORNIA-OREGON-WASHINGTON)

The Pacific Northwest is a portion of the Oregonian zoogeographic province, a cool water area, replete with local upwelling, and rich in species. The broad boundaries of the province extend from Point Conception (north of Santa Barbara) to near Juneau, Alaska.

A 5,000-barrel diesel oil spill occurred in May, 1971 in the vicinity of Anacortes, north of Seattle and east of the San Juan Islands in the Greater Puget Sound area. The biological effect has been studied by a team from Coastal Ecosystems Management Incorporated (on a subcontract from Texas Instruments, Inc.) This study focused on short-term acute effects of the spill. Most clams in the intertidal zone died, and in those subtidal areas receiving diesel oil, species diversity was lower than in similar areas studied in 1958. The Anacortes spill study indicated that Puget Sound has a bacterial flora with low metabolic rates that "preclude their consumption of large quantities of oil."[10]

There are great distinctions between the effects of crude oil and diesel oil, the latter having immediate acute toxicity to many marine species. This study does identify problems of assessment of oil spills in the Puget Sound area, which is probably unique in its short- and long-term climatic and hydrographic changes, especially in terms of rapid water movements and salinity fluctuations.

Much of the coastline in the Pacific Northwest is relatively unpolluted in comparison with major metropolitan developments in other coastal U.S. locations. Although conclusive evidence is not available, in theory such an area may be more affected by an oil spill than, for example, Southern California. Kanter, Straughan, and Jessee have found that, in areas of natural seeps, organisms may be more tolerant of oil pollution than in less polluted areas.[11] This suggests that the relatively oil-free coastline north of Central California may suffer more severe impact than the well-documented Santa Barbara Channel oil pollution incidents.

CALIFORNIAN

The area from Point Conception south into Baja California has a warm-temperate fauna, although some northern species are present. Over the past several decades, pollution and other human activities have decreased the species diversity markedly. Surveys conducted in 1959 and 1969 indicate that from 28 percent to 78 percent of the species have disappeared from selected Southern California areas, with an average reduction in variety from Gaviota to Dana Point of 63 percent.[12] It is likely that during the several decades prior to these surveys, species variety also decreased, so that perhaps only 10 to 30 percent of the original population remains in accessible locations. The wealth of warm-temperate species is now only observable in areas of Northern Baja California.

Most studies of the Santa Barbara blowout were not able to establish a direct link between the decrease in the marine biota and oil pollution. Because of the number of variables involved (weather, other pollution sources), the directly attributable effects were a decimation of about 10 to 25 percent of the channel bird population, most of which were the less abundant swimming birds (loons, grebes, and cormorants) rather than the common gulls and shorebirds. Barnacles' breeding and larval settlement were adversely affected, and mortality in barnacles and in several marine plants was observed. The weight of living material (biomass) in a subtidal Santa Barbara Channel community was reduced by a factor of 3 to 10 in certain locations over a 10-year period, but the cause is unknown.[13] In intertidal areas where smothering or mortality occurred, recolonization took place. Some habitats of oil-struck areas seemed particularly hard hit, however. Oil often accumulates in the upper intertidal zone, especially in crevices. Evans found that a beetle, the dominant species of the crevice community, is absent from heavily oiled beaches in Santa Barbara, but present in less oiled areas to the north and south.[14]

The Santa Barbara Channel oil spill indicated that certain faunal and floral elements and certain habitats are affected by acute doses of oil, as evidenced by the mortality and absence of species. The subtle role that hydrocarbons and crude oil may play in contributing to the deteriorated southern California shallow-water marine communities is not clear at this time. The pollution effects from numerous sources must be isolated, and the long-term, chronic, and low-level physiological impairments and adaptive adjustments to polluted conditions must be understood.

GULF OF MEXICO AND FLORIDA AREAS

The shallow waters, numerous estuaries, and uniform warm temperatures make the Gulf of Mexico a diverse and productive marine area (the largest fishery area in the U.S.). Waterfowl are abundant in this area, especially during winter migration. The coastal marshes also support fur-bearing mammals and alligators.

A survey following the Chevron oil spill did not establish detrimental environmental effects, and other accidents in the Gulf area have not resulted in any clear documentation of substantial impact.

It is reasonable to expect a major impact on birds in the Gulf, but only one spill has resulted in documented destruction of bird life. In this spill, an accumulation of oil from an unknown source resulted in the loss of about 600 ducks from Pelican Island off Louisiana in 1967.[15] Nearshore spills may have an effect on spawning and nursery grounds, wildlife refuges, estuaries, and marshlands. Mackin, of Texas A&M University, has studied several Gulf Coast oil spills. In discussing loss from a "wild" well, he found that "the oil loss was in a narrow channel which connected with small oyster embayments where water depths were only about two to seven feet. The oil spread over several square miles of shallow water. No adverse effect was found."[16]

Crude oil pollution has not resulted in persistent environmental damage in the Gulf of Mexico along the U.S. coastline. This is also true for the *Ocean Eagle* spill in Puerto Rico, although short-term effects did include mortality and tissue damage to thousands of fish and invertebrates.[17] During a year following the spill, however, a survey of shallow areas indicated recovery of the biological resources.[18] In Panama, a tropical mangrove community has not recovered from a spill of Bunker C and diesel.[19] This may reflect the greater toxicity of these oils as well as the delicate nature of the mangrove associations, which are also present along the Florida Coast.

Thus, among the Gulf habitats, the mangrove communities and coral associations in Florida could be expected to be particularly sensitive.

Table 36. Annotated Bibliography of Some Recent Oil Pollution Investigations

Location	Author/Publication	Subject	P or S*	Oil Type	Summary	Statistical Evidence
Alaska	Fornari, D. J., 1972; report for Univ. Wisconsin, Madison	Effects of oil contamination on the marine fauna and flora of Arctic Seas	S	General	If a spill occurs during winter, damage may be restricted and minimal; but during summer, damage may be widespread as the oil will have a greater tendency to come in contact with plant and animal life.	None
Alaska	Kinney, P. J., et al, 1970; Report, Institute of Marine Science, Univ. Alaska	Quantitative assessment of oil pollution problems in Alaska's Cook Inlet	P&S	Crude	Flushing and biodegradation capacity of Cook Inlet result in no measurable hydrocarbon accumulation.	Adequate
Alaska	Glaeser, J. L. 1971; Proceedings of Joint Conference on Prevention and Control of Oil Spills, API, EPA, and USCG	Oil pollution problems in Arctic	P&S	Crude	Although lighter fractions evaporate, mechanisms for biodegradation are not active in Arctic water, even during summer.	Adequate
Canada	Sprague, J. B. and Carson, W. G., 1970; Technical Report No. 201, Fisheries Research Board, Canada	Toxicity tests with oil dispersants in connection with oil spill at Chedabucto Bay, Nova Scotia	P	Bunker "C"	Ten oil dispersants selected by "Project Oil" were tested on salmon, flounders, lobsters, clams: toxicity ranged from lethal to practically non-toxic with concentration of 1–10,000 mg/l.	Adequate

Canada	Ages, A., 1971; Report No. 8, Atlantic Oceanographic Laboratory, Bedford Institute, Canada	Oil reconnaissance in the Magdalen Islands	P	Bunker "C"	Compared to Arrow spillage, this spillage presented minimal damage owing to wind and wave action. Principal factor in minimizing pollution threat was high pour point of oil (52° C).	None
Canada	Task Force—Operation Oil, 1970; Canadian Ministry of Transportation	Clean-up of the Arrow Oil Spill in Chedabucto Bay	P&S	Bunker "C"	Oil results in suffocation of certain benthic invertebrates. Fauna ingest and retain oil. Possible suffocation of seals, widespread bird losses observed.	Adequate
Canada	Loucks, R. H., Lawrence, D. J., May, 1971; Marine Pollution Bulletin, pp. 92–94.	Reconnaissance of an oil spill	S	Fuel oil	When oil is spilled in the sea at a temperature near its pour point, it can become invisible to aerial reconnaissance through fragmentation by wave action.	None
Canada	Zitko, V., Tibbo, S. N., 1971; Bulletin of Environmental Contamination and Toxicology, 6 (1), pp. 24–25.	Fish kill caused by an intermediate oil from coke ovens	P	Coke by-product	Thousands of dead herring observed in a Nova Scotia harbor. Samples of skin, muscle, and intestines from 4 dead herring were analyzed for oil. Detection of oil and high toxicity of oil to herring implied death from intermediate oil.	Adequate
Canada	Zitko, V., Carson, W. V., 1970; Technical Report No. 217, Fisheries Research Board, Canada	The characterization of petroleum oils and their determination in the aquatic environment	S	Fuel oils	Petroleum oils are persistent and in the environment and are taken up readily by aquatic animals.	Adequate

Table 36. Annotated Bibliography of Some Recent Oil Pollution Investigations (cont.)

Location	Author/ Publication	Subject	P or S*	Oil Type	Summary	Statistical Evidence
Washington	Clark, R. C., Jr., Finley, J. S., 1971; *Proceedings of the Joint Conf. on Prev. and Control of Oil Spills*, API, EPA, and USCG	Puget Sound fisheries and oil pollution— a status report	S	Crude and other oils	Pollution problems are primarily associated with ports and the major cause is human error. Even though there has been a reducing of spillage caused by human error, there remains a marked threat to animal and plant life.	None
Washington	Watson, J. A., Smith, J. P., Ehrsam, L. C., May, 1971; Report, Texas Instruments, Inc.	Biological assessment of diesel spill in the vicinity of Anacortes, WA	P	Diesel	Ecological effects difficult to document. Diversity was lower in areas associated with accumulated oil. Oil may be toxic to micro-flora.	Adequate
California	Kanter, R., Straughan, D., Jessee, W. N., 1971; *Proceedings of the Joint Conf. on Prevention and Control of Oil Spills*, API, EPA, and USCG	Effects of exposure to oil on *Mytilus Californianus* from different localities	P	Crude	Mussels from areas of natural oil seepage found to be more tolerant than those species which had no exposure to natural oil seepage.	Adequate

California	Turner, C. H., 1969; Cruise Report 69-A-2, Resources Agcy. California Dept. of Fish and Game	Inshore survey of Santa Barbara oil spill	P	Crude	Though unsightly, the oil seemed to have little adverse affect on animal and plant assemblages observed along shoreline and near shore Anacapa Island and Santa Cruz Island.	None
California	Hamilton, L., Pinkas, L., 1969; Cruise report 69-5-3, Resources Agcy. Calif. Dept. of Fish and Game	Pelagic fish and trawling survey of Santa Barbara oil spill	P	Crude	Trawl survey of 2,647 fish; all appeared healthy. In a Pelagic survey of 96.6 miles of echo sounding, 3 fish schools were recorded. No apparent adverse effects observed.	Adequate
California	Mais, K. F., 1969; Cruise report 69-A-4, Resources Agcy. Calif. Dept. of Fish and Game	Pelagic fish survey of Santa Barbara oil spill	P	Crude	Acoustic survey and midwater trawling found no ill effects of the oil on the pelagic fish in the affected area.	None
California	Jow, T., 1969; Cruise report 69-A-3, Resources Agcy. Calif. Dept. of Fish and Game	Trawling survey of Santa Barbara oil spill	P	Crude	No evidence of oil contamination of the bottom was noted at depths between 6–62 fathoms. Oil emulsion occurred in the dredge sample taken inside Santa Barbara Harbor.	None
California	Evans, W. G., 1970; The Pan-Pacific Entomologist 1970, 46 (4), p. 233	Thalassotrechus barbarae (Horn) and the Santa Barbara oil spill	P	Crude	This beetle was used as an indicator because of its general behavior and habitat; it cannot be found in its type habitat due to oil contamination.	Adequate

Table 36. Annotated Bibliography of Some Recent Oil Pollution Investigations (cont.)

Location	Author/ Publication	Subject	P or S*	Oil Type	Summary	Statistical Evidence
California	Straughan, D., 1971; Hancock Foundation, Los Angeles	Biological and oceanographical survey of the Santa Barbara Channel oil spill 1969–1970: biology and bacteriology	P	Crude	Widespread damage was not documented. Those populations affected were "recovering." The study was complicated by unusual freshwater runoff and other pollutants which did not permit determination of the cause of widespread changes from previous surveys.	Limited
California	Kolpack, R. L., 1971; Allan Hancock Foundation, Los Angeles	Biological and oceanographical survey of the Santa Barbara Channel oil spill 1969–1970: physical, chemical, and geological studies	P	Crude	Oil from the spill covered major portions of the channel bottom, and eventually accumulated in the basins. Most estimates of the amount spilled appear to be conservative.	Adequate
California	Chan, G. L., 1972; Report, College of Maria, CA	A study of the effects of the San Francisco oil spill on marine organisms, Part I	P	Bunker "C"	Smothering produced substantial mortality in many intertidal species but marked recovery was observed within 10 months; thousands of birds were killed.	Adequate
Wake Island	Gooding, R. M., 1968; Special Scientific Report— Fisheries, No. 636, U.S. Dept. of Commerce	Oil pollution on Wake Island from the tanker R. C. Stoner	P	High octane aviation fuel, Diesel, Bunker "C"	In spite of large number of fish killed, relatively few were killed compared to remaining population. Of the invertebrates, turbinid snails and sea urchins were the ones found dead in large numbers. A typhoon is given credit for cleaning the shores and moving the oil away from the island, thus minimizing the actual damage.	None

Location	Reference	Title		Oil	Effects	
Canal Zone	Glynn, P. W., et al, 1971; Report, Smithsonian Tropical Research Institute	Fundamental analysis for determining the effects of oil pollution on the ecology of a tropical shore	P	Crude	Mangrove community suffered more than any other of the marine communities. Major elements of the fauna have not returned after 33 months.	Limited
Puerto Rico	Pearce, J., and Ogren, L., 1968; Bureau of Sport Fisheries and Wildlife, Sandy Hook Marine Lab., New Jersey	Observation of the effects of oil from Tanker *Ocean Eagle* on marine organisms of San Juan Bay and Vicinity II; observation one year after the catastrophe	P	Crude	Observations one year after spill indicated no major change in or deterioration of the marine environment. Chronic oil pollution conditions continue. Long-term effects not well understood.	None
Puerto Rico	Cerame-Vivas, M. J., 1968; Univ. Puerto Rico, Report to U.S. Commerce	The *Ocean Eagle* oil spill	P	Crude	In littoral zone, Sessile and slow-moving forms covered with oil were killed. Fish not drastically affected. Detergents in concentrations 0.001 ppt showed toxicity to invertebrates.	None
Puerto Rico	Pearce, J. B. and Ogren, L., 1968; submitted to *Marine Pollution Bulletin*	The long-term effects of oil contamination which resulted from the sinking of the tanker *Ocean Eagle* in San Juan Harbor, Puerto Rico	P	Crude	Crude oil itself not highly toxic. Long-term damage due to hardened oil. Limited application of emulsifiers and other chemicals probably saved biota of Puerto Rico from extensive damage.	None

Table 36. Annotated Bibliography of Some Recent Oil Pollution Investigations (cont.)

Location	Author/ Publication	Subject	P or S*	Oil Type	Summary	Statistical Evidence
Texas	Mackin, J. G., 1971; Report, Interstate Oil Compact Commission	Environmental effects of petroleum production on marine communities	P&S	Crude	Produced water (brine) decreases species diversity of benthic communities near the discharge site; several thousand yards from the discharge, diversity is above normal, perhaps because of organic chemicals in the brine.	Limited
Louisiana	Resources Technology Corporation, 1972; Report, Resources Technology Corp., Dallas, TX	Studies and investigations of the fate and effects of the Shell oil spill, Platform B, Block 26, South Timbalier Bay, Dec. 20, 1970	P	Crude	The study documents decreased megafaunal counts near the platform, possibly related to hydrocarbon content of sediments. Gills of fish captured near the spill showed loss of cells.	Limited
Louisiana	Dept. Interior, 1970; Report, U.S. Dept. Interior	Interim evaluation of environmental impact from the Chevron Company fire and oil spill of coastal Louisiana	P	Crude	No confirmation of environmental damage. But circumstances were mitigating, and persistent pollution may have previously eliminated sensitive species.	Limited

Location	Reference	P/S	Oil type	Findings	Data
Louisiana	St. Amant, Lyle S., 1971; transcript of 36th North American Wildlife and Natural Resources Conference, Washington, D.C.	S	General	Large spills usually result in bird kills but no major losses are noted. Sessile animals are affected most, however. Oyster will purge itself if removed from contaminated area. Fishing is hindered primarily by physical obstruction. Construction and dredging activities may be the greatest impact of the industry.	None
Massachusetts	Blumer, M. et al. 1971; Environment 13 (2), pp. 1–12.	P	No. 2 Fuel oil	Massive, immediate destruction to intertidal life. Oil remained in sediments in spite of biodegradation. Shellfish sustained significant damage.	None
Massachusetts	Blumer, M., Souza, G., Sass, Jr., 1970; Marine Biology 5 (3), pp. 195–202.	P	No. 2 Fuel oil	Oil pollutant present in whole individuals of *Crassostrea virginica* and adducter muscles of *Aequipecten irradians*. Aromatic hydrocarbons remain in scallops months after the accident. Uncontaminated *Aequipecten irradians* contain hydrocarbons in lesser amounts and of different type.	None
Massachusetts	Blumer, M. et al. 1970; Report, Woods Hole Oceanographic Institute, Ref. 70-44.	P	No. 2 Fuel oil	Aromatics not affected by biodegradation. Oil still is detected in sediments. 1970 crop of shellfish are polluted over last year's crop. Mussels which survived developed few eggs.	Adequate

Table 36. Annotated Bibliography of Some Recent Oil Pollution Investigations (cont.)

Location	Author/ Publication	Subject	P or S*	Oil Type	Summary	Statistical Evidence
Maine	Dow, R. L., 1971; Report, Maine Dept. Sea and Shore Fisheries	Pollution in Maine	S	Bunker "C"	Foul taste in marine animals from several weeks to two or more years has resulted from oil spill in a lobster area.	None
Maine	Green, R. W., 1969; Testimony before Maine Legislative Research Sub-Committee on Coastal Conveyance of Petroleum	Coastal pollution	S	Crude	Most consistent result of oil pollution in marine coastal waters is on clams, quahogs, mussels, oysters, and lobsters. These are unmarketable owing to odor and flavor for weeks to years. Dispersants, emulsifiers, or detergents combine with oil fractions and sink to the bottom and affect an entirely different community of marine plants and animals. Worms are readily affected.	None
Saudi Arabia	Spooner, M., 1970; *Marine Pollution Bulletin*, 1 (2) pp. 166–167	Oil spill in Tarut Bay, Saudi Arabia	P	Light crude	A storm helped alleviate any serious damage to fisheries. Oil immediately affected the fauna; crabs, bivalves, and limpets were killed by smothering. Bird populations not severely affected.	None
USSR	Kasymov, A. G., 1970; *Marine Pollution Bulletin*, 1 (2), p. 101	Industry and the productivity of the Caspian Sea	P	General	Each year 100,000 tons of petroleum are lost into the Caspian Sea. Reduction of phytoplankton has been documented. Greatest reduction in benthic fauna found in breeding grounds of fish. Fish are subsequently affected owing to insufficient food.	Adequate

* Primary (P) is a report of primary data gathering; Secondary (S) means the report is based on the primary research of others found in the literature.

Table 37. Survey of Some Incidents of Oil Spills and Bird Kills, 1907–1971

Date	Type	Location	Product and Barrels Spilled	Birds Killed	Species and Reference
1907	Tanker	England	Crude; 50,000	Up to 100,000	Puffins[a]
1917–18	Ships	Worldwide	Oil; unknown	Up to 100/day	Guillemots[a] Razorbills, etc.[a]
1921–35	Ships	England	Oil; unknown	75–90% of colonies	Guillemots, gulls, cormorants[a]
1929	Ships	England	Oil; unknown	Large numbers	Scoters[a]
1936	Ships	Great Lakes	Oil; unknown	Large numbers	Wildfowl[a]
1937	Tanker	San Francisco	Crude; 70,000	10,000	Shore birds and murres[b]
1936	Ships	Coast of Kent	Oil; unknown	1,400	Sea birds[a]
1938	Unknown	English Channel	Oil; unknown	Large numbers	Scoters[a]
1938–45	Ships	Europe & U.S.	Oil; unknown	Decimated populations	Many species[a]
1948–58	General survey	England	Oil; unknown	50,000 to 250,000/ year	Auk colonies[a]
1951–52	General survey	England	Oil; unknown	100,000	Many species[c]
1952	Tankers	Massachusetts	Oil; 150,000	Up to 300,000	Eiders[b]
1955	Tanker	Germany	Crude; unknown	275,000	Unknown[a]
1956	Tanker	Washington	Fuel oil; unknown	2,900	Scoters and guillemots[a]
1959	Ships	North Sea	Oil; unknown	Tens of thousands	Ducks, scoters, and auk colonies[a]
1961	Discharge	England	Oil; unknown	Locally severe	Scarce diving species[a]
1966–67	75 incidents	Alaska	Oil; 1,000+	1,200–2,000	Ducks[d]
1966	Tanker	England	Crude; 10,000	2,772	20 species[a, d]
1967	Tanker	Virginia	Crude; 1,000	Unknown	Waterfowl[d]
1967	Unknown	Cape Cod	Oil; unknown	Unknown	Ducks and other waterfowl
1967	Tanker	England	Crude; 700,000	At least 30,000	Auks, razorbills, puffins, gulls, cormorants[a]
1967	Unknown	Louisiana	Oil; unknown	600	Ducks[e]
1968	Tanker	Puerto Rico	Crude; 84,500	Limited damage	Unknown[f]

a W. R. P. Bourne, "Oil Pollution and Bird Populations," in *The Biological Effects of Oil Pollution on Littoral Communities*, Field Studies Supplement Number 2, ed. by J. D. McCarthy and R. D. Arthur, pp. 99–121 (London: Field Studies Council, 1968).

b Battelle Memorial Institute, "Biological and Ecological Effects of Oil Pollution," in *Oil Spillage Study: Literature Search and Critical Evaluation for Selection of Promising Techniques to Control and Prevent Damage* (Richland, Wash.: Battelle-Northwest, 1968), p. 47.

c Marvin Zeldin, "Audubon Black Paper #1: Oil Pollution," *Audubon*, 73 (May, 1971), pp. 99–119.

d Julian McCaull, "The Black Tide," *Environment*, 11 (November, 1969), pp. 2–16.

e U.S., Department of Interior, *Statement, Questions and Policy Issues Related to Oversight Hearings on the Administration of the Outer Continental Shelf Lands Act, Held by the Senate Committee on Interior and Insular Affairs Pursuant to S. Res. 45, March 23, 1972,* p. 99.

Table 37. Survey of Some Incidents of Oil Spills and Bird Kills, 1907–1971 (cont.)

Date	Type	Location	Product and Barrels Spilled	Birds Killed	Species and Reference
1968	Tanker	South Africa	Crude; 30,000	High kill	Unknown[f]
1968	Tanker	South Africa	Crude; 117,000	High kill	Unknown[f]
1969	Barge	Connecticut	No. 6 oil; unknown	Small kill	Unknown[f]
1969	Rig blowout	Santa Barbara	Crude; 500 barrels/day	At least 3,600	Grebes, cormorants, mergansers, pelicans and loons[d]
1969	Tanker	Scotland	Crude and residue; 1,000+	20,000	Eider, scoter, auk, and other species[d]
1969	Tanker	Sweden	Unknown	Unknown	Seabirds[f]
1970	Tanker	Nova Scotia	Oil; unknown	7,100	Many species[c]
1970	Tanker	Alaska	Oil; unknown	10–100 thousand	Unknown[e]
1971	Tankers	San Francisco	Bunker C; 20,000	7,000	Sea and shorebirds[g]
1971	Pipe Break	Richmond, CA	Oil; unknown	25% loss (55 oiled)	Unknown[h]

[f] Dillingham Corporation, *Systems Study of Oil Spill Cleanup Procedures*, Vol. I. *Analysis of Oil Spills and Control Materials* (La Jolla, Calif.: Dillingham Corporation, 1970), pp. A1–A39.

[g] U.S., Department of Interior, Bureau of Land Management, *Final Environmental Statement: Proposed [December] 1972 Outer Continental Shelf Oil and Gas General Lease Sale Offshore Louisiana*, p. 117.

[h] Recovery of cleaned birds was 75 percent. James L. Naviaux, *Aftercare of Oil-Covered Birds* (Pleasant Hill, Calif., National Wildlife Health Foundation, 1972), p. 8.

ATLANTIC COAST

Information is not available on the impact of crude oil on central Atlantic Coast marine life. Diesel and Bunker C oil spills have been monitored in Massachusetts, Maine, and Canada, and extensive, persistent damage has been documented.[20] In the cool-temperate Maine coast, casual studies of a 25,000-barrel crude oil spill by the Liberian tanker *Northern Gulf* indicate that residues of crude are present on rocky areas seven years after the spill and that clams were tainted for several years.[21]

In addition to lack of knowledge of the effects of crude oil in general, the composition of potential Atlantic crude is, of course, completely unknown. One might expect that most Atlantic Coast areas may respond to pollutants in a similar manner as Gulf areas, but this hypothesis remains to be tested. As Atlantic offshore oil is expected to be 30 or more miles from shore, the more toxic aromatic fraction may have dissipated prior to arrival onshore, but pipeline breaks could occur close to shore.

Table 38. Recent Research Funding on the Environmental Effects of Oil Pollution

Agency[f]	Fiscal Year Dollar Expenditures[a]				Total 1970–1973
	1970	1971	1972	1973	
Dept. Commerce					
NOAA	—	423,000	—	276,300[b]	699,300
Dept. Defense					
Navy	—	17,000	—	—	17,000
Dept. Interior					
OWR	—	—	33,529	—	
BSFW	—	—	11,000	—	
Total	—	—	44,529	—	44,529
USGS	10,000	0	0	0	10,000
Dept. Transportation:					
U.S. Coast Guard	50,000	—	—	75,000[c]	125,000
EPA	82,000	2,292,379	—	—	2,374,379
NSF	—	375,000	13,500	44,550	433,050
Smithsonian	—	—	84,375	—	84,375
States	59,400	—	—	—	59,400
Industry[d]	—	10,000	50,000	1,500,000[e]	1,560,000
Other	—	105,000	—	—	105,000
Total	201,400	3,222,379	192,404	1,895,850	5,562,033

[a] Unless footnoted, data was provided by the Smithsonian Science Information Exchange, Incorporated, Washington, D.C. For certain projects, funding information was not available.

[b] Personal communication from J. W. Angelovac, Technical Advisory Division, NOAA, November 20, 1972.

[c] U.S., Coast Guard, *Coast Guard Answers to Questions and Policy Issues related to Overview Hearings on the Outer Continental Shelf Lands Act, before the Senate Committee on Interior and Insular Affairs on Senate Resolution 45, May 24–26, March 23, 1972*, p. 48.

[d] American Petroleum Institute, Committee on Air and Water Conservation and Committee on Public Affairs, *Environmental Research, A Status Report* (Washington: API, January, 1972), p. 1-2. Specific marine project funding is not listed. The API Committee on Air and Water Conservation spends over $3 million annually.

[e] "Oil Industry Sponsors $1.5 million Gulf Study," *Under Sea Technology*, 13 (September, 1972), p. 42.

[f] Dashes indicate funding information not available

SURVEY OF INCIDENTS OF OIL SPILLS AND BIRD KILLS

Table 37 lists documented bird kills from a variety of petroleum industry activities, and indicates that tanker accidents have been most responsible for the widespread destruction of bird life. Most of this information is derived from a review article by W.R.P. Bourne, entitled "Oil Pollution and Bird Populations," published in *The Biological Effects of Oil Pollution on Littoral Communities.*

RECENT RESEARCH FUNDING

Table 38 lists approximate levels of funding for federal, state, and industry research on the environmental effects of oil pollution. It does not include research on clean-up technologies. Funding levels of certain agencies, such as the Army within the Department of Defense, are not available, and information is generally inadequate for fiscal year 1973.

1. Joel W. Hedgpeth, "Marine Biogeography" in *Treatise in Marine Ecology and Paleoecology*, Geological Society of America, Memoir 67, ed. by Joel W. Hedgpeth, Vol. 1: *Ecology*, New York: Geological Society of America, 1957), p. 360.

2. John L. Mohr, Personal Communication, Letter, February 27, 1972.

3. Environment Canada, Inland Waters Branch, Hydrologic Sciences Division, *Oil Pollution Research Program*, (Ontario, 1971), p. 2.

4. P. J. Kinney, D. K. Button, D. M. Schell, B. R. Robertson, and J. Grover, *Quantitative Assessment of Oil Pollution Problems in Alaska's Cook Inlet* (College, Alaska: Institute of Marine Science, University of Alaska, 1970), p. 5.

5. Lt. (jg.) John L. Glaeser, "A Discussion of the Future Oil Spill Problem in the Arctic," in *Proceedings of Joint Conference on Prevention and Control of Oil Spills*, June 15-17, 1971, Washington, D.C., sponsored by American Petroleum Institute Environmental Protection Agency and U.S. Coast Guard (Washington: American Petroleum Institute, 1971), p. 480.

6. *Ibid.*, p. 479.

7. Kinney, *et al., Oil Pollution Problems in Alaska's Cook Inlet*, p. 5.

8. R. J. Miget, Personal Communication, March 20, 1972.

9. Kinney, *et al., Oil Pollution Problems in Alaska's Cook Inlet*, p. 5.

10. Texas Instruments Incorporated and Coastal Ecosystems Management Incorporated, *Biological Assessment of Diesel Spill, Anacortes, Washington, May 1971: Final Report*, (Dallas: Texas Instruments Incorporated, 1971), p. II–75.

11. Robert Kanter, Dale Straughan, and William Jessee, "Effects of Exposure to Oil on *Mytilus Californianus* from Different Localities," in *Proceedings of Joint Conference on Prevention and Control of Oil Spills*, p. 485.

12. Nancy L. Nicholson, and Robert L. Cimberg, "The Santa Barbara Oil Spills of 1969: A Post Spill Survey of the Rocky Intertidal," in *Biological and Oceanographical Survey of the Santa Barbara Channel Oil Spill*, Vol. 1: *Biology and Bacteriology*, comp. by Dale Straughan (Los Angeles: Allan Hancock Foundation, University of Southern California, 1971), p. 351.

13. Kristian Fauchald, "The Benthic Fauna in the Santa Barbara Channel Following the January, 1969 Oil Spill," in *Biological and Oceanographical Survey of the Santa Barbara Spill*, Vol. 1, p. 76.

14. William G. Evans, *"Thalassotrechus barbarae (Horn)* and the Santa Barbara Oil Spill," *The Pan-Pacific Entomologist*, 46 (October, 1970), p. 233.

15. U.S., Department of Interior, *Statement, Questions and Policy Issues Related to Oversight Hearings on the Administration of the Outer Continental Shelf Lands Act, Held by the Senate Committee on Interior and Insular Affairs, Pursuant to S. Res. 45, March 23, 1972*, p. 99.

16. John G. Mackin, "Environmental Effects of Petroleum Production on Marine Communities," a paper presented to the Interstate Oil Compact Commission, Biloxi, Mississippi, December 1972, p. 9.

17. M. J. Cerame-Vivas, "The *Ocean Eagle* Oil Spill," Special Report to Office of Naval Research, (Washington: ONR, Ocean Biology Program, 1968), p. 2.

18. Jack Pearce and Larry Ogren, "Observations on the Effects of Oil from the Tanker *Ocean Eagle* on Marine Organisms of San Juan Bay and Vicinity; II. Observations One Year After the Catastrophe" Manuscript, (2 vols.: Sandy Hook Marine Laboratory, U.S. Bureau of Sport Fisheries and Wildlife, 1969), p. 2.

19. Peter W. Glynn, "Fundamental Analysis for Determining the Effects of Oil Pollution on the Ecology of a Tropical Shore, Monthly Progress Report for the period September 1-30, 1971," (Balboa, Canal Zone: Smithsonian Tropical Research Institute, 1971), p. 4.

20. Max Blumer, J. Sass, G. Souza, H. Sanders, F. Grassle, and G. Hampson, *The West Falmouth Oil Spill: Persistence of the Pollution Eight Months After the Accident*, Reference No. 70-44, (Woods Hole, Mass.: Woods Hole Oceanographic Institution, November, 1970), p. 26; Canada, Ministry of Transport, "Report of the Task Force, Operation Oil: Cleanup of the Arrow Oil Spill in Chedabucto Bay," Dartmouth: Atlantic Oceanographic Laboratory, 1970), Vol. II, p. 44; and Robert L. Dow, "Estuarine Communities and Pollution" (Unpublished manuscript, Maine, Dept. of Sea and Shore Fisheries, 1970), p. 14.

21. Dow, "Estuarine Communities and Pollution," p. 15.

Appendix E. Leasing Procedures

DURING the course of our study, the Division of Marine Minerals within BLM furnished two items which clarify and illuminate leasing and pre-leasing procedures. Since these items are not widely known, they are reproduced here with the Division's permission. The first lists step-by-step procedures for each five-year lease schedule and the second describes the pre-nomination resources evaluation report.

STEP-BY-STEP PROCEDURES FOR FIVE-YEAR LEASE SCHEDULES

Step 1. Pre-nomination resource evaluation report. (Explained in the following section.)

Step 2. Issuance of a call for nominations to determine industry's interest in broad offshore areas.

Step 3. Tract selection, including:
  a) Selection of tracts proposed to be offered at a particular lease sale. (BLM and USGS operate under a formal tract-selection agreement concluded in August, 1971.)
  b) Public announcement of tracts proposed to be offered.

Step 4. Preliminary pre-sale evaluation.

Step 5. Preparation of an environmental impact statement on those tracts selected to be offered, including:
  a) Preparation of a draft statement.
  b) Holding a public hearing.
  c) Preparation of a final statement.
  d) Preparation of a program decision option document (PDOD).
  e) Publication of sale notice.

Step 6. Final pre-sale evaluation to determine individual tract estimates of value.

Step 7. Holding the sale by sealed competition bidding for each tract.

Step 8. Post-sale analysis, including:
  a) Post-sale evaluation.
  b) USGS recommendation to accept or reject a bid.
  c) BLM determination on a tract-by-tract basis of whether leases shall be issued.

Step 9. Post-sale operational responsibilities.

BLM has the lead responsibility for five of the nine components. USGS has responsibility for Items 4 and 6, with inputs from BLM on Item 6. Joint BLM–USGS responsibility is involved in Step 3a—tract selection.

PRE-NOMINATION RESOURCES EVALUATION REPORT

Section 3301.2 of Title 43 CFR, the OCS leasing regulations, provides for BLM, at such time as an area is initially considered for mineral leasing, or as the need arises, to request the Director, USGS, to prepare a summary geologic report of the area. It also provides for BLM to request other interested federal agencies to prepare reports describing to the extent known any other valuable resources contained within the area and the potential effect of mineral operations on the resources or on the total environment.

The summary geologic report prepared by USGS describes the general geology, structure and stratigraphy, presence or absence of productive trends, extent and thickness of potential horizons and resource or recoverable reserve estimates for the area to be opened for nominations. Information contained in past reports has been general in nature, being based primarily on published and other data available to the public, and does not reflect the total knowledge the government may have on a particular area because of the proprietary nature of much of the government's data.

Previous practice has been to request such reports 30 days prior to a call for nominations. In addition to the geologic report from the USGS, resource reports are requested from the Bureau of Mines, National Park Service, Bureau of Sport Fisheries and Wildlife, and the Bureau of Outdoor Recreation. At present, requests for reports are being planned 90 days prior to the call for nominations.

Plans are being formulated to expand the use of pre-nomination resource reports in order to obtain the broadest spectrum of multiple use information as early in the leasing process as possible and to insure sound decisions later on in the leasing process. This expanded effort will essentially consist of (1) forwarding requests for resource information to interested agencies outside of the Department of the Interior, principally those offices that have worked with BLM in the preparation of environmental impact statements, and (2) the identification in the request of specific data requirements and/or questions that need to be answered which lie within the province or particular expertise of each individual agency.

Within this framework, BLM also plans to relate carefully the scope of future calls for nomination to the subsequent need to select tracts for sales of up to one million acres. This would allow the respondents to focus on fairly specific areas and, it is hoped, either to endorse the action or to develop initially any issues or differences on multiple-use problems in the area or portions of the area under consideration. Such information would allow these issues to be resolved or settled before the time when they become public information through release of tract-selection lists or draft environmental statements. All participating agencies would, of course, have a further chance to provide inputs or comments into the subsequent environmental statement drafts.

Appendix F. NASA, NAE, and University of Oklahoma OCS Petroleum Studies: Description and Comparison

THE University of Oklahoma (OU) technology assessment is one of three recent studies focusing on how offshore petroleum technologies can be made safer and less environmentally threatening. The other two were conducted by the National Aeronautics and Space Administration (NASA)[1] and the National Academy of Engineering (NAE).[2] The NASA study was prepared for and funded by the U.S. Geological Survey (USGS); the Department of the Interior contracted for the NAE study; and the OU study was supported by a grant from the Research Applied to National Needs (RANN) Division of the National Science Foundation. In this appendix, these three studies will be generally described and compared in terms of objectives, how they were conducted, and their conclusions and recommendations.

OBJECTIVES

NASA: At the request of USGS, the NASA study was undertaken to examine the feasibility of improving the reliability of safety and anti-pollution equipment used in offshore oil operations through the use of NASA advanced engineering techniques. Specifically, the study was to determine: (1) the practicality of NASA quality management techniques; (2) the applicability of Failure Mode and Effects Analysis (FMEA); and (3) the impact of these management and analysis programs and the legal changes needed to implement them. This narrow but well-defined series of objectives contrasts markedly with both the NAE and OU studies.

NAE: The NAE study focused on the safety of offshore petroleum development. Its purpose was to recommend reasonable technical and regulatory procedures to minimize petroleum intrusions into the marine environment. Although the NAE review addressed a broader set of questions than the NASA study, it utilized the NASA study as an element of its data base. In general, the NAE review dealt with certain problems of management of technology but did not address itself to the broader issues of the management and control of OCS resource development.

OU: The quite broad objectives of the OU study were to assess the ade-

349

quacy and impacts of OCS petroleum technology and to recommend new equipment, procedures, and policies for optimal development of OCS oil and gas resources.

NASA, NAE, and OU: These three studies are similar in their focus on technologies. However, they contrast sharply in scope: The NASA study focuses on the applicability of a particular approach to safety and quality management. The NAE study examines a range of issues, but largely restricts its coverage to technologies, primarily because the NAE panel specifically defined its objectives to avoid confronting issues such as environmental risk and social benefits and ruled out recommendations which would require changes in the law. The OU study, on the other hand, had objectives in addition to those of the NASA and NAE studies and proposed to examine the impacts of a wide range of OCS operations and their relationship to a broader set of energy, social, and environmental issues; the OU technology assessment team examined both physical and social technologies and made recommendations ranging from improving specific hardware items to an overall management plan for optimal OCS development.

CONDUCT OF THE STUDIES

NASA: The NASA team consisted of five engineers with extensive backgrounds in aerospace technology and systems safety together with a USGS representative (see Table 39). This group interviewed responsible personnel and viewed operations in managerial, manufacturing, and oil production facilities, concentrating on 16 subject areas. These included, for example, enforcement, specifications, organization, inspections, analysis,

Table 39. Summary of Scope, Duration, and Team Composition

	NASA	NAE	University of Oklahoma
Scope	Applicability of NASA procedures to OCS oil and gas management	Review of OCS operations to minimize oil spills	Assessment of technologies used in OCS oil and gas operations
Duration	2 months	16 months	20 months
Team composition	Engineers-aerospace (5) Liaison-USGS (1)	Executives-industrial (5) Engineers-marine (2) Engineers-petroleum (1) Liaison-Coast Guard (1) Liaison-Interior (1)	Biologist (1) Engineers-aerospace (2) Engineer-industrial (1) Lawyer (1) Physicist (1) Political Scientists (2)

and procurement. The study formally commenced August 16, 1971, and continued through October 8, 1971; however, acquisition of background knowledge and data actually began earlier. Following documentation and discussion with government agencies, suppliers, contractors, and operators, the applicability of established NASA procedures was considered. Recommended changes in USGS and operator activities were issued in a 36-page mimeographed report to USGS in November, 1971. This report has subsequently been widely disseminated throughout the industry and, despite certain reservations and initial hostile reactions, has been generally well received. A number of the team's recommendations are currently being implemented by USGS.

NAE: The eight-man NAE panel represented a variety of engineering, scientific, and management backgrounds in industry and universities, including three presidents of marine engineering companies, and vice presidents from Westinghouse Electric Corporation and Esso Production Research Company, for example. In addition, the panel included liaison representatives from the technical divisions of the Coast Guard and the Department of Interior. The panel met in ten working sessions from May, 1971, to August, 1972, combining field trips and meetings with government and industry spokesmen. In addition, a one-day technical session at the 1972 Offshore Technology Conference was co-sponsored by the panel.

Contents of the report are the product of panel deliberations. As acknowledged in the NAE foreword, the text does not always support the conclusions and recommendations, owing largely to the diverse background, competence, and experience of the panel members. The 197-page report, which included 101 pages of appendices composed of the NASA study and Offshore Technology Conference papers, was published by NAE Marine Board in December, 1972, and is being widely circulated.

OU: The OU study was conducted by an eight-man interdisciplinary research team drawn from the social, physical, and life sciences as well as engineering and law. The study continued from September, 1971, through April, 1973. The general research strategy employed is described in Chapter II. In general, initial background data were acquired during a series of initial briefings by government and industry representatives, field trips to offshore drilling and production facilities, and extended interviews with persons from a variety of petroleum companies. Team members also participated in a five-day Engineering Foundation Conference at which an informal atmosphere facilitated discussion of future OCS technologies with some 60 technical and administrative representatives of government, industry, and universities.

Following a systematic assessment of OCS technologies and their impacts, the consequences of alternative equipment, procedures, and policies were examined, and a general management system was defined. The NASA study was an element of the data, and during the final portion of this study, the NAE review was examined. A draft report was issued for review in April, 1973. This book incorporates revisions made in response to comments and criticism of that draft.

A COMPARISON OF THE THREE STUDIES

The three studies differ in terms of team composition and approach. The NASA team was comprised of a group of engineers, as seems appropriate given the team's objectives. Although members of the team were aerospace engineers, the elements of quality control and systems analysis described in the NASA report have been successfully used in a number of industries. A major benefit of the NASA team's composition was that it provided a new perspective on OCS technologies and operations.

In terms of expertise, the NAE panel was broader than the NASA panel, including engineers, scientists, and industrialists. However, in contrast to both the NASA and OU teams, the NAE panel included persons whose interests could be directly affected by the panel's conclusions and recommendations.

All members of OU's core research team were drawn from the University of Oklahoma. This was in keeping with the goal of insuring to the maximum possible extent that the study be conducted impartially. The OU study is one of the first attempts at technology assessment as a means of providing a broad, interdisciplinary overview of two problem areas. Given this goal, the OU team incorporated a greater breadth of expertise than did either the NASA team or the NAE panel.

The NASA study observed the extent to which formal quality control organizations and procedures are used in the OCS and how inspection is used in quality control. (See Table 40.) The progress that has been made in achieving safe operations was noted as was the general philosophy of production operations. Specific hazards, such as with fuels and corrosion, for example, were identified. It was concluded that NASA's contractual quality management techniques were applicable to OCS activities, that systems safety analysis should be in widespread use, and that it would not be necessary to change the law to implement these changes. The team noted that full-scale investigations to develop a systems safety program were not desirable, and that the general OCS order program is acceptable as presently structured. However, it was noted that it would be desirable to add OCS orders for certain specific equipment items.

Table 40. Summary of Conclusions

NASA

1. Technologies characterized by an absence of formal quality control organizations & procedures.

2. Significant progress has been made in past 2 years in achieving safer operations.

3. "Production first" philosophy has delayed problem resolution.

4. Basic NASA contract approaches are applicable to OCS operations.

5. Hazards analysis is applicable to OCS operations. Current design documentation is inadequate.

6. No changes in law required to implement NASA procedures.

7. OCS orders are developing in the right direction to provide essential guidance to industry. However, greater standardization is needed, and orders require further revision.

NAE

1. Present technology is adequate to support current operations.

2. Improvements are possible in damage control and fire fighting.

3. Nuisance spills can be almost eliminated with present methods.

4. Most oil releases are caused by accidents of error and equipment.

5. Oil spills have temporary effects, but little agreement exists on long-term effects.

6. OCS orders have been effective but the criteria of effectiveness are vague.

7. Government inspectors lack standards, resulting in requirements for *ad hoc* judgments.

8. The OCS industry suffers from a lack of publicly recognized standards.

9. Individual companies often have complete and high-quality standards.

10. Industry/government relations are closed to public view; industry research is held private.

11. Accident data are generally unavailable.

12. Although skilled personnel are required, training is limited in scope.

University of Oklahoma

1. OCS operations are not technology driven. Technological changes have been evolutionary and incremental.

2. Until recently, the governing criterion of technological development has been economics.

3. Recent safety and environmental demands seriously challenge the present system for managing OCS development. Participation has been limited to Interior and the petroleum industry.

4. Selected physical technologies presently being used on the OCS need to be improved or more widely utilized. However, industry's state of the art technological capabilities are adequate to meet new safety & environmental requirements.

5. The major problems to be resolved for optimal OCS development are managerial.

6. Effective management requires more adequate resource & impact data, more effective cooperation & coordination by responsible agencies in planning and policy-making—and a specific statement of the portion of energy demand to be supplied by the OCS.

7. OCS development is socially preferable to increased imports and TAPS.

The NAE study observed a need to develop OCS petroleum, and that present development has resulted in only limited or conjectural environmental degradation. The panel did not consider esthetic values, ruling them out because of their subjective nature. Technologies were found to be adequate to support current operations. The NAE panel did, however, identify weaknesses in regulation, inspection, information acquisition, standards, and training and indicated where substantive changes could be made.

The OU study focused on a wide range of social and physical technologies. Conclusions reached relate the administration and management of OCS resources to energy supply and environmental and social issues. The team's conclusions covered both equipment and procedures as well as the present management system.

The NASA study concluded that although the NASA safety approach is applicable, the limited complexity of OCS technologies does not warrant the adoption of many NASA procedures. Similarly, the NAE study found that technologies were adequate; and the OU study found that the present technologies will change only incrementally and that the deployment of present state-of-the-art technologies within a responsive management system would achieve a number of desirable social goals. According to the OU team, difficulties within the present system are less technological than policy problems. The principal conclusions of the three studies are enumerated in Table 40.

RECOMMENDATIONS

As previously indicated, jurisdictional and general administrative aspects of OCS operations were covered only in the OU study. This followed from the belief of the OU team that a number of significant issues dealt with international, federal-state, and agency jurisdictional problems. Indeed, the long-term administrative problems of energy and land-use planning and environmental impacts were treated as a central issue to OCS development.

In general, the management recommendations made by the OU and NASA studies advocate a more active federal role whereas the NAE study advocates continuing present procedures and returning to a pattern of establishing regulations in terms of objectives rather than specifying how objectives are to be achieved. The NASA and OU studies suggest that USGS should involve outside participants in developing standards for all safety and anti-pollution equipment. OU would extend this procedure to include the formulation of OCS orders. The NAE study suggests the development of industry consensus standards; in contrast, the OU study suggests that participation in setting standards should include qualified persons from outside government and industry. All three studies advocate a more active accident-investigation role for government and call for the public disclosure of accident information.

All three studies found that personnel safety and training programs need to be improved. NASA and OU advocate an explicit supervisory role for USGS; NAE, on the other hand, calls only for some kind of general "government participation."

In terms of information exchange, all three of the studies encourage more widespread dissemination of information throughout industry. The NAE and OU studies also recognized a need for increased information on biological effects of crude oil intrusion to inform assessments of environmental and esthetic modification. The OU study also suggests several monitoring activities and a policy of minimal environmental intrusion rather than a coordinated program to specify "reasonable limits of crude oil intrusion" as suggested by NAE.

In terms of research and development, the NAE and NASA studies advocate possible R&D assessment and sponsorship in the area of safety and pollution-mitigating technologies. However, the NAE recommendations are limited to various damage-limiting technologies. The OU team recommends additional R&D programs to be undertaken in a number of areas by both government and industry. Both the NASA and OU teams advocate more widespread use of systems safety analysis techniques and a need for periodic review of specific equipment inadequacies. The NAE panel concluded that the technologies are adequate and recommends only that certain damage-limiting technologies receive additional technological refinement.

Recommendations of the three studies are listed in Table 41.

1. Morris K. Dyer, *et. al.* "Applicability of NASA Contract Quality Management and Failure Mode Effect Analysis Procedures to the USGS Outer Continental Shelf Oil and Gas Lease Management Program" (unpublished report to the U.S. Geological Survey, November, 1971.)

2. National Academy of Engineering, Panel on Operational Safety in Offshore Resources Development, *Outer Continental Shelf Resources Development Safety: A Review of Technology and Regulation for the Systematic Minimization of Environmental Intrusion from Petroleum Products* (Washington: National Academy of Engineering Marine Board, December, 1972), 197 pages.

Table 41. Summary Listing of the Recommendations of the NASA, NAE, and University of Oklahoma OCS Petroleum Studies Grouped in 10 Functional Categories

NASA	NAE	University of Oklahoma
	JURISDICTION	
		National Boundaries. The outer limit of national jurisdiction should be established as soon as possible along with an international authority to manage and control the development of seabed resources beyond this fixed limit.
		Federal-State Agreements. Continuing efforts should be undertaken to establish interim agreements allowing oil and gas development in those areas where OCS development is scheduled and where the states claim jurisdiction beyond the three miles provided in the Submerged Lands Act.
		Agency Jurisdiction. The Congress should act to clarify ambiguities concerning the six-mile zone between the outer limit of the territorial sea and the beginning of the OCS off the Gulf coasts of Florida and Texas.
		Energy Coordinator. A top official of the executive branch, either a departmental secretary or a White House officer, should be designated energy coordinator for the federal government.
	GENERAL ADMINISTRATION	
		Impact Statement Hierarchy. The OCS management process should include preparation of a hierarchy of impact statements that starts with a general programmatic statement.
		Promotion and Regulation. Promotion and regulation functions should remain divided within Interior between BLM and USGS. These two functions should be strictly separated.

Ten-Year Schedule. BLM should formulate a ten-year schedule for the development of OCS oil and gas resources.

Coastal Planning. The Department of Commerce should be designated as having special responsibilities for providing the coastal-zone planning component in OCS impact statements.

Lead Agency. The Department of Interior should be assigned lead agency responsibility for all 102 statements prepared for the OCS.

Programmatic Statement. USGS should lead, with the close cooperation of Commerce, in preparing programmatic impact statements for each of the regions included in the ten year-development schedule.

Define Lease Areas. Using the programmatic statements as a base, BLM should, in consultation with USGS, select sale areas (not tracts) defined by co-ordinates for inclusion on its five-year lease schedule.

Lease Impact Statement. Based on the programmatic statement and nominations from industry, BLM, in cooperation with USGS, should prepare a lease sale draft impact statement to be available at least fifteen months prior to the sale and three months prior to the public hearing. EPA approval on impact statements.

Committee Review. An ad hoc committee should be constituted by CEQ to review draft impact statements for lease sales. Review to be public.

Bonus Bid. BLM should continue to administer the lease sale using present procedures including the bonus bid system. Selected experimentation with the staggered bonus system should be considered.

MANAGEMENT AND REGULATION

Development of OCS Order Management Program Plan. The USGS regional office should extend current efforts by staffing, at the earliest possible time, with personnel experienced in quality management and capable of developing, documenting, and assisting the Regional Supervisor in implementing this type program. The NASA documents NPC 200-1A, "Quality Assurance Provisions for Government Agencies," and NHB 5330.7, "Management of Government Quality Assurance Functions for Supplier Operations," should be used as guidelines.

Operational Use of USGS Water Resources Division Data Development Techniques. A portion of the planned OCS Order Management Program referenced in the previous recommendation includes the Water Resources Division study. It is understood that the Conservation Division intends to adopt the data development techniques used in the study for continued use.

Objectives Oriented Regulations. In order to avoid inhibition of technical development and to take maximum advantage of advances made in equipment and methodology, government policy should be to establish regulations in terms of the objectives to be achieved and not in terms of specific methods of achieving them.

Refine Current Procedures. In permit procedures, there should be continuation and refinement of the current practice of requiring submission of plans of applicants in terms of equipment and including personnel qualification and training procedures which will be used to control hazards. The government should continue to make granting and continuance of permits contingent upon adherence to regulation and submitted plans.

Updating Regulations. Regulations established for the control of offshore oil operations should take into account on a continuing basis the results of failure analysis as well as consideration of the natural environmental hazards (such as hurricanes, earthquakes, or large waves, and the state of the art of working in the marine environment).

Table 41. Summary Listing of the Recommendations of the NASA, NAE, and University of Oklahoma OCS Petroleum Studies Grouped in 10 Functional Categories (*cont.*)

NASA	NAE	University of Oklahoma
	MANAGEMENT AND REGULATION (*cont.*)	
		USGS Management. With limited exceptions, post-lease management should be concentrated in USGS, including a number of safety, environmental, pipeline rights-of-way, and pipeline safety, and certain data gathering and assessment functions.
		Apply FWPCA to OCS. The FWPCA Amendments of 1972 should be amended specifically to apply discharge provisions to the OCS.
		Cleanup Cooperatives. The Coast Guard should establish specific equipment and performance standards for cleanup cooperatives.
	OCS ORDERS DEVELOPMENT	
OCS Order Development. The USGS Regional Office should organize an OCS order development and implementation function. This function, technical in nature, involves many hours of research, investigation, and discussion, and should be assigned to a small committee of qualified people selected by the Supervisor.		*OCS Orders: Preparation.* All OCS orders should be reviewed in advance by committees representing both industry and other interested parties selected by the Director of the Conservation Division of the USGS.
		OCS Orders: Coverage. All design specifications and regulations for which USGS has administrative responsibility, including those resulting from interagency agreements (OSHA, OPS, EPA) should be detailed in OCS orders for each USGS area.
	STANDARDS AND CERTIFICATION	
Standards/Specifications Development and Use. USGS should take the lead in insuring the rapid development	*Consensus Standards.* Government should encourage and support the development of a comprehensive sys-	*Standards.* USGS should establish equipment requirements in terms of the objectives to be achieved. While

and use of adequate standards/specifications for all safety and anti-pollution equipment to be used on the OCS. Also:

a. That USGS seek API cooperation in establishing a committee to function under USGS guidance for the purpose of determining specific needs, and to write, review and approve standards/specifications for safety and anti-pollution equipment. The committee must function under the guidance of USGS.

b. That specifications developed by the committee contain requirements for a basic quality control system, and where equipment is to be used in a deleterious environment, an environmental test program.

c. That the USGS, through OCS orders, require the use of approved standards/specifications.

tem of industry consensus standards and should make use of the resulting standards system in the regulation and inspection of the offshore industry, and make adherence to such standards a consideration in the issuance of permits.

Joint Standards Development Under ANSI. The American National Standards Institute (ANSI) should be used jointly by government and industry to integrate the efforts of government, industry, and the professional societies for the development of industry consensus standards for personnel, equipment, and operating procedures.

Standards Development Participation. Government personnel associated with offshore resource development should participate in the standards preparation procedures and there should be means of assuring that such government personnel can participate as equals.

Deep-water Technology Standards. Industry and the government should establish a working relationship for the joint development of standards for advanced deep water technology. Industry consensus standards for completion and workover safety procedures should be developed. Special consideration should be given to hazard control and damage limiting methods.

these requirements should include detailed performance standards for all pieces of equipment affecting safety and environment, design specifications should not be allowed to act as a deterrent to technological development.

Certification of Drill Rigs. In addition to its present responsibilities for safety, the Coast Guard should establish formal certification and inspection requirements for jack-up drilling rigs.

RESEARCH AND DEVELOPMENT

Research and Development (R&D). The USGS should establish a method to determine needs and conduct or direct the research, testing and development necessary to improve equipment and methods for an increasingly safe and pollution-free operation on the OCS. Alternatively, the USGS should work with the industry in establishing an organization such as the American Petroleum Institute (API) to serve as the **R&D** focal

Clean-up R&D. The government should make quantitative studies of the effectiveness of the various present and potential methods of cleaning up oil from the marine environment, and of their potential marine environmental impact.

Government R&D Utilization. The government should encourage and utilize industry research and development programs by means of promotion of industry con-

Environmental R&D. A single federal agency EPA or NOAA should assume responsibility for monitoring, coordinating, and filling gaps in environmental research.

Clean-up R&D. EPA should assume responsibility for monitoring, coordinating, and filling gaps in government and industry R&D aimed at improving clean-up and containment technology.

Table 41. Summary Listing of the Recommendations of the NASA, NAE, and University of Oklahoma OCS Petroleum Studies Grouped in 10 Functional Categories (cont.)

NASA	NAE	University of Oklahoma
	RESEARCH AND DEVELOPMENT (*cont.*)	
point, with all companies contributing toward resolution of problems.	sensus standards on offshore technology so that it can act to ensure that information on improvements in safety technologies becomes available to participants in offshore resource development. *Environmental Research.* The government should sponsor a coordinated program to specify reasonable limits of crude oil intrusion in accordance with biological and aesthetic standards. These standards should be set in a manner that will take full account of site variables. The effort should be carried out on a continuing basis in order to take advantage of improvements in the technology of offshore petroleum operations. The program should be specifically directed to provide a basis for engineering design and standards for components and systems to be used in offshore petroleum operations.	*Government R&D.* USGS should undertake an expanded research, development, and testing program as necessary to insure optimal regulation and rapid development of new equipment and procedures. *Industry R&D.* Industry should expand its R&D programs with the objective of developing technologies that are responsive to broader criteria such as those associated with safety and environmental concerns.
	PHYSICAL TECHNOLOGIES IMPROVEMENT	
Hazard Analysis. The USGS Gulf Coast Regional Office should be authorized to implement the proposed "design review" group. The region should require submission from offshore operators a list of critical operations to be performed during drilling at time of permit request. The requirement for submission of complete Hazard Analysis should be phased into system starting with new work, with time limits on existing wells. The analysis group should work with operators to eliminate (reduce) hazardous operations by recommending redesign of hardward or operations and develop new inspection criteria. *Wearout Prevention.* Development of a reliable sand erosion probe should be accelerated under USGS spon-	*Damage Control Technologies.* The government should actively encourage and sponsor the development and testing of damage-limiting and fail-safe systems and techniques in the areas of damage control, fire fighting, and well control.	*Review Technology.* USGS should appoint an independent and representative committee of experts to review state-of-the-art in OCS technologies periodically or when an accident investigation or 102 statement process indicates a need to recommend desirable changes in equipment and performance standards. *Systems Approach.* Industry should undertake a self-conscious program aimed at increased use of the systems approach in designing its technologies. Specific efforts should focus on increased redundancy and fail-safe designs. *Inadequate component.* USGS should compile a list of components that need to be developed, improved, or more widely deployed, and publish an annual sum-

mary review of the progress achieved in correcting weaknesses.

Subsea Production Systems. USGS should encourage early deployment and use of subsea production systems.

Failure Reporting. USGS should establish improved reporting and systematic analysis procedures for failures, malfunctions, and equipment defects, as well as issue appropriate notices and warnings.

Accident Investigation. Interior should establish a board similar in function to the National Transportation Safety Board to investigate major OCS accidents.

sorship (including a specification). A requirement should exist for rigorous test and inspection (X-ray/sonic) of wells upon sand erosion detection.

Failure-Reporting and Corrective-Action System. Monthly summaries from each operator of failure causes and corrective action should be required for all safety equipment specified by OCS Orders. All accidents and oil spills should follow similar procedures. For the procedure to be effective, its object should be recurrence prevention, with emphasis placed on the determination of causes, preventive action, and follow-up.

FAILURE REPORTS, INSPECTIONS, AND TESTING

Test Sites. The government should develop a policy regarding the testing of offshore equipment, including the establishment of criteria for selection of test sites for such equipment in the marine environment.

Company Inspection. Routine inspection procedures in the offshore industry should be carried out by the specific companies involved for compliance with industry consensus standards. Government inspection should be confined to spot-checking to ascertain compliance to regulations.

Oil Spill Analysis. A careful analysis should be carried out after every major offshore oil spill to determine the precise manner in which the spill occurred—taking into account any equipment failures, personnel errors, or design inadequacies, their causes and what can be done to prevent such future occurrences.

Performance Analysis and Disclosure. The information resulting from accident investigation and evaluation of component performance should be analyzed by a competent organization (similar to the National Transportation Safety Board or the Marine Safety Council), and its conclusions should be made public promptly.

Table 41. Summary Listing of the Recommendations of the NASA, NAE, and University of Oklahoma OCS Petroleum Studies Grouped in 10 Functional Categories (cont.)

NASA	NAE	University of Oklahoma
PERSONNEL SAFETY AND TRAINING		
Training and Certification. Operators should develop methods to insure that company or contract personnel performing inspection and tests of safety or anti-pollution equipment are properly trained in USGS requirements, the equipment functions, test methods, etc., prior to performing these services and that training is periodically updated as equipment is modified or new types of equipment are utilized. Operator or outside-source certification of personnel following demonstration of skill should be required. Operators provide USGS with a description of the methods to be employed in accomplishing the above, and that these methods be approved in advance by USGS.	*Training Program.* Since operator training programs are essential to safety in offshore resource development, the U.S. government should: a. Actively encourage and support such training programs; including the objective of safe and reliable operation, installation, maintenance, and repair of equipment systems and components; b. Sponsor industry-government standardization of training criteria; c. Give weighted consideration to the existence and quality of job qualification requirements and permit procedures; d. Ensure the participation of U.S. government personnel involved in standard setting, regulation, and inspection or permit procedures in such training programs.	*Personnel Standards.* USGS should develop uniform standards and certification requirements for personnel who perform inspection and test functions. *Personnel Training.* USGS should develop a program to establish improved and standardized training and procedures for operating personnel. This program should utilize the expertise of organizations and individuals such as behavioral scientists who specialize in training. *Human Factors Criteria.* Industry should focus specific attention on the use of human factors criteria in equipment design aimed at minimizing human-error accidents.
Safety and Anti-pollution Motivation Program. The USGS should initiate an OCS-wide safety and anti-pollution motivation program. Such a program could be effective in terms of obtaining industry response and favorable publicity.		
INFORMATION AND DATA		
Information Exchange. The USGS should investigate the legal question of a possible anti-trust law violation regarding formal exchange of hardware and method problem information within the oil and gas industry.	*Public Disclosure.* The official reports stemming from investigation of major accidents should receive prompt and full public disclosure, and should be available in a readily accessible form.	*Data Collection.* Based on the inclusion of areas on the five-year lease schedule, USGS should initiate its own data-collection program for each area to the extent required to prepare a lease sale impact statement.

If a favorable ruling is obtained, USGS should encourage and participate in the development and operation of the system.

Standardization of Forms. The USGS should revise the Pollution Report form presently being utilized in the District offices and require its use by the operators for those spills presently requiring written confirmation. USGS should develop a form for the recording of test results that would standardize this type of reporting by operators or "third party" personnel. The form should include cause of and action taken to correct discrepancies found during performance of required tests. It should provide the form to operators and require its use; or require operators to develop their own forms which will include the same layout and required information.

Engineering Documentation. The USGS should require that certain minimum engineering documentation be available at the operator's lowest level onshore engineering office.

Information Exchange System. The government should directly sponsor, encourage, and provide the means for a public exchange of information on the causes and effects of accidents, and on the performance of specific items of safety—related equipment in the offshore industry.

Self Incrimination Consideration. In addition to, and separate from, the inspection procedures, there should be a government-sponsored system of reporting safety-related information for the purpose of improving the safety of offshore operations and the inspection system by additions and eliminations. This system, in order to be effective, must take into consideration and allow for the problems of self-incrimination.

Hydrocarbon Studies. NOAA should initiate continuous hydrocarbon baseline and toxicity tests at the point that areas are included on the five-year lease schedule.

Environmental Monitoring. With the start of exploratory drilling operations in any OCS area, EPA should assure continuous monitoring of commercially useful and sensitive marine species for sublethal effects and possible tainting.

Industry Cooperation. USGS should actively promote greater industry cooperation in the development of safety, accident prevention, and environmental protection technologies.

Glossary

Acidizing—The application of acid to a producing zone to dissolve hard carbonate and thereby open passages through which oil or gas can enter the well bore.

Annulus—The space around a pipe suspended in a well bore. Its outer wall may be either the wall of the bore hole or the casing.

Articulated joint—A moveable joint. Such joints are expected to be used on lay barges and on bouyant tower platforms.

Associated gas—Free natural gas in immediate contact, but not in solution, with crude oil in the reservoir. (See dissolved gas).

Ballasting—The taking on by tankers of water to replace off-loaded oil and thereby improve stability.

Barite—Barium sulphate, a mineral used to increase the weight of drilling mud. The specific gravity of barite is 4.2 (i.e., it is about 4.2 times as heavy as water.)

Barrel—A unit of volume for petroleum products. One barrel is the equivalent of 42 U.S. gallons, or 35 imperial gallons, or 159 liters. One cubic meter equals 6.2897 barrels.

Bed scour—Scouring of the floor of the sea. May be by ice or rocks.

Benthic fauna—Animals whose habitat is in deep water or on the sea-bottom.

Biodegradation, biological degradation—Degeneration or deterioration of a substance through biological processes.

Biological agents—Living organisms which contribute to the biodegradation of oil.

Biomass—The total amount of living matter in a given area or environment.

Biosynthesis—Production of a chemical compound by a living organism.

Biota—The flora and fauna of a region.

Blind ram—Integral part of the blowout preventer. Rams whose ends are not intended to fit around the drill pipe, but to seal against each other and shut off completely the space below.

Blowout—An uncontrolled flow of gas, oil, and other well fluids from a well to the atmosphere. A well blows out when formation pressure exceeds the pressure being applied to it by the column of drilling fluid.

Blowout preventer—Equipment installed at the wellhead for the purpose of controlling pressures in the annular space between the casing and drill pipe, or in an open hole during drilling and completion operations.

Bore hole—The well bore; the hole made by drilling or boring a well.

BTU (British thermal unit)—Amount of heat required to raise the temperature of one pound of water one degree Fahrenheit. The BTU is a very small unit of measurement, and when one adds up large quanities of energy, one must count in large multiples of the BTU. Thus, the energy balance tables in this report are expressed in trillions (10^{12}) and quadrillions (10^{15}) of BTU's.

Carcinogen—A substance or agent which produces or incites cancer.

Casing—Large steel pipes placed in an oil or gas well as drilling progresses to "seal-off" or "shut-out" water and prevent caving of loose gravel formations.

Christmas tree—The assembly of pipes, valves and fittings at the top of the casing which is used to control the flow of oil and gas from a producing well.

Common carrier transmission line—Pipelines which may be used by more than one producer and are regulated by the Federal Power Commission or the Interstate Commerce Commission.

Condensate—Liquid hydrocarbon obtained by the condensation of vapors or gases produced from oil wells and ordinarily separated at the production site and run as crude oil.

Consolidated formation—A formation in which the sand, clay, rock, and other constituents have been stabilized around the well bore in the production zone.

Contiguous zone—Areas adjacent to the territorial sea over which coastal nations claim jurisdiction for some special purpose such as fishing, customs, and sanitation. Limited to a maximum of twelve miles from the coast by the 1958 Convention on the Territorial Sea and Contiguous Zones.

Continental margin—The submerged prolongation of adjacent land extending to an average water depth of 200 meters (approximately 660 feet).

Core sample—A cylindrical sample taken from the formation for purposes of examination. A sidewall core is one taken from the wall of the bore hole by special lateral coring devices.

Dead weight—The difference, expressed in tons, between a ship's displacement at load draft and at light draft. It comprises cargo, bunkers, stores, fresh water, etc.

Depletion allowance—A proportion of income derived from mining or oil production that is considered to be a return of capital not subject to income tax.

Development well—A well drilled in a proven field for the purpose of completing the desired pattern of production. Sometimes called an exploitation well.

Directional drilling—Controlled drilling deviation from a vertical plane for the purpose of reaching subsurface points laterally remote from the point at which the bit enters the earth.

Dissolved gas—Natural gas in solution with crude oil in the reservoir. (See associated gas).

Downhole safety equipment—Valve or other devices installed below the Christmas tree in production wells to prevent blowouts.

Drainage tract—A tract adjacent to one from which oil and gas are being produced. As production continues, oil and gas may be drained from formations in the drainage tract.

Drill pipe—In rotary drilling, the heavy seamless tubing used to rotate the bit and circulate the drilling fluid. Individual pipe lengths are normally 30 feet and are coupled together with tool joints.

Drill string—A "string" or column of drill pipe.

Exploratory well—A well drilled in unknown territory to find and define oil and gas deposits. If territory is completely unknown the well is called a wildcat.

Failure mode effect analysis—Analysis of the effect of a failure of a low level element upon successively higher levels of an assembly until the ultimate effect on the total system is determined.

Fast breeder reactor—Nuclear power source for electrical generation presently under development. Not only does it generate electricity, but it also produces nuclear fuel and is therefore a major hope for eliminating the energy crisis.

Flaring—The disposal of unwanted gas by burning in the atmosphere.

Fracturing—Applying pressure or using explosives to increase porosity.

Free-water knockout—A tank for separating water from oil.

Gas lift—Process by which crude oil is forced to the surface through formation pressure.

Gathering lines—Flow lines which run from several wells to a single tank battery.

GNP (gross national product)—The total market value of the goods and services produced by the nation before the deduction of depreciation charges and other allowances for capital consumption; a widely-used measure of economic activity.

Isobath—Lines connecting points of equal water depth.

Jack-up rig—A mobile drilling platform with extendible legs for support on the ocean floor.

Kelly—The heavy square or hexagonal steel member which is connected to the drill pipe to turn the drill string. It has a bored passageway that permits fluid to be circulated from the swivel into the drill stem and up the annulus.

Lay barge—A barge used to lay underwater pipelines.

LACT (Lease Automatic Custody Transfer)—An automatic system for measuring and monitoring produced oil and gas prior to sale.

Log—A record of downhole formation and well bore data.

LOT (Load/on top)—Tanker loading and unloading procedures designed to minimize oil loss.

Marine riser—A telescopic pipe running from a floating drilling rig to the ocean floor used to direct the drill stem and carry mud.

Mass flow monitoring—A procedure for metering flow through pipelines for the purpose of early identification of leaks.

Mud—A water or oil based slurry used to counteract downhole pressure and remove cuttings during drilling operations. It is circulated by pumps.

Mud pump—A large reciprocating pump used to circulate the mud on a drilling rig. Also called a slush pump.

Multi-phase pumping—A procedure for moving simultaneously through pipeline systems various combinations of oil, gas and water.

Oil shale—A convenient expression used to cover a range of materials containing organic matter (kerogen) which can be converted into crude shale oil, gas, and carbonaceous residue by heating.

102 statement—The environmental impact statement required by section 102 (2)(c) of the National Environmental Policy Act of 1969.

OCS (outer continental shelf)—The submerged lands extending from the outer limit of the territorial sea to some undefined outer limit. In the U.S., this is the portion of the shelf under federal jurisdiction.

Perforating—The cutting of holes in the casing to permit oil or gas to flow from the formation into the well hole.

Phytoplankton—Floating or weakly swimming plant life.

Primary fuel—Fuel consumed in original production of energy as contrasted to a conversion of energy from one form to another.

Redundancy—The provision of backups for critical elements of equipment or systems for the purpose of improving reliability.

Reel barge—A pipelaying barge which lays pipe by winding it off a reel or spool rather than by welding sections as is the usual practice.

Reinjection—An alternative to flaring or venting in which non-marketed gases are pumped back to the producing formation to maintain gas lift capability.

Relief well—A well drilled to intersect another well at some point below the surface, used to regain control of wells that are out of control.

Residual fuel oil—Crude petroleum or viscous residuums obtained in refinery operations. Commercial grades of burner oils Nos. 5 and 6 are residual oils and include Bunker fuels.

Rotary drilling—The method by which a hole is drilled by a rotating bit to which a downward force is applied. The bit is fastened to and rotated by the drill string. The drill string also provides a passageway through which the drilling fluid is circulated. New joints of drill pipe are added as drilling progresses.

Sacrificial anodes—A non-structural block of highly conductive metallic material preferentially corroded through the process of electrolytic action to maintain platform structural integrity.

Sand probe—A device used to warn of excessive sand erosion in wells containing velocity actuated downhole safety valves.

Second order consequences—Technologies often produce more than the intended initial or first order effect. For example, the automobile has had effects on land use, air pollution, development of suburbs, etc. These often unanticipated effects are known as second order consequences.

Secondary recovery—Oil and gas obtained by the augmentation of reservoir energy often by the injection of air, gas or water into a production formation.

Seismic survey—A geophysical exploration technique in which generated sound waves are reflected or refracted from underlying geologic strata and recorded for later analysis.

Sonar—A device for detecting the location of submerged objects by means of reflected sound waves.

Step-out wells—A well drilled adjacent to or near a proven well to ascertain the limits of the reservoir.

Stinger—A hinged structure attached to the after part of a lay barge to support the pipe as it moves from the deck to the ocean bottom.

Storm choke—Velocity actuated downhole safety devices are commonly known as "storm chokes."

Subsea completion—A production well in which the Christmas tree assembly is located at or near the ocean bottom.

SPS (Subsea production system)—The complex of piping, valves and related equipment used to produce oil and gas from individual or connected subsea completions.

Subsoil survey—Investigation of shallow focus ocean bottom conditions, usually for the purpose of setting platforms or rigs.

Tender—The barge anchored alongside an offshore drilling platform. Usually contains living quarters, storage space and the mud system.

Tension leg platform—Floating platform for drilling or production which is restrained and located by tension cables or articulated supports from the ocean bottom.

Territorial sea—The sea area immediately adjacent to a coastal nation within which it claims comprehensive jurisdiction.

Tertiary recovery—Use of heat or methods other than fluid injection to augment oil recovery.

Tool pusher—Supervisor of a rotary drilling or workover rig operation.

Transit rights—A right of passage on the surface of the water. Being proposed to prevent closing off a large number of straits and international maritime routes if territorial seas are extended.

Trip—Hoisting the drill string out of and returning it into the well bore, usually for the purpose of changing bits or preparing to take a core.

Tubing—Conduit for routing oil or gas to the surface.

Venting—Releasing unwanted gas directly to the atmosphere.

Water column—Used in distinguishing the various jurisdictional areas in ocean space: the seabed and subsoil; the water between the seabed and the surface; living resources in the water; and activities on the surface of the water.

Well bore—The hole made by the drilling bit.

Wellhead—The equipment used to maintain surface control of a well. It is formed of the casing head, tubing head, and Christmas tree. Also refers to various parameters as they exist at the wellhead: wellhead pressure, wellhead price of oil, etc.

Wildcat—Any well in unproved territory.

Workover—Performance of one or more remedial operations on a producing oil well with the hope of restoring or increasing production. Examples of workover operations are deepening, plugging back, pulling and resetting the liner, squeeze cementing, shooting, and acidizing.

Zooplankton—Floating or weakly swimming animal life.

Indices

INDEX OF NAMES